Your Child Is Asleep
early infantile autism

THE DORSEY SERIES IN PSYCHOLOGY

EDITOR   HOWARD F. HUNT   *Columbia University*

BARNETTE (ed.)   *Readings in Psychological Tests and Measurements*   rev. ed.

BENNIS, SCHEIN, STEELE, & BERLEW (eds.)   *Interpersonal Dynamics: Essays and Readings on Human Interaction*   rev. ed.

COURTS   *Psychological Statistics: An Introduction*

DESLAURIERS & CARLSON   *Your Child Is Asleep: Early Infantile Autism*

DEUTSCH & DEUTSCH   *Physiological Psychology*

FISKE & MADDI   *Functions of Varied Experience*

FLEISHMAN (ed.)   *Studies in Personnel and Industrial Psychology*   rev. ed.

FREEDMAN (ed.)   *The Neuropsychology of Spatially Oriented Behavior*

HAMMER & KAPLAN   *The Practice of Psychotherapy with Children*

KLEINMUNTZ   *Personality Measurement: An Introduction*

MADDI   *Personality Theories: A Comparative Analysis*

RATNER & DENNY   *Comparative Psychology: Research in Animal Behavior*

ROZEBOOM   *Foundations of the Theory of Prediction*

VON FIEANDT   *The World of Perception*

Your Child Is Asleep
EARLY INFANTILE AUTISM
Etiology · Treatment · Parental influences

Austin M. DesLauriers, Ph.D.
Professor and Director of Research and Training
University of Missouri Medical Center

Carole F. Carlson, Ph.D.
Director of Research and Chief Psychologist
Osawatomie State Hospital
Osawatomie, Kansas

1969
THE DORSEY PRESS, Homewood, Illinois
IRWIN-DORSEY LIMITED, Nobleton, Ontario

First Printing, January, 1969

Library of Congress Catalog Card No. 68–56869
Printed in the United States of America

To all those children who, like

Kathy, Connie,
Elizabeth, Tommy, June,

await their awakening to a
brand-new vision of a brand-new day.

While He was still speaking, there came from the ruler's house some who said, "Your daughter is dead. Why trouble the Teacher any further?" But ignoring what they said, Jesus said to the ruler of the synagogue, "Do not fear, only believe." And He allowed no one to follow Him except Peter and James and John the brother of James. When they came to the house of the ruler of the synagogue, He saw a tumult, and people weeping and wailing loudly. And when He had entered, He said to them, "Why do you make a tumult and weep? The child is not dead but sleeping." And they laughed at Him. But He put them all outside, and took the child's father and mother and those who were with Him, and went in where the child was. Taking her by the hand He said to her, "Tal'itha cu'mi"; which means, "Little girl, I say to you, arise." And immediately the girl got up and walked; for she was twelve years old. And immediately they were overcome with amazement. And He strictly charged them that no one should know this, and told them to give her something to eat.

Mark V: 35–43

Preface

We have asked ourselves to whom should this book be addressed: to parents, to educators, to child psychologists, to scholars and researchers, or to workers in the field of community mental health?

This book presents our views on the education of a child. More specifically, it might be said to be a book on "special education" since its main concern is with a special child: the autistic infant. Yet as its central thesis, this book asserts that the autistic child's condition and behavior represent, in a dormant and arrested stage, that same ferment of life which in any normal child finds expression in his insatiable appetite for living and in his tireless drive to know and possess the world in which he lives. Thus, the education of the autistic child is seen as an "awakening"—an awakening to an exciting experience of aliveness and of love for life as well as an awakening to an ever-widening world of people and objects to relate to and from which to find personal enrichment.

Closely related to education, the central issues of meaningful human communication constitute also an all-pervasive theme in this book. The growth and development of a child, his "education," cannot proceed outside of the security and support which the early communicative ties with his parents give to his infinite expectation that his appetite for living will be nourished and that his presence in this world will be truly welcomed. We define communication as the felt presence of one human being to another. The child and the mother communicate when, in the amount and variety of stimulating interactions which they enjoy and in the reciprocal patterns of activities through which they meet their mutual needs, their presence to each other—a direct, physical, sensory, affective presence—is arousingly made available to each other. Such a bodily, preverbal communication can be viewed as the model or exemplar of all meaningful communications between human beings because only such a communication, which brings one's presence to another's presence, permits the separation and the differentiation of the individual to be asserted and his individuality to be enriched. In the autistic child such a capacity for human communication does not exist.

This book is also the report of a research program wherein our views on communication and education were to be put to test by applying them in a therapeutic-educational effort at "awakening" the arrested development in a group of autistic infants. In its final design, this research evolved out of a broad study of the Parental Influences on Early Ego Development in the Child (a project supported in part by a grant from the State of Illinois Research Authority; grant No. 17–151). In this study we had been attempting to circumscribe and define patterns of parental communications and to evaluate the impact of the child's presence in shaping these patterns. If a child could not communicate his presence to his mother, the mother would never know how to be a mother to this child. Such was the "autistic anlage" as we understood it; and our program set out to determine whether a human communication pattern could be aroused in the autistic children of our project and whether, if it did develop, it would have a direct impact on shaping a normal pattern of communicative response in the mother. The present report covers two years of work in this effort. In publishing it now we are quite aware that this effort is just a beginning—a beginning that holds promise, however, for broader efforts in this area and possibly more effective ones.

A novel and somewhat timely aspect of our research design may make this book quite appealing to parents and to workers in the field of community mental health. Our program with autistic children was carried out on an out-patient basis; the parents of each child in the project were recruited as the main psychotherapists and educators; and as many resources as were available in the community—teachers, pediatricians, ministers, etc.—were all made active coparticipants in the attempt we were making to awaken the child.

In many ways this book is also an expression of faith. Faith in human life. Faith in the unique capacity which man possesses, through the awakening of his reflexive consciousness, to direct and control his discovery of a world without which he would be nothing, but over which he constantly strives to assert his mastery. Man is part of this world; and his place in it has to become, for each individual, a personal experience of achievement and secure satisfaction. Yet for every individual, the awakening of a personal consciousness which makes him deeply aware of himself in the very process of becoming aware of others emerges through a series of simple and humble steps. In these steps are asserted his appetite for living as well as his infinite expectation that he truly belongs in this world and will surely be accepted as part of it. In order to communicate this faith in human life we have alluded, at various points in this book, to a story from the Bible in which a child who was thought to be dead was "awakened" by the Teacher and turned over to her parents so that "they would give her something to eat."

The tragedy of early infantile autism is not the tragedy of death but rather the mystery of dormant life. The pages of this book report how we went about trying to awaken the sleeping child. The awakening which we attempted had neither the pomp and solemnity of a religious ritual, the drama of a miraculous happening, nor, even less, the loftiness of a spiritual experience. The awakening took place in an atmosphere of pleasure and fun—pleasure at being alive, fun in being part of life. This we tried also to convey in the style of this book, where the sober qualities of scientific research are covered at times by the enthusiasm of the research workers.

To the parents of our group of autistic infants we obviously owe our deepest debt of gratitude: their devotion to their child and their dedication to our program made the task of "awakening" their child a most encouraging and gratifying enterprise. We also wish to thank Mrs. Pat Jones, director of the Pied Piper Nursery School, and the warm and responsive staff of teachers who worked with Kathy; Mr. Michael Debowski, principal of the Jack and Jill Nursery School, who made available to us the amazing teaching talents of both Mrs. Iris Mosteller and Mrs. Clare Garneau in shaping up Elizabeth; and Miss Vesta Reever who, as principal of a public school, ensured that June could feel like a normal school girl.

We wish to acknowledge gratefully the substantial and matchless contributions to our program of Dr. Vita Krall, who not only tested all the children many times but also rated them and their parents during her visits as home-observer. To Dr. Gerald Motz we express our thanks for the careful evaluations he made, at periodic intervals, of the parents of our subjects. Many other colleagues have helped us by critically evaluating our methods or discussing our views. Especially are we grateful to Dr. Robert I. Watson, Dr. Aryeh Routtenberg, and Dr. Robert Sekuler for their invaluable assistance in defining some basic concepts and in developing our experimental design.

To those wonderful assistants who have read, edited, typed, and retyped the manuscript—Jeanne Fox, Ellen Dunlop, Mary Ann Holloman, Vivian Polhamus, Thelma Haddock, and Helen Porter—we also express our most sincere and affectionate gratitude.

Finally, to our families, whose interest in our work and patience with our long absences have sustained our courage and made our efforts worthwhile, we give our deepest and most heartfelt thanks.

Kansas City, Kansas   CAROLE F. CARLSON
December, 1968   AUSTIN M. DESLAURIERS

Table of Contents

The general psychological context in which this study on early infantile autism was developed is discussed in this Introduction, where we set forth the conditions of human personality growth, and the language or communication means which the child utilizes in insuring that his parents provide him with the conditions of his own personality development.

In this section the problem of early infantile autism is set forth in the context of parent-child interaction and communication. The syndrome is described and the literature concerning it is reviewed and critically evaluated. An interpretation is given of the behavioral manifestations of infantile autism as symptoms of sensory and affective deprivation, and a neurophysiological model is developed to account for the type and quality of this deprivation.

Part II   Can the child be aroused?

In this section the therapeutic implications of the neurophysio-
logical model are derived, and detailed steps are described which
could be used to reinstate in the autistic child a growth process
that would enable communication with the parental environ-
ment to take place. On this basis a research hypothesis is presented
and the methodological steps to carry it out are outlined. The
children and their families are introduced.

Part III   Arise!

This section gives a detailed account of the procedures used in carrying out the therapeutic program with the children and in involving the parents and teachers as first line therapists with the children.

Part IV   And the child arose: the results

Each child and his family are discussed here in terms of the ratings, tests, and observations made during the project, and crucial questions raised by the results obtained are discussed.

Part V   "In the beginning is relation . . . " (Buber)

In this section an effort is made at extending the implications of the theory, the approach, and the results of our project, to other forms of developmental deviations in children (such as the congenitally blind or deaf, the mentally retarded, children with severe learning disabilities, etc.) and to general problems of education. These broad views, stated from a scientific point of view, are then re-stated in a somewhat philosophical context of human aspirations and human dignity.

Appendix

Bibliography

Indexes

The Language of Childhood

a psycho-somatic model of
human communication

To speak of a relationship between a mother and her child in the early phases of development in this child is to assume that some sort of communication exists between these two human beings. This assumption, like so many which we make in discussing problems of early personality or ego development, does not, however, make clear either the type of communication that is presumed to take place or the conditions under which the communicated message can be transmitted or received. If, for instance, 2 days after birth, the baby is heard crying, nobody knows for sure what the baby is crying about; 6 months later, however, the baby's cries, though still open to many possible interpretations, will appear to have a much clearer reference to some specific meaning; 20 months later, crying will be clearly related to a specific cause. Obviously, communication is of a different type in each of these three instances, and, therefore, the type of relationship. Yet in all three situations, the element in common appears to be, on the part of the baby, an expressive sound accompanied by more or less diffuse or specific body gestures and movements; and, on the part of the mother (the environment), an alert, attentive response which brings the mother in direct contact with the child.

That communication or relation with a child, in the early phase of its personality development, is established through direct physical con-

1

tact would seem to be a well-confirmed fact, readily observed and demonstrable. Yet the relationship of such contact to the personality or
ego growth of the child is far from being clear. Experiments designed
to determine the value of such contact-communications with a variety
of young animals have served to emphasize their importance in the
animal's future adult patterns of responses to a variety of stimulating
and/or stressful situations (for a review of such experiments, see Levine, 1962), but the experimental results remain nevertheless ambigu-
ous with regard to the conditions under which such contacts must take
place to have a noticeable differentiated effect on future behavior.

In this connection, the concept of "critical periods," which was
brought forth by ethologists (Lorenz, 1935, 1958; Thorpe, 1961), has
been utilized as a possible hypothesis to explain, or at least clarify, the
problem at issue here. (See Scott, 1960; Gewirtz, 1961.) This concept had
the real advantage of taking into account *time sequences* in the development of the organisms under study, and therefore allowed for the possibility that certain conditions needed to be met, in the animals, before
a certain response to their behavior could bring about a relatively stable (learned) change in their behavior. Thus a critical period would be
certain moments in time, with reference to the growing organism, when
the communication made to the animal would be received and appropriately responded to with a predictable and stable pattern of behavior.
For instance, for a short while after hatching, the young of many species of birds and fowl will tend to follow closely, at a more or less constant distance, almost any moving object to which they might have
been exposed. The exposure of these young to such an object for a
brief period (a critical period) in the early hours of life (within 54 hours
for one species of bird; within 32 hours for another) can establish the
"following-behaviors" in great strength (see Hess, 1959). It is important, however, not to confuse this "following" behavior with "imprinting" which reflects a natural (instinctual) inclination on the part of animals (all animals and possibly humans also; see Thorpe, 1961; Scott,
1963; Gewirtz, 1961) to form primary (basic and elementary) social attachment to other animals close to them. The "following" behavior can
be viewed either as evidence that the primary social attachment has
been formed or as the process by which this attachment is established.
What is implied here appears to be that it is the physical presence of
one animal to his young which brings about the imprinting (primary
socialization) phenomenon, and that this is such an innate striving in

the young that some animals, like birds, will be driven to "follow" in order to maintain the physical presence of the other.

In human beings, such critical periods as ethologists have demonstrated in the case of certain animals have not been unequivocally observed. Spitz (1955; 1965) speaks of a number of such critical periods in the development of the child, but more as useful and convenient points of reference in understanding different patterns of behavior than as truly predictable instinctual responses to specific communications or contacts. Yet he brings attention also to the importance of the "presence," in a stable and predictable way, of the mother, the father, the siblings in a family, on the development of the primary socialization process in the child. Bowlby (1957; 1958) made even more explicit this need, in the child, for the physical presence of the mother and viewed as "critical," in the child's early relationship to his mother, those moments when through the instinctual expression of some behaviors—such as sucking, clinging, following with eyes or ears, smiling, and crying—the infant would act as a "releaser" in the parent of effective and appropriate modes of responses to his needs. The term releaser, which Bowlby directly borrowed from ethologists, has the value of emphasizing the idea of mutual correspondence between the infant's and the mother's organism; the crying or the smiling of the baby triggers off maternal responses in the mother which, in every way she can, affirm and assert the immediate availability of her physical presence to him.

Though Bowlby's hypothesis emphasizes the critical aspects of these communication patterns between the infant and his mother, it leaves out, however, the specific or critical time period at which such events should take place to have an effect in establishing learned patterns of responses in the child and his mother. In this connection, J. McV. Hunt (1961) writes: "What is important in the hypothesis of critical periods is the fact that various kinds of circumstances have effects when they occur at one period but not when they occur at another period. Whether or not circumstances have an effect appears to be a function of whether or not the organism has already developed within its repertoire schemata which are relevant to those circumstances and which can be accommodatively modified by them" (p. 290). It would thus appear then, that, as Hunt says, "every period along the line of development must be critical for experience with certain types of circumstances." The specific experience, however, of personal attachment and relationship to another human (mother) in the early environment of the child appears to be directly related to the immediate physical presence, pleasurable or unpleasurable, of the mother; on this basis, says Scott (1963) "we must therefore postulate the existence of an independent process of social attachment," independent, that is, of reward or punishment. "However," he adds, "we also have evidence that an intense emotional experience, whether rewarding or punishing, will increase the speed of forming the primary attachment" (p. 37). It would seem that what makes a period critical in the development of the child is not only the time at which it occurs but also the emotional climate and possibly the many other events that exist at the time when it occurs.

Because of this inadequacy of the concept of critical period to reflect truly the conditions of growth in the human child, another construct has been added which attempts to correlate somehow the changes in the child's behavior to the existing conditions in the neurological substrates of this behavior. Hebb (1949) has been able to demonstrate that, especially in infancy, organisms exposed to a multiplicity and variety of sensory contacts and stimulations will respond much more effectively, in a differentiated and appropriate way, to new situations of sensory contact and stimulation that those whose sensory experience, so to say, has been limited in variety or in amount. In the interaction between the organism and the environment, the possibility of behavioral changes taking place in the organism's response to the environment rests, according to Hebb, on two main factors: one is the existing intrinsic organization of the neural activity going on in the young organism; the other is the steadily increasing stimulating influence of the infant's environment. The activity of the neural intrinsic organization in the infant involves not only the active reception of the sensory stimulating field but also the active transmission of such sensory events along associative pathways; the more the same sensory event can be associated with a variety of sensory stimulations and circumstances, the easier it will be for the organism to acquire a stable response (learning) to that sensory event. In order to understand how the environment impinging on the organism can help the infant modify and adapt his behavioral response to the demands of the environment, Hebb postulates, between the sensory receptive areas of the cortex and the associative areas, a ratio (the A/S ratio) of stimulations received (contacts, communications) to the existing amount of associative pathways capable of linking this stimulation with a wide variety of previous experiences when such a stimulation was received. The greater the field of possible expression of any stimulation, the easier it is to fit any stimulation into existing "familiar" and stable patterns of behavioral responses. The child learns and grows to the rhythm of variety within stability. The more variety he experiences in the sensory stimulations he receives, the easier it is for him to fit any new stimulation into the widening intrinsic organization which develops in his central nervous system. From that point of view, it would be understandable that what could be a so-called critical period in one organism, as far as learning new, appropriate, and adaptive behavioral responses (if by "period" we refer only to the amount of time the organism has been developing) might be an uneventful period if that organism has not undergone, during that time, some *structural* changes conditioned by the amount and, especially, the variety of contact-stimulations provided by the environment (the mother).

Thus we are faced with the intriguing and paradoxical situation of a growing organism whose structural organization determines what is good or not for its growth in the environment, and whose environment determines what will be at any time the condition of its structural organization. Once we have set forth the problem of human relationships in those terms, the question of communication between mother and child, in the early phases of the child's ego or personality development, takes on a significance of much more far-reaching implications in our understanding of normal, or of pathological, personality growth.

The first implication is that the child *needs* his mother, and that the mother, in order to be such, *needs* the child. Now this sounds very much like a truism so thoroughly understood that it should go without saying. Yet, in the light of our preceding discussion, this commonplace statement assumes a much deeper sense. To say that the child needs his mother means that without the multiplicity and variety of stimulations which help shape the internal structural organization of the organism's total field of experiences, this organism—the child—will not grow and develop in a fully human way. To say that the mother needs the child means that without the incessant demand of the child upon the environment (the mother) for varied and numerous stimulations and contacts, the mother will be unable to know how to be a mother to that child. There is a reciprocity here at the ego developmental level which parallels very much the biological correspondence which exists, between mother and child, at the level of elementary life maintenance.

To carry this statement a step further, it is important at this time to define more clearly the terms of our statement. We speak of child and mother; of a relationship or communication between them; of a reciprocity which, at the psychological level of personality growth, parallels the biological correspondence between mother and child at the level of physiological development. The child is a living human organism which has detached itself from another organism, the mother, and which in this condition of separation can now develop and maintain, provided certain conditions are met, an independent existence. From the moment of conception to the moment of birth, there is a movement from one organism to two organisms, from one body to two bodies, from one human being to two human beings. There is now physical separation between the two, because each one has physical boundaries in which its mass, its weight, its volume are contained. All the formal properties of a physical mass can be attributed to these two organisms. They have dimensions and they have exteriors; there is distance and space between them; and all these can be measured with mathematical accuracy.

Withal, these two are living organisms, specifically human, endowed with sensory, affective, and motoric functions through which are expressed what has been conceptualized as those structures which make a human being human. It is through these structures and functions that mother and child relate and communicate.

Concerning this relationship and communication, some central features, important to a clear definition of the language of childhood, need to be made explicit now. First, not only do mother and child communicate, through the instrumentality of structures and functions available to them, but they want to and are built to do so. The simple model of Stimulus-Response is inadequate here to represent observed behavior; the dimensions of autonomy and initiative in the child and in the mother complicate the simple Stimulus-Response paradigm. The child anticipates (provokes) and reaches out for the stimulus to which he needs to respond. Very careful studies involving micro-motion analysis (Blauvelt, 1961) have demonstrated this initiative in the child, even in those behavioral reactions, observed soon after birth, that seem to be reflexes. In their study on the human newborn's capacity for orientation, as a central feature of the infant's interaction with the mother at feeding time, Blauvelt and McKenna (1961) were able to show that, immediately after birth, the infant and his mother possess the capacity to properly and mutually orient themselves to each other in an active and purposeful way. "The demonstration of the infant's response to specific stimulation makes possible the study of the mutual action of mother and baby. The continued orientation to their baby's face, observed in many parents, suggests that all or some of them sense and respond to this early response of their infants. At the level appropriate to his phase of development the neonate possesses capacity for such an interaction." And in our own work,* involving the careful observation of the transactional processes that go on between a child of two years and the mother, evidence has accumulated to support the view that, when in each other's presence, in conditions where neither can escape the other, mother and child demonstrate in their activities a type of anticipatory set that reflects dramatically, on the one hand, the initiative of the child in moving toward the mother and inciting from her a movement toward him, and, on the other hand, the initiative of the mother in giving support to any movement of the child towards her.

We speak here of movement between the mother and child, and this is the *second* important feature of the communication between these two which needs to be emphasized. Their presence to each other, specifically what brings mother and child in communication and relationship, is overwhelmingly expressed in reciprocal activities, in motility, and in spatial displacements. Sylvia Brody (1956) was led to this conclusion in her intensive observation of mothering patterns toward babies, and acknowledged the dominant role of activity and movement over any specific sensory stimulation as such. The mother defines herself to her child through the variety of activities she engages in with him. Our concern in the research on parental influence in the early ego development of the child was to determine those factors in the behavior of the mother which contribute most directly to the process of separation and differentiation that the child must undergo in his normal ego development. The data which we have accumulated in this connection give unquestionable priority to motility and action in the separating and differentiating efforts of the child. It is not enough for the child that the mother remain in passive attendance when she is with him. Whatever activity the child may engage in seemingly always includes some effort to get the mother actively involved with him. If the mother remains too far off by herself, or close by but aloof, or detached and passive, then the child's behavior in alerting the mother and in forcing her to move with him, and towards him, assumes an urgency which increases in tempo to the point where the child is seen as making a

* "Parental Influences on Early Ego Development in the Child." Research project supported in part by State of Illinois, Grant No. 17-151.

complete nuisance of himself. If, on the contrary, the mother becomes so active that her behavior leaves no room for any initiated movement of the child towards her, we see the child actively resetting some distance between himself and her, either by "spoiling" the game, pouting, and stubbornly refusing to move, or aggressively fighting her off. Thus motility, with its concomitant or resulting sensory pleasure or displeasure, appears as the central instrument of communication and relationship between mother and child, because it brings both in active, "alive" presence to each other. (See Escalona, 1965.)

Through her activities, the mother defines herself to the child by providing him with sensations of varied intensity and quality. In moving towards her or away from her, in "mixing it up," so to say, with her, in this back and forth movement, the child not only varies the degree and quality of his sensory experiences, but he also encounters the boundaries which define the mother in space; these boundaries are physical. We come then to a *third* important feature of the communication between mother and child: It is concretistic and physical. It is truly a language of the body; of its mass; its weight, dimensions, and extensions; and its appearance and external qualities. This is truly the "silent language," the social importance of which Edward T. Hall (1959) illustrated so dramatically. Here, truly, actions speak louder than words, and communication is made by movement in space. Thus physical conditions of communication appear to be necessary and present from the very first contacts between child and mother soon after birth, and Blauvelt (1961) has demonstrated that not only does the baby position himself as best he can in physical relation to the mother, but she herself tends to follow the movements of the baby so as to be on an identical axis to that of the baby's body.

The meaning of space in which activity takes place appears also central in our work. So much so, that we consider the observation room in which we place the mother and her three-year-old child as a most important, independent variable in bringing about qualitative changes in the transactional processes between these two.

This room situation creates a living condition the likes of which is rarely encountered at home. Though mother and child have lived together many months before they come to us, seldom have they been confronted with each other in such a way that they cannot escape each other. Under these conditions, the mother gives evidence of having to make radical adjustments to what might be referred to as her perceptual cognitive style (cf. Holzmann, Klein, Gardner, 1959). Whether "field dependent" or "field independent" (see Witkin, 1954), whether a "leveler" or a "sharpener," her outlook on her child is challenged to the maximum, because the child is constantly on top of her, so to say, and there is no place to hide. Even the wall-mirror in the room prevents escape by relentlessly reflecting to her gaze the narrow limits of her life space in this research room. To the observer, each movement between the child and his mother seems to be magnified in this small space, and our shorthand symbolic technique of recording these movements demonstrates what we are tempted to call the mathematics, or at least the geometry, of love (of affects, of feelings, of communication).

As the child moves toward the mother, the distance between the two is diminished. To this movement the mother can respond in several different ways: She can move to meet the child; she can attend to the movement of the child and encourage it; or she can move away from the child, by turning her back to him, by attending to something else, by actively discouraging him, and so forth. There is language to these bodily movements of the mother by which she defines herself to him in space. Mother is close; mother is far; mother is reachable; mother is unreachable; mother is with me; or mother is not with me. Various parts of the body play roles at different times in this communication. The position of the mother's head, for instance, as she looks at the child involved in some task, will determine whether the child "knows" that she is with him and be satisfied, or whether she is just "looking through him," leaving the child worried and dissatisfied. Extending her hand and touching the child will very often bring the mother in close enough communications with him that it will prevent restlessness and disorganization in his activity. Dramatizing with her entire body her presence to him appears to be a most natural and spontaneous form of histrionics for many mothers; the response the child gives to such performances makes it clear that in so doing she becomes very "alive" to him and he shares in this life.

A central hypothesis of our research work has been that in his relationship (his contacts) and his communication to his mother, the child is constantly seeking to define himself, that is, discover his own limits, and experience himself as a separated and differentiated individual. In this communication, which involves so many physical attributes of the child, the response of the mother is given through a reciprocal activity involving spatial displacement of her body. It is through such movements in space accompanied, and/or followed, by sensory stimulations that the mother defines herself to the child. As he reaches out for her, as he moves towards her, the child encounters his mother first as a body, as a physical object with dimensions, extensions, volume, and mass. The sensations he experiences as he moves toward her, with her, on her, constitute for the child what we would like to suggest as the precursor of his body image. There is no representational quality to this "image," but rather it is a total sensory experience in which, at various times in the child's development, one sensory modality appears to dominate over the other. Thus, for instance, whereas tactile sensations are probably the dominant aspect of the experience in the early mother-child contact, auditory and visual qualities would seem to assume a greater and greater importance in this total experience as the child distances himself physically from the mother. Our research findings in this connection, however, suggest that the various modalities within tactile experiences remain fundamental in the development of the child's definition of his own body, so that even when visual communication takes over, this visual experience retains a tactile quality, a sensuous one, if you want, rather than a representational image or an esthetic experience. The more the mother is physically available in a direct contact-communication with her child, the easier it is for him to separate himself from her and move independently.

The preceding discussion of the basic modes and patterns of communication and relationship between the child and the mother can provide a clearer understanding of the concept of body image. The observations which form the empirical basis of this concept lead us to the following proposition: The body of the mother, with its living, physical, qualities is an integral part of the child's progressive experience of himself as a separated and differentiated individual. This means that the body of the mother is an integral part of the development of the child's own body image. But precisely because such a development takes place in the actuality of a physical contact-communication between the child and the mother, in which are involved a wide variety of motoric activities and sensory stimulations, our discussion leads us to offer a formal counterpart to the suggested empirical definition of the child's body image. Stated formally, the concept of body image can be defined as an *organ of communication* where the image—not in its representational value, but in its experiential sensory qualities—is a complex matrix of all the bodily movements which bring the child in contact with the mother's own body, and of all the sensory experiences which accompany these movements and these contacts.

Thus we can speak of the language of the childhood as both the source and the expression of the child's body image. The source, because the physical sensory communication which the child makes to the mother helps him define himself in relation to her. The expression, because the clearer the experience in the child of his separation and differentiation from the mother, the easier it is for him to move freely toward or away from her, as a developing, individuated organism. That is, separation and differentiation lead to more separation and differentiation—which eventually culminate in a separate unique identity. The child speaks with his body, moving toward the mother to receive responses that make him feel alive and real. The mother responds with her body, to provide the external physical sensory stimulations that keep alive and real the child's experience of his separation from her and communication with her. In this interactional reciprocity or, as Grinker puts it (1953), in this "transactional process," the foundations of human communications are laid. Only after this separation has taken place can a real relationship between two separated and differentiated individuals take place. This is the "psychosomatic" model of human communication, and its implications are far-reaching for a better understanding of pathology in early personality development and of the therapeutic process that can be used in dealing with pathology.

First, the sensory-motor qualities of the earliest forms of human communication, fundamental as they are to normal personality growth, antecede any symbolic or verbal representations and cannot truly be encompassed by them. Piaget's (1954) observations, experiments, and demonstrations offer ample support to such a statement. The first, and immediate, implication of such a state of affairs is that between human beings, regardless of age and the specific language they may use, there exists a commonality in the basic instruments of communication; this common instrumentality is the human body in its organismic and experiential sensory motor components. In any human interaction, communication is possible only if the following conditions are met: One, that each party in the interaction experiences himself as separated and differentiated from the other; second, that a movement is initiated by one which, through its sensory stimulation of the other, makes his presence felt and experienced by the other. The response given by this other to the felt presence of the one who initiated the communication, will maintain and develop the communication only if it represents a similar sensory-motor activity which stimulates in the first one the experience and awareness of his physical presence to him. What we are saying here is that what brings two people together has little relationship to the number, type, or variety of symbols, signs, and words that may be used. Somehow the very early experience of the immediate and direct impact of the body-image language must be reinstated in order for the communication between individuals to be personal, meaningful, and enriching. The basic form of communication cannot be reduced to words, and therefore cannot be reinstated through verbal associations or imagery. This means that there are certain difficulties in human relationships and communication that cannot be expressed except through the body, and that there are certain individuals who retain the capacity to speak to others more easily through body language than through the more distant, abstract instrumentality of verbal communication. There is no room here for a conceptual framework which assumes a duality of body-psyche and which would lead to a vain search for bodily correlates of psychological events. Rather, the somatic event is the behavior "bit" which communicates the individual's personal need and difficulties because there is no available symbolic representation of this need, or of these difficulties, in the individual. There is no available symbolic representation because these basic needs existed prior to symbol-formation ability; i.e., they are pre-verbal and pre-symbolic.

In a searching essay, Grinker (1963) raised the question of communication with severely depressed patients and emphasized the frustrating condition created by verbally expressing to such patients whatever seemed therapeutically appropriate, only to find that what had been said and seemingly understood by the patients, never really became effective or meaningful to them. Obviously, the therapeutic verbal effort was not communicating anything to these patients. A language was being used here which was not the language of the patient's plea for help. If, however, in the light of our preceding discussion, the "depression" is accepted, in its concrete, physical qualities of a severe drop in energy level, then the only language that can establish any degree of true communication with a depressed patient has to be physical and concrete, reflecting the basic body-image foundations of human relationships. The success achieved in the therapy of depressed patients, where strong and insistent demands are made that the patients work physically and hard, attests to the validity of such a level of communication with the so-called psychological condition of "depression" (Hollon, 1962).

A second implication of this body-image theory of communication is that any form of barrier or obstacle to the receiving of adequate sensory messages, in the child, will have severe effects on this child's capacity to separate and differentiate himself from others, establish a meaningful relationship with others, and communicate with them. This is the same as saying that any significant degree of sensory deprivation in the pre-verbal or presymbolic period of the child's life adversely affects the child's personality or ego development, preventing the possibility of object relationships and meaningful human communication. The depri-vation can be viewed as primary when the sensory receptors of the child are damaged peripherally (such as in deaf and blind children) or are prevented from reaching an adequate level of sensory "arousal" in the child because of central impairment or dysfunction in the brain. In such cases, we are confronted with developmental deviations that cannot be subsumed under general headings of somatic or psychological patholo-gies, but rather need to be understood, because they are directly related to the preverbal levels of human experience, as truly psychosomatic im-pairments of communication.

Unlike these primary forms of impairments, which bring about ex-treme deviations in the normal rate of childhood personality develop-ment, many so-called atypical forms of personality growth in the child appear related not to any major defect in the child's sensory receptive functions, but to an environmental deprivation of adequate and ap-propriate sensory stimulating responses. Here the capacities of the child to separate and differentiate himself from others would be potentially adequate were it not that, for a variety of reasons, the maternal sensory impact on the child is either too weak (inattention, rejection, apathy) to reach the child, or is forcing the child to a regressive position of sen-sory unavailability as a defense against an inordinately painful over-stimulation. In either case, such "secondary" forms of sensory depriva-tion, or overload, produce serious developmental personality defects in the child, which can be viewed less as deviations from a normal growth process than as a breakdown of previously attained levels of personality organization. Yet here also the central defect in the child's capacity to relate to others and communicate with them appears consequent to a loss of bodily sensory experiences essential to an adequate development of body image, which is the basic instrument of human personal com-munication (DesLauriers, 1962).

Thus from the concept of body image, empirically described as the sum total of physical, sensory contacts between the child and the mother, and formally defined as the instrument of relationship and communication between these two, a truly psychosomatic model of human communication can be derived. In this model, any stated or implied duality between body and mind has no place. The sensory motor quality of the behavior which brings the child in the presence of the mother, and the stimulating response which the mother gives to the physical presence of the child, lay the foundation of an interactional process of growth in which the separation and differentiation of the child, as an individual, is constantly enhanced and fostered by the pattern of physical, bodily communication. The entire organism of the child, in its internal and external behavior, speaks to the mother, and demands of her those physical sensory responses which will stimulate in the child an increased awareness of the mother's physical presence to him, and an expanding experience of his own individuated and defined reality. This primitive dialogue is beyond symbolic representation, translation, or interpretation; it cannot be encompassed by words. Yet, by the same token, it cannot truly be said to be nonverbal. Basically and developmentally, this dialogue is preverbal; its content is the totality of those varied sensory-motor behaviors that place mother and child in physical presence to each other. In this primary form of human communication, the child, through his body, says to the mother: I am alive and I exist because I can feel, smell, taste, see, hear your body, and know you are here; and the attentive mother, through her body, responds: I am here, and you can be alive and exist now, because I touch you, hold you, feel you, and so forth. Such a psychosomatic communication, because it is the most basic form of human relationship and because without it the early ego (personality) development of the child would be crippled, remains even in adult life a most expressive instrument of human communication. This language is truly primitive; its physical, somatic, sensory-motor directness reaches the original sources of life in the developing human individual. Its primitivity is not truly regressive because this language always says everything that needs to be said. Thus, for some adults, whose distress in life is "beyond words," this form of communication becomes the only way they have of crying out: I need you here, physically present to me, touching me, holding me, feeding me, etc., to know that I am alive and exist. The response to that appeal should be just as simple, as direct, as primitive.

"In the beginning is relation," writes Buber (1923). "Consider the speech of 'primitive' people, that is, of those (like the child) that have a meagre stock of objects, and whose life is built up within a narrow circle of acts highly charged with presentness. The nuclei of this speech, words in the form of sentences and original pregrammatical structures, mostly indicate the wholeness of a relation. We say 'far away'; the Zulu has for that a word which means, in our sentence form: 'There, where someone cries out: O Mother, I am lost.' "

The body-image language, the language of childhood, reflects, even more directly, this primitivity. When the mother is not there, when she is "far away," she is, for the child "there (at that distance) where someone (the child, with everything that he is) cries out: 'O Mother, I am lost! Hold me, touch me, let me feel that I'm alive with you.' "

There are some children who are "far away" from their mother, because they seem incapable of crying out: "O Mother, I am lost!" This book is about such children. In seeking to determine the quality of the relationships, between the child and his parents, which influenced most profoundly the growth and development of the child's personality, a most convincing answer, we felt, could come from an understanding of those children whose behavior alienates them from any close contact with their human environment, and prevents them from receiving from this environment those stimulating responses necessary to their growth. Such is the condition of the early infantile autistic child. The early infantile autistic child not only does not reach out for human contacts, he is also unreachable by those around him who try to contact him. Here we have, it seems, a dramatic illustration of the essential importance of the reciprocal communication pattern, which we described earlier, between the child and the parent, where the initiative of the child in seeking stimulating responses from the environment is central to the possibility of bringing about in the parent an adequate parental response. The autistic infant has no initiative, he does not reach out, he does not cry out: "O Mother, I am lost, and I need you"; and therefore the parent not only has no response to give, but the incentive to give a response progressively dies, and the parent eventually appears just as distant from the child as the child is from the parent.

But what would happen if somehow we could arouse such a child? What would ensue if somehow we could alert the initiative of this child to the point where he would begin to reach out to the parental environment? If we could do this, we could expect that the parent, distant and alien without such messages from the child, would then discover and give those parental responses necessary to the child's growth. And if this happened, then we would expect to see the child, isolated and alone until then, begin a reciprocal exchange with his environment which would lead to a normal process of personality development.

The answers to these questions constituted the central challenge of our concern with autistic infants. To meet this challenge meant that we had first to understand what the autistic position represented in the picture of human life; is the autistic infant's behavior a defensive rebellion against a world which does not want him, or the mute isolation of a child who does not know how to reach out to the world? In the second place, we had to find some explanation for this autistic position in the child if we were to assess in what way or to what extent it could be changed; what type of explanation would best encompass and give sense to this child's behavior, and would offer a possibility of changing it? The first part of this book deals with these issues and presents our answers as hypotheses to be tested.

In the second part, we describe the method we used in putting our theory to test. The therapeutic implications of the explanation we give of the autistic behavior are outlined first, and the setting and conditions under which we applied them are given. How we approach the autistic child, what measures we use in assessing whatever change takes place in his development, what role the parents are asked to play in this effort and what changes can be measured in their own response to their autistic youngster, these questions represent the steps we took in putting to test our theory.

The results of our work are reported in the third part of this book and are followed by a general discussion of the meaning of our investigation for the understanding of personality development in children in the light of the psychosomatic theory of human communication which we described in the earlier part of this chapter. If, as Buber wrote (*op. cit.*), "In the beginning is relation," and if relation is more important to communication than words, could it be that a better understanding of the "mystery" of early infantile autism could lead us, as was suggested by Sarason (1958), to a clearer awareness of those fundamental factors in human relationships which are basic to meaningful and enriching human communication! We hope, through this book, to shed some light on the "mystery" of early infantile autism, and make some contributions to a better understanding of human relationships.

Part I

. . . Your child is not
dead, she's asleep . . .

Mark V : 39

Chapter I

The Circle of Silence

the autistic infant and his parents

What is wrong with Kathy*

The first year. We were unaware of anything wrong with Kathryn. In fact we were very happy and content to have such a sweet and good baby. We did not realize she was too good to be true. We had an older child—Mark. As an infant he was active, restless, and a continual case of hunger. Kathryn was so content and good that it was sheer joy to have such a baby. People looked shocked and probably doubted the veracity of my statement that Kathryn had never cried for food or milk since she was three months old. She never cried at all! This did cause me some concern as I had heard that crying strengthens the lungs, and I was sure she would have weak lungs.

Another sign of trouble during her first year that should have alarmed us, but didn't, was that she never cried for attention. She had no need to be held or cuddled as a normal baby does.

Still another warning sign was Kathryn's ever-increasing fear of anything, anyone, or any place new to her. She would cry and not be consoled until she was safely home again. Just getting in the car frightened her, and she would cover her eyes. This fear of change or newness began around six to eight months as she became aware of her environment. We couldn't go to church, to the grocery store, or anywhere as a family

* These pages about Kathy were written by her mother.

19

because poor little Kathryn would cry the whole time. We catered to her fears and went on errands singly, always taking Mark so he didn't miss out on so much.

Her fears included our dog, which surprised me. Children are often afraid of dogs but usually not if they have a dog, and certainly not of their own dog. Bessy was quite a large and clumsy dog so I thought perhaps her size explained Kathryn's fear. She was so small compared to Bessy.

Kathryn's physical development went along very normally. She sat, crawled, stood holding on, and walked holding on to furniture all within a normal range. She started to crawl at seven and a half months and was a very proficient little girl. She was walking around the furniture by 9 to 10 months. But she was still walking by holding on to the furniture at 16 months. It was during this interim that we began to have apprehensions about her. Why wouldn't she let go and try to walk? She wasn't hanging on for balance, only touching for security.

I took her to our former family doctor for her first year physical checkup. I told him of her fear of everything. To my chagrin he just chuckled and commented that he had no pill for that, and we would have to let time take care of it. Of course, she was crying all the time in his office. He told me to bring her back another day when she wasn't crying because he couldn't examine her while she was so upset. That was the last time I ever went to that doctor. I came home and immediately called the pediatrician to whom we had always taken Mark and made Kathryn's first appointment. I knew she would cry no matter when I took her, so there was absolutely no point in waiting for a day when she wouldn't. Dr. L. examined her thoroughly and pronounced her in fine health. On the day of our appointment the doctor's waiting room was so crowded that I decided to save my questions of her fears for the time being.

Feeding became more of a problem as each month passed. She showed no interest in food at all, and even less in feeding herself. I just brought her to the kitchen at mealtime, and she ate passively as I gave her each spoonful. I never knew for sure when or if she was full. When the food on the plate was gone that was okay with her. I did get a rather wry chuckle out of a statement in Dr. Spock's book. He said that no child would starve to death if food was in front of them. I thought to myself —he just hasn't seen Kathryn, because I know she would. I even skipped two meals one day in hopes she would accept new food. It failed completely and I didn't have the courage or strength of determination to starve her any more. It was clear that she wasn't aware of being hungry anyway.

For her first birthday her Daddy gave her a small pink animal. We all called it Fuzzy. Fuzzy became Kathryn's constant companion. He seemed to give her some sort of warmth and security that we couldn't give her. He slept with her, and she carried him and hugged him most all of the time. Not until we began her therapy sessions at nearly three years of age did she part with her beloved Fuzzy.

She made no sounds or coos as a baby, and there was no hint of the beginnings of speech. At this time I wasn't concerned since Mark was slow to start talking, but certainly made up for it once he started. I am not the kind of mother who talks to babies. I feel uncomfortable and even silly carrying on a one-sided conversation with a baby. I knew very well that the sound of mother's voice is pleasant to the baby and probably did encourage the baby to mimic at an earlier age, but I still couldn't do it.

During her second year my husband and I faced the fact that something was wrong with our little girl, but we were at a complete loss to know what. We decided to try and do something about it ourselves. This job was largely up to me, since my husband, of course, was gone all day.

The second year.   The first thing I decided to do was to make her realize that I was her mother and I wanted to hold her. I would pick her up and carry her out to the living room and sit in my rocking chair. She would cry and try to get off my lap, but I held her close and talked to her. In a surprisingly short time she stopped rejecting this form of attention and acted as though she enjoyed it. I was greatly encouraged.

Next on the list of problems was her eating. She was still drinking milk from a bottle, and we thought she should use a cup now. We tried offering her a cup and were met with total rejection. We then took the bottle away completely, hoping that a physical need or craving for milk would work on our side and make her try the cup. It didn't, so we took a rather drastic step which upset us both quite a lot. It seemed so cruel. One of us held her head and the other gave her milk from the cup. Again this effort was successful in a very short time. After only two or three crying and fighting sessions she found out that it was really okay to drink from a cup and she drank readily thereafter. However, she insisted on drinking from only one cup, her cup, limiting her drinking only to mealtimes, and only to milk or orange juice. She would never drink any water.

From these two experiences we concluded that we couldn't be gradual about necessary changes. We had to decide what was right to do, and then do it amid her screams of fear and protest.

She got too big for her little plastic bathtub as we knew she would, but she screamed when I put her in the bathtub. This time I felt it was unnecessary to force her to accept this change. I just couldn't do it. She hung on to me so tightly and was so frightened that we both ended up crying. After that I put her in the kitchen sink. She was frightened, of course, the first time, but after that she was fine.

She stayed withdrawn in her own room and we either went in there or carried her out if we were to see her. She spent hours curled up on her bed clutching her beloved pink Fuzzy animal, scratching at the wall or flickering her fingers in front of a light. When in bed she often rocked with such vigor as to move her bed halfway across the room.

The third year.   After her second birthday we faced the problem more realistically and knew we needed help. We had to know what was wrong. I was emotionally torn apart as it was so difficult to face these changes. I was in constant fear that I would make her worse. I was certain that her problem, whatever it was, was psychiatric in nature and that she needed professional help.

This was a period of extreme anguish for us. My first step was to consult Kathryn's pediatrician, Dr. L. I told him of her problems and difficulties, and he suggested that we take her to the Pediatrics Evaluation Center of a hospital in a large metropolitan area. He mentioned the possibility of a personality change. That was the only clue I needed to assure myself that her problem was indeed psychiatric. I consulted with Dr. L. in September, and we immediatedly applied to the Evaluation Center. It was not until February that we started the evaluation, and these months were indeed black ones for us. I went over in my mind, until I could no longer, everything that I could think of that could have affected her emotionally. I was sure it was my fault that she was disturbed. I became psychosomatically ill myself during these months. This was never diagnosed, only my own opinion, but it seemed accurate. A few weeks after talking to Dr. L. I became hoarse and could barely talk. This condition lasted during these months of anxiety and disappeared completely once we started the evaluation process. I knew it was psychosomatic, but that didn't help at all.

Once the evaluation started, a calm of sorts settled down on us and we didn't feel the anxiety and dread so intensely. We were frightened but it didn't gnaw at us anymore. We had confidence in the people who would examine Kathryn, and we were sure that we would have positive answers to our questions. Knowing the truth, no matter how bad, is always easier than fearing the unknown. During her evaluation she was tested in every conceivable way—eyes, hearing, neurology, EEG, brain X-ray, pediatrics, occupational therapy, speech therapy, psychology, psychiatry, etc.

Throughout all the tests she cried and there was no cooperation at all. She would start to cry as soon as we walked in the door of the clinic and didn't stop until we left. During brief times in the waiting room she would quiet down and walk around a little, seemingly intrigued by the different floor tiles, but mostly she sat on my lap and clung to me in fear. The worst ordeal of all was the X-ray. We had to lay her on the X-ray table while she screamed in terror. We had to tape her to the table and forcibly hold her down. I was so upset and felt so sorry for her that I came very near grabbing her and running out. It was a dreadful ordeal for both of us, but I stuck it out and she had no other choice.

Anecdote: One doctor came in to examine her reflexes and brought two interns along. He was telling them how to get a baby's attention and keep the baby happy. Well, with Kathryn his method was a total failure and he looked a bit foolish. She cried and threw his "objects of interest" on the floor.

We had to cancel our first appointment for our final conference at the Evaluation Center. Mark was sick; John called Mrs. G. to cancel and arrange for a new time. He told me that Mrs. G. seemed quite anxious to see us soon and reassured John that they had something planned to help us. We had no idea what she meant, and she didn't volunteer any information. During the time of Kathy's evaluation I had become rather puzzled and uncertain. It seemed at times that the various ways they examined her had little to do with her problems. I knew her eyes and ears and muscles and reflexes were okay so I suppose I was mostly impatient. I was very anxious for the psychologist to see her, and when he did I deluged him with questions. He couldn't answer them so he was evasive and noncommital. This bothered me a little but I rather thought he wished I would keep quiet so he could observe Kathryn. All

I could think of was why?—why?—why? Why won't she chew her food? Why does she throw everything down? Why can't I hold her on my lap? Why is she so afraid of everything? and so on ad infinitum. A little later we were called and asked to bring Kathy in again because a psychiatrist wanted to see her. I was sure now that they were on the right track. When we took her up for the final visit she was in better shape and didn't cry and cling to me. When the psychiatrist came in she was standing on the flood studying the tile. He tried to hug her and she pulled away instantly. He asked me if she let us hug her. I said, "No, she only clings to me if she is afraid." He said that was all he needed to know. He had evidently satisfied himself, but I was a little disappointed that the whole thing was over in so short a time. From then on until our conference I was bewildered about Kathy's problem. I had seen a number of children with various problems all getting the same tests as Kathy, but none seemed at all like Kathy. Everyone there was so nice to us and seemed extra nice to Kathy. I wondered if her problem, whatever it was, had any hope for help.

Finally the conference day came and I was not only relieved that at last we would know what the problem was but also very frightened of the truth. I felt that I could accept any problem, no matter how serious, if there was just some way to help her.

We had to wait only a few minutes, and then Mrs. G. led us into Mrs. A's office. I had scarcely sat down when Mrs. A. said, "Kathy has a very serious problem." I went numb all over and just sat there staring at her.

Kathy is an autistic child

In 1943 Kanner published an article entitled "Autistic Disturbances of Affective Contact." It contained extensive case history and observation material on 11 children between the ages 2½ and 8½ years, who he felt came "into the world with an innate inability to form the usual biologically provided affective contact with people." From this material he abstracted a number of essential common characteristics forming, in his opinion, a syndrome never before reported. Kanner considered these characteristics to be unique to this syndrome, which subsequently became known as "Early Infantile Autism." Rimland, in a recent book (1964) *Early Infantile Autism*, using Kanner's original observations in conjunction with a critical and comprehensive review of the available literature on early infantile autism, has attempted to further delineate the characteristics of the syndrome, especially as it is differentiated from childhood schizophrenia. The symptom complex outlined below is based primarily on the Kanner and Rimland formulations, with some additional information from more recent literature and from observations by the present authors of children with early infantile autism.

The most distinct characteristic of the syndrome is what Kanner (1943) referred to as extreme autistic aloneness; i.e., the child's inability to relate himself in an ordinary way to people and situations from the beginning of life. Indeed, it is because this characteristic was so striking that Kanner, in his original article, was led to consider the disorder as a "disturbance in affective contact." This "aloneness" is described as an aloofness, a preoccupied air, an inability to adjust emotionally to humans, even to the extent of complete indifference to the comings and goings of the child's own parents.

A second extremely important characteristic is the child's insistence on the preservation of sameness. The child is often extremely upset by environmental changes; e.g., changes of routine, of furniture arrangement, or of the order in which everyday acts are carried out.

In conjunction with the above two characteristics the child himself appears unoriented (as opposed to disoriented), detached, and disinterested in events occurring around him. He is aloof and indifferent to the surroundings as long as the sameness he requires is maintained. He will often occupy himself for hours with some repetitive activity involving either the manipulation of an object or of some part of his own body (as in rocking, wall scratching, twirling an object, or in ritualistic or bizarre hand movements). Throughout these activities he appears independent, self-sufficient, and self-absorbed.

Physically the children appear healthy and are frequently described as beautiful and well formed. They usually present a history of general good health, except for early (during the first year) eating difficulties and continued peculiar eating habits such as failure to show any sign of hunger, refusal to chew, very late acquisition of self-feeding skills, insistence on using only certain dishes, etc. There are usually marked difficulties in toilet training and, if and when acquired, it is usually at a much later than normal age.

In terms of physical responsiveness these children are remarkably unpliable, stiff and unresponsive, failing to adapt themselves to their mothers or other adults when being carried or held. In this connection,

Kanner (1943) mentions the recollection by many mothers that these children failed to assume at any time an anticipatory posture preparatory to being picked up.

Motorically the children frequently appear somewhat clumsy in gait and gross motor performance (Kanner, 1943). However, quite often they are very skillful in terms of finer muscle coordination; e.g., they often exhibit a high degree of skill in twirling, spinning, or picking up small objects. Also, as mentioned earlier, they frequently engage in bizarre or ritualistic hand movements and in body rocking.

Only about half of the reported cases are able to use speech. The language, when present, is of a very peculiar nature. It is characterized by one or several of the following features: (1) affirmation, by repetition of a question (absence of the word "yes"); (2) pronominal reversal (absence of word "I"); (3) delayed echolalia type of repetition of whole phrases; (4) irrelevant and metaphorical use of language (e.g., Kanner's child who referred to his grandmother as "55").

The question of the presence of normal or abnormal electroencephalographs in children with early infantile autism is still a moot one. Rimland (1964) in his survey of the literature concluded that they are usually normal, but occasionally equivocal or borderline. However, a study published in 1964 (not included in Rimland's survey) by White and his associates reported that 58.6 percent of the autistic children studied had abnormal EEG's including such phenomena as focal slowing and paroxysmal spikes. Thus, at this point it is probably safe to conclude that as often as not the EEG's of autistic children are abnormal, but these abnormalities never seem to be associated with seizures or any detectable neurological deficit.

Hallucinations are considered to be absent in autistic children. However, some authors postulate the existence of negative hallucinations; i.e., the autistic child pretends that the world doesn't exist.

Another area which has received considerable discussion regarding the occurrence of early infantile autism is that of family background. Time and again the high educational and intellectual background of progenitors has been emphasized, and this fact forms a major cornerstone in most genetic and psychogenic theories as to the etiology of the syndrome. The present authors feel that this is best interpreted as a spurious correlation for several reasons. It is a commonly noted fact that autistic children are frequently misdiagnosed the first time around as mentally defective, brain-damaged, deaf-mutes, or as cases of childhood schizophrenia. Due to the high cost of the extensive procedures in most evaluation centers, it would seem reasonable to expect that only those families in higher economic brackets could afford to go through these procedures a second and third time. Higher income is generally correlated with higher educational and intellectual backgrounds. Further, there is reported a high preponderance of the diagnosis of early infantile autism among children of Jewish descent (Rimland, 1964). This particular ethnic group is well known for its psychological sophistication and its intensive provision of facilities in this area. It also contains a higher percentage of educated and professional people than the general population.

Another family characteristic which may be more pertinent is the much lower than average rate of psychosis in parents, grandparents, and siblings. However, if the above statements regarding economic selection factors are operative, one might also expect these educationally and professionally successful people to be emotionally stable relative to the rest of the population.

In summary, the syndrome of early infantile autism is a condition which is present from the beginning of life, although not usually suspected until the latter part of the first year of life. It is characterized by extreme autistic aloneness, personal detachment, lack of orientation, and insistence on the preservation of sameness. The children are frequently described as beautiful. Health is generally good though there are often difficulties with eating habits and toilet training. Physically they are unresponsive to other humans. Motorically, they are somewhat clumsy in gross motor performance, though often very skillful in the area of fine muscular coordination. Often they display bizarre or ritualistic hand movements and body rocking. Language (present in only about 50 percent of the cases) is very peculiar in nature and hardly at all useful as a method of communication. The EEG may or may not be abnormal but there are no seizures and no evidence of neurologic deficit. Hallucinations are absent. Familial background similarities which may or may not be genuinely characteristic, are: (1) high educational and intellectual background; (2) low incidence of psychosis. In order to be diagnosed as suffering from early infantile autism a child need not exhibit all of the behavioral features discussed above, although obviously the more of them he exhibits the more sure one can be of the accuracy of the diagnosis. However, the diagnosis of autism cannot be made if the child fails to display: (1) the characteristic autistic aloneness; and (2) the insistence on the preservation of sameness; i.e., these two characteristics are considered necessary though insufficient criteria for making the diagnosis of early infantile autism. Further, the history of the child should warrant assuming that these symptoms were notice-able, if only in retrospect, within approximately the first 6 to 18 months of life.

Chapter II

The Communication Barrier

autistic behavior and
sensory and emotional deprivation

In the face of such behavior the first question must be: What does this behavior reflect? Is it a response to an environment which is rejecting or insufficient in providing developmentally effective gratification? Or is it the direct manifestation of a neurological defect in the child such that it is the child's organism itself which is lacking in developmental potential and that it would be hopelessly naïve to expect, in this situation, anything but minimal ego development?

The autistic child seems to lack the natural propensity toward provoking from the parents (or any human being) those types of responses which foster and enhance his progress toward separation, differentiation, and identity. This child is isolated and alone. One is confronted here with what appears to be such a minimal degree of human ego functioning that Bettelheim (1959; 1967) was led to compare the autistic behavior to that of feral primitivity. The behavior syndrome described by Kanner and Rimland reflects what might be viewed as primitive antecedents to ego functions; in all areas—perceptual, affective, motoric, and cognitive—there is evident a serious developmental lag. The autistic child is so isolated from any communication with others that not only is he, for all practical purposes, unreachable through ordinary modes of personal or social contacts, but he has no interest in, or response to,

29

such contacts, being contented, apparently, with the unending repetition of simple, stereotyped, manneristic forms of behavior. In a family where there are other children, parents of the autistic child, while completely helpless in reaching or understanding this one, seem quite capable of having normal and gratifying relationships with the other children. In other words, the autistic child somehow cannot provoke from the parents the responses he needs and therefore they cannot be truly present to him as parents. It is as if this child were not "in tune" with them; he stands "by himself" in the most literal sense of this expression. There is no communication here, because there is no relationship, and this situation, in a negative way, illustrates best the basic requirements of ego development. The "isolation" of the autistic child cuts him off from his parents, and the parents progressively cease to have any effective response to him.

The effects of sensory deprivation

In attempting to understand the quality of this "isolation" in the autistic child, we were led to view it in the light of the extensive reports on sensory isolation, restriction, or deprivation (see Fiske & Maddi, 1961; Solomon et al., 1961; Schultz, 1965). In the mass of experimental evidence accumulated in the past 10 years on the behavioral effects and consequences of sensory restriction, it is striking to note how every area of ego functioning is, in one way or another, seriously affected when a human individual is left with minimal or unvarying sensory stimulation. Duane P. Schultz, in his recent book *Sensory Restriction, Effects on Behavior* (1965), has summarized most dramatically this evidence. These sensory restriction or deprivation experiments have been conducted under a number of conditions involving an attempt either to decrease all kinds of stimulus input to an absolute minimum, or to reduce patterning and meaningful organization of sensory input while maintaining a somewhat normal level of input. The sensory modalities most frequently involved are the visual, the auditory, and the proprioceptive-kinesthetic (via body immobilization). Under such conditions of minimal or unchanging sensory stimulation the human individual finds himself "out of touch" with an object; the experiences that he undergoes have a discrete and discontinuous quality which prevent any real, meaningful integrations; his perceptual processes, his capacity to learn, his memory and associative functions, his capacity to control his feelings and emotions, and his thoughts and ideas have such a disconnected and disparate quality that they cease to contribute to any real or effective object relationship. He becomes detached, apathetic, and irritable. Even at the motoric level there is evidence of a peculiar kind of gross motor incoordination; spatial relationships are disturbed; repetitive and ritualistic muscular patterns appear; and yet in these manneristic-like forms of motor behavior, there remains a capacity for finer and more delicate and discrete movements. The striking similarity of such effects of sensory restriction with the description of autistic behavior in children strongly supports the view that the "isolation" of early infantile autism represents a severe case of sensory deprivation.

However, laboratory experiments on the effects of early sensory deprivation are, for obvious reasons, restricted to the use of very young animals (see especially the works of Hebb, 1949, 1958; Reisen, 1961; and others). Nevertheless, it is possible to glean some very good evidence as to the effects of sensory and perceptual deprivation on human infants by referring to the maternal deprivation studies of institutionalized children, and to studies of children born with specific sensory defects such as blindness. What is of particular interest here are the obvious similarities between the behavior of these children and the behavior of children with early infantile autism.

Rimland (1964), Keeler (1958), and Eveloff (1960) have commented on the similarity between autistic children and those institutionalized infants suffering from "hospitalism" or anaclitic depression. According to Eveloff, ". . . the major differentiating factor is affect. The autistic child is affectless, if not disturbed in his preoccupation, while the anaclitically deprived children may closely resemble autistic children in advanced stages." Most investigators in this area have chosen to place the blame for this condition (anaclitic depression) on maternal deprivation, i.e., specific absence of maternal stimulation and love. However, any careful inspection of the general descriptions of the institutional settings in which these children spend the first 12 to 18 months of their lives clearly shows that these children exist in an environment which is lacking not only in the presence of maternal stimulation, but is strikingly devoid of nearly all kinds of stimulation (Spitz, 1945, 1946a, 1946b; Bowlby, 1951; Aubry, 1955). Indeed, after reading Spitz's description of the environmental conditions surrounding the foundling home infants, whom he studied, one would be hard put to suggest further sensory or perceptual stimulus restriction short of tube feeding, tube evacuation, elimination of daily baths, and maintenance of perpetual darkness.

If we turn next to a consideration of studies of children who were born blind (see Keeler, 1958; Sandler, 1963; and Burlingham, 1961), especially those suffering from the condition of retrolental fibroplasia, we find another example of children who present autistic patterns of behavior to a more or less severe degree. In his attempt to establish overoxygenation in infancy as the causative factor in brain damage leading to the behavioral manifestations of early infantile autism, Rimland (leaning heavily on Keeler's study) strongly stresses the similarity between the behavior of autistic children and those with retrolental fibroplasia, a condition known to be associated with prematurity and oxygen administration. However, he fails to note that unlike other children who are born blind, these children, because of their premature condition, not only receive oxygen, but also spend the first several months of their lives in hospital incubators.

Certainly the availability of all types of stimulation under these conditions is curtailed; and the one type of stimulation which might be available to any other child living in an incubator, visual stimulation, is also denied these children. Likewise, Rimland chooses to ignore Keeler's observations that the five original children with retrolental fibroplasia in his study, those who display most markedly the autistic symptomatology, came from homes (their initial referral was for psychiatric disorders) where they were almost totally ignored by the mother, posing a further stimulus deficit. On observing 35 other children with retrolental fibroplasia (who were normal in the sense of not having been referred for psychiatric disorders), he found their behavior to be similar to that of the original 5 except that the symptoms and deviations in development were more marked in the latter. Keeler then extended his study further and observed a group of 18 children who were congenitally blinded at birth, but from causes other than retrolental fibroplasia. In these children, "one did not see the same degree of autistic patterns of behavior. . . . Abnormalities in motility were noted but were not so prevalent and not so severe. . . ."

In the final extension of his study, Keeler observed a group of children who were blinded later on in infancy or in early childhood. Of this group he reported that abnormalities in development and in behavior were least conspicuous, although they showed more anxiety; were disturbed by changes in their environment; and showed "blindisms" in the form of putting their fingers in their eyes, head and body twisting, turning in a circle, and so forth.

These four groups of Keeler's exhibit an interesting hierarchy of sensory and perceptual deprivation. The first two groups, the children with retrolental fibroplasia, have in common the features of prematurity and consequent encapsulation in incubators for the first few months of life. In addition, the original first group of five children with retrolental fibroplasia are described as existing in bad psychological environments in which there existed, in fact, neglect on the part of the mothers.

It is obvious that these are the children whose behavioral characteristics most strikingly resemble those of the autistic syndrome. In the other groups, in whom the manifestations of early infantile autism are less marked, the degree of sensory deprivations described is less severe and does not appear to affect as severely the personality development of the children.

Rimland's view, which attempts to explain the condition of early infantile autism in the child by postulating an organic deficit in the reticular formation of the central nervous system, does not sufficiently and specifically take into account this picture of sensory deprivation in the child. Thus the implication of his position seems to be that the autistic condition, in all its behavioral features, is so closely tied up with a central nervous system incapacitation that it is, for all practical purposes, irreversible. Because of the postulated irreversible impairment in the reticular formation, no meaningful association of experiences can become established in the autistic child; no memory or integration of events; no control or coordination of movements; and experiences are discrete and discontinuous. In short, Rimland suggests, as an explanation to early infantile autism, an organic defect which directly impairs, in the child, the capacity to connect previous experiences with the current ones; in contrast to Kanner's position which had emphasized an affective impairment, Rimland's view points to a cognitive deficit in the autistic child.

Rimland himself, however, recognizes the limitation of his hypothesis in accounting for the entire complexity of the behavioral syndrome of early infantile autism. The clinical descriptions given by Kanner (1943), and the specific behavioral patterns which he underlined (especially, for instance, with regard to metaphorical language in the autistic youngster), could not be easily encompassed by the assumption which Rimland makes of a central nervous defect of cognitive functions. The current body of empirical data and experimental studies on the effects of sensory restriction appears to be of significant relevance in attempting to understand the behavioral syndrome of infantile autism. Further, a more comprehensive hypothesis would seem required here, one which not only would account for the specific syndrome of childhood autism, but also for the wide variety of autistic-like behavioral patterns which exist in children, who, for one reason or another, have suffered very early in life from sensory deprivation, and whose personality growth, therefore, has been arrested.

Early infantile autism and the "Reizschutz" (internal barrier)

What then are the very basic requirements of early personality or ego development? First, the child must be capable of receiving the parental and environmental sensory stimuli; second, the sensory stimuli must reach him on some fairly consistent and continuous basis, to enable him to integrate them, so that he will have available to him sensory experiences to perceive, to integrate, to coordinate, to remember. That is, the child must not be deprived of, or restricted from, receiving sensory messages. In what way is the child with infantile autism so deprived or restricted? He begins life in a parental environmental situation which has sufficed for the normal growth and development of his siblings. Extensive examinations indicate that his eyes and ears are normal and functioning at least at the receptor level. Yet he does not seem to "see" and "hear" as the normal child does. He can make sounds and often can speak, though late and in a somewhat bizarre fashion. He can walk and run, though somewhat later than normal and, initially at least, with a strange stiff clumsy gait as though he were not aware of walking or running. He frequently shows no reaction to pain in the normal way. That is, he may reflexively withdraw an injured appendage, but this is rarely accompanied by the cry of a normal child and never by the search for comfort for his pain. Yet this is a child who rarely exposes himself to injury. Thus, it appears that at the peripheral level the visual, auditory, tactile, proprioceptive receptors are intact and capable of functioning as receivers; and further, that some kind of transmission takes place since all the reflexes in these children at local, spinal, and cortical levels are intact—that is, that the direct reflex sensory-motor pathways are functional. In terms, however, of ability to integrate, to organize, to remember—in short, to learn—these children show a very severe deficit.

Yet autistic children do learn a few things, and it is interesting and important to look at what these few things are and under what circumstances they are learned. First of all, they learn routines. Routines are by definition things that are repeated over and over again. And although no one has commented on how long it takes them to learn a routine, it has escaped no observer of autistic children that they do learn them; and further, that even after they have learned them, they insist upon their repetition to the last detail. This is interesting for two reasons. First, it illustrates that repeated encounter with the same stimulus situation on the part of the autistic child results in the display of some ability to learn, some ability to integrate, to organize, and to remember experiences. The second interesting aspect of this is that adults under conditions of prolonged sensory restriction often come to rely very heavily on the compulsive ritualistic repetition of ordinary routines.

Ruff, Levy, and Thaler (1961) observe that after prolonged stays in a room designed to create a situation of reduced sensory input the subject will try to restore meaning to the environment by structuring the experiment to provide a sense of conformity with previous experience. He will do this in a very concrete manner, by attempting to reinstate spatial orientation (e.g., establishing direction, establishing relations between objects in the experimental room); time orientation (e.g., occurrence of hunger, state of beard growth); and by engaging in compulsive thought and activity (e.g., repeating poems, carrying out familiar routines). These investigators suggest that ". . . isolation destructures the environment, the subject responds by restructuring to create a sense of continuity with his previous experience. The experiment will be tolerable only as long as the sense of continuity is maintained."

In an article entitled "The Cognitive Consequences of Early Sensory Deprivation," Bruner (1961) speaks even more directly to this point. He maintains that an organism must develop a model of the environment in order to operate effectively. If sensory restriction or deprivation is imposed early in life, the organism fails to develop such an environmental model and consequently later adult transactions with this environment are impaired. He states, "Without such prior learning, the centrifugal control functions of the nervous system are without a program, without a basis for predicting that certain events are more likely than others, or preclude others, and have no basis for selectivity toward stimuli."

Relating this to the nature of perceptual development and perceptual differentiation, he states that "continued contact with a rich sensory environment . . . permits the development of differentiation of spheres of activity, of sensory modalities, of events within modalities." Further, he believes that ". . . part of the process of perceptual development consists of the capacity to utilize cues, to extract information from cue-significant encounters . . . ," and that early deprivation prevents development of efficient strategies for information evaluation; that is, for finding out what leads to what and with what probability. Deprived of this development, the organism has great difficulty in utilizing probable, rather than certain, cues. What better example of this difficulty than the child with early infantile autism!

In one of his concluding paragraphs Bruner states, ". . . When one prevents an organism (*and one might add—when an organism is prevented*) from monitoring the fittingness of his percepts and his cognition structures (*or is prevented from even forming percepts and cognitive structures*), one is cutting him off from one of his principal sources of maintaining adjustment."

Thus far it would appear then that the autistic child can learn, especially if a stimulus situation is repeated many, many times; and further, that once he has learned something—e.g., a routine—he insists that it be repeated in its detailed structural entirety. Might it not be so, then, that his other types of repetitive bizarre behaviors (hand movements, rocking, and so forth) are also attempts, though extremely primitive developmentally, at some sort of structure and some sort of escape from absolute absence of stimulation?

There is a second type of learning which the autistic child often displays. It is best illustrated in his speech, which has been described as echolalic, metaphorical, and irrelevant. In an article dealing exclusively with these speech peculiarities, Kanner (1946) noted that the repeated phrases of an autistic child which may at first glance appear as metaphorical or irrelevant, if traced back to their original source assume definite meaning and are rooted in concrete, specific, personal experiences of the child who uses them. Kanner further notes that the source situations or experiences to which these phrases refer are always of high emotional tone. It is as though the autistic child is capable of affect;

i.e., of feeling himself and responding to affect in others, but only in high emotional impact situations.

Rimland's assumption of a cognitive deficit stemming from an organic impairment in the central nervous system seems to take no account of the importance of affective or motivational factors in cognition, learning, and integration of experiences. The autistic child, he said, cannot learn, because he cannot relate one experience to another; and, therefore, there is little meaning or continuity to his experiences. There is ample evidence, empirically and experimentally, that the continuity and integration of sensory experiences is much more related to affective and emotional conditions than to perceptual or ideational processes as such. Freud had suggested this in a negative way by offering clinical evidence that we cease to learn from, or we forget, those experiences we dislike. But on a more experimentally positive and systematically controlled basis, Piaget, Werner, and many others have demonstrated the central place of affect in perception, memory, and the organization and integration of sensory experiences. The continuity of experience in life is impossible without memory, and the meaningfulness of experience requires that each experience be somehow related and integrated with other experiences. Whatever one chooses to view as the prerequisites of a functioning memory, it has become abundantly clear that "emotional factors," "affect," "drives" or "strivings," and attitudes serve as the organizing catalyst of sensory experiences and give them meaningfulness (Rapaport, 1950). This point has been amply demonstrated by the experimental works of Bartlett (1932), in his extensive studies on the relationship of attitudes and social influences to the various aspects of memory functioning. The studies of Katona (1940) on memorizing and organizing, and of Zeigarnik (1927) on retention, underline also the central place of affective elements in the functions of memory. The most recent studies on perceptual meaningfulness and selectivity of sensory experiences (Gardiner et al.) give a central role to affectivity, needs, and attitudes. Furthermore, the consensus of researchers in the field of sensory deprivation—the effects of which, as mentioned earlier, are so frequently the loss of experiential continuity and integration—is that affective and emotional factors appear basic to the individual differences in response to such restrictions (Schultz, 1965). More directly in line with the concern of this study, however, are the impressive clinical materials which Kanner has accumulated and evaluated over the years, and which underline very forcefully the place of emotional and affective factors in those experiences of the autistic child which are fixated and retained, and serve as an integrating and associative link to other experiences.

In summary, thus, the condition of early infantile autism presents a situation in which: (a) the child appears so "isolated" and indifferent to the world about him that much of his behavior could be viewed as a consequence of sensory restriction; and (b) those sensory experiences which do reach the child, and do display some degree of integration, organization, and memory—in short, learning, however discrete, discontinuous, and meager—are all associated with high stimulus strength, either because of excessive repetition (reinforcement) of the stimulus constellation, or because they are characterized (reinforced) by the impact of an unusually strong affective or emotional climate.

Chapter III

The "Reizschutz" (Stimulus Barrier)

etiological considerations in sensory deprivation and early infantile autism

Sources of early sensory and affective deprivation

In viewing the early infantile autistic behavior as a dramatic instance of sensory and affective deprivation, we are confronted, however, with the central issue of the source or cause of this deprivation. Are we dealing here with a condition created by an impoverished and possibly rejecting environment, where the parents, the mother especially, has little capacity to provide the child with appropriate stimulating experiences, so that the child finds no response to his developmental needs and no "releaser" to his instinctual drives? Or is the problem here one of a deficient organism, suffering from an inborn limitation in the capacity to receive sensory messages or affective stimulations? Some research workers in child development have felt that this dichotomy may not be very crucial, since a child does not grow in isolation but only through interaction with the parental environment. To quote Escalona (1963):

> The controversy as to whether infantile autism is "due to" inadequate mothering, or "due to" inborn deficit loses its significance. It is a result of lack in experiences which may come about through

extreme variations in either intrinsic or extrinsic determinants, or both. . . . It (infantile autism) is caused by the absence of those vital experiences in early childhood which we regard as the necessary condition for ego synthesis.

Bettelheim's views

The question, however, as Bettelheim (1967) puts it, remains "exactly how it comes about, in the lives of some children, that these vitally needed experiences do not occur."

Bettelheim himself (1967), who never truly clarifies whether he is talking about primary autism (early infantile) or secondary autism (childhood schizophrenia), chooses to view the parental environment as responsible for the fact that "vitally needed experiences do not occur" in the early life of the autistic child. Basing his view on the many years of clinical experience he has accumulated in working with a variety of disturbed children, Bettelheim reached the conclusion that the autistic condition in a child is directly consequent to the wish of the mother that this child "did not exist." The child, very early, according to Bettelheim (who refers to Sontag, 1941; Escalona, 1949; and Spitz, 1964, in this regard), senses somehow this basic rejection by the mother, and tries, in defense, "to blot out what is too destructive an experience" for him. In so doing, the child, his back turned on the world, so to say, remains unavailable to it. In protecting himself from the destructive designs of his mother, he ends up by defending the deprived and "empty fortress" of his life.

Bettelheim (1967) recognizes certain weaknesses in his position. He concedes:

What is difficult to know is what triggered the reaction. The more intimate the relation, the more difficult it is to know what belongs to which partner. If we assume that the investment in the mother is both intense and disappointing, then it may cause the child to turn his back on the world. That part is easy. What is much more difficult to say, at this shadowy age of the mind, is what made things go so sour for the child.

. . . It would be very hard to know if what goes on between the infant and his surrounding world is due to his heightened sensitivity, to over-stimulation, or to an absence of stimulation.

In choosing to resolve this dilemma by ascribing the autistic condition to the interaction of a highly sensitive child with an extremely destructive mother, Bettelheim rejects the possibility of the inborn nature of autism or of an organic basis to it. Against Rimland's neurological theory of early infantile autism, Bettelheim points, on the basis of his work with autistic children, to the reversibility of the process. Against any others who might offer arguments for the inborn nature of the condition, he holds that "there is reason to question the inborn nature of autism until such time as it is actually observed in newborn infants before mothering can have made a difference." Obviously since "such time" never occurs, we are left with the ineluctable conclusion that early infantile autism comes about as a consequence of an infant's reaction to a dangerous and destructive maternal environment, and reflects behaviorally the sensory and emotional deprivation which such an environment entails and which the child himself compounds by turning his back on it.

Choosing the environment as a central causal factor in the etiology of early infantile autism was "the easy part," as Bettelheim himself stated. But even there, things are not that easy. Environmental deprivation and its pathogenic effects on the child have received considerable attention in the past years (see Spitz, 1945; Provence and Lipton, 1962; Bowlby, 1952; etc.). Following Bettelheim's argument, one is left to seriously wonder why an infant, who from the very first hours of his life senses the destructive attitude of a mother who wishes he did not exist and, in consequence, turns away from and blots out such a destructive experience, would not end up in marasmus and possibly die rather than live on forever as an autistic child?*

It is true that environmental limitations in sensory and affective stimulation do not always lead to a marasmic, languorous reaction in the infant; in some cases, it creates only a form of pseudomental retardation, as Goschen (1963) has demonstrated. Bettelheim recognizes and discusses these observations. But he fails to indicate why in one situation a sensorily deprived child dies in a marasmic state or develops in a mentally retarded fashion, while in another, he becomes autistic. It is not enough to say, as Bettelheim does, that it all depends on the circumstances and the endowment of the child. There are great and significant behavioral differences between the mentally retarded, the maras-

* Note: An extensive discussion of the marasmic condition is given in Chapter IV.

mic, and the autistic child. The mentally defective is neither out of this world, nor against it; he seems rather incapable of meaningfully relating himself to it, because he cannot understand it. Affectively, he is responsive, in an appropriate way, to simple, direct, and elementary stimulations; but his initiative, drive, and autonomy in giving responses have a diffuse, unstructured, and undifferentiated quality. The marasmic child, described by Spitz (1945), is sad and languorous; his behavior reflects deep depression, and though some of his activities resemble, in their stereotypic and self-stimulating aspects, those of the autistic child, what comes across to the observer and is communicated appears to be the dark despair of one who has lost everything.

In this connection, Eveloff writes (1960), "The autistic child is affectless, if not disturbed in his preoccupation, while the anaclitically deprived child is sad, forlorn, and later apathetic." The crucial word here, in contrasting the autistic child to the mentally retarded or to the marasmic child, is that the former is "affectless"; he is aloof and indifferent to his surroundings; he looks "through" and "beyond" people; he has nothing, apparently, to communicate to his environment. If we were to assume that each one of these various types of children has been, in one way or another, sensorily deprived, the specific effects of the sensory deprivation on the child are very different in each case.

Yet in each case the developmental process is impaired and crippled. In the early infantile autistic child there is hardly any development at all. There is communication, or relationship, with but a very small fraction of the parental and home environment, as if the "receiving set" in the child were not at all tuned in to the normal sensory and affective messages transmitted by the environment. Bettelheim says that this state of affairs exists because the child, in self-protection, has turned off the set. The evidence he offers of cold, distant, rejecting, and destructive parents is not too convincing, and certainly does not fit with the data we have accumulated on the parents of the children in this study, which will be reported in detail later. As indicated earlier, if Bettelheim's views on the destructive effects of the mother's "death wish" for her child has the value of a loss of love object and of sensory and emotional deprivation in the child, it would be plausible to expect a marasmic and depressed reaction to set in rather than an autistic condition. From Spitz's (1945) report on his group of "marasmic" infants, it is clear that these children were "normal" before being subjected to the deprivations inherent in "hospitalism." This means that these children possessed a "receiving set" that was tuned in to the sensory and affective stimulations expected in a normal environment. It was because of the absence of such stimulations in the environment of the foundling home that they were adversely affected. They were abandoned, so to say, and they died in this desert of love.

Rimland's views

The autistic child does not die; quite the contrary, his behavior continues to express in a minimal fashion a reaching out which is inherently ineffectual and sterile because it lacks affective quality. The barrier to affective communication appears to be an internal one, rather than consequent to a parental rejection. In recent years, a number of attempts have been made to understand the autistic behavior as an inborn neurophysiological defect, and this point of view deserves consideration at this time. In his book on early infantile autism (1963), Rimland, after admirably reviewing all the literature to date on the subject, concludes that the defect in autistic children is basically a cognitive one. He traces the diversity of symptoms and manifestations of early infantile autism to a single critical disability: "The child with early infantile autism is grossly impaired in a function basic to all cognition: the ability to relate new stimuli to remembered experience" (p. 79). Rimland then goes on to suggest, on a highly speculative basis, the brain stem reticular formation as a possible site of the organic impairment which resulted in those cognitive problems. He further speculates that the condition is the result of a hereditary disposition to oxygen damage in the area of the reticular formation. This oxygen damage produces the early infantile autistic behavior, which he considers to be a rare type of oligophrenia, in a child who was hereditarily destined to be a genius.

Two major criticisms of Rimland's position are offered at this point. First, as was discussed in Chapter II, he fails to deal with that aspect of the disorder which Kanner considered to be the outstanding, pathognomonic, feature of the disorder; i.e., the disturbance of affective contact. Many brain-damaged, retarded children show as severe cognitive deficits as those seen in autistic children, but without the concommitant severe affective deficit. Second, the case for early oxygen damage is a very weak one, not supported by the majority of prenatal histories of autistic children unless one is willing to assume that the ordinary levels of atmospheric oxygen, to which the child is exposed at birth, are sufficient to "trigger off" the hereditary predisposition to oxygen damage. However, since the reasoning behind this hypothesis was based on the damage caused by oxygen to the rapidly developing eye tissue in those infants blinded by retrolental fibroplasia, one wonders why all children with early infantile autism are not also victims of retrolental fibroplasia (RLF). It is further worth noting that the damage caused by oxygen in RLF is a vascular damage, with a pathological vascularization of the retina, followed by obliteration and fibrosis. The reticular formation of the brain stem, as it is classically circumscribed, is not an area of high vascularization. However, the limbic-midbrain region (to be discussed in more detail later), particularly the hypothalamic area, is one of the most highly vascularized areas in the brain. Therefore, if Rimland's oxygen damage hypothesis as a causative factor was correct, the limbic-midbrain area, and particularly the hypothalamus, would be more likely sites of damage than would the area of the classical reticular formation (Wicks, 1966). This is particularly interesting when one considers the affective disturbance in early infantile autism in light of the fact that the limbic-hypothalamic area has long been associated with emotional phenomena. We will return to this question in greater detail in Chapter IV.

Other neurophysiological positions

Another recent study which has implicated the reticular formation is that of Hutt and Hutt (1964). Their hypothesis is that in children with early infantile autism nonspecific activity of the reticular system is sustained at a chronically high and relatively inflexible level; that is, these children are in a chronically high state of arousal. This hypothesis is based on a study of children, age three to six, with Kanner's syndrome. The several observations (discussed below) which Hutt and Hutt suggest as supporting their hypothesis are based on an N ranging from two to six children. The observations and their interpretations are as follows:

1. Observations of the electroencephalograms of these (no N specified) children are consistently desynchronized or of higher frequency than is usually found in children of this age (two to six). Hutt and Hutt suggest that this may be evidence of an unusually high level of electrocortical activation or arousal in the waking state.

2. Behavioral withdrawal and the continued performance of stereotyped behaviors, which are the two main characteristics of the syndrome, have been shown in animal research to be associated with
states of high arousal.

3. In the potentially exploratory type of situation, observations of six
autistic children found increased stereotypy with increasing environmental complexity and least evidence of stereotypy when the child
was alone in an unfurnished waiting room. The authors suggest that
if stereotypy is a function of level of arousal, then increased sensory
bombardment (in the complex situation) would result in more stereotyped behavior. They further suggest that the stereotypies may be a
device to prevent level of arousal exceeding critical limits by blocking further novel sensory input.

4. Telemetric EEG's of two autistic children, together with simultaneous
behavioral observation of their free-field activities, found in the unfurnished room less stereotypy and more synchronized higher voltage
EEG's than in the complex environments. Stereotypies were more frequently accompanied by desynchronized EEG activity than rhythmic
activity.

5. The frequent observation that autistic children often appear deaf
and manifest a higher threshold to pain than normal children is
thought by Hutt and Hutt to be the result of blocking of sensory
pathways produced by the chronically high level of arousal.

6. The insistence on sameness is again seen (as was stereotypy) as an
attempt on the part of an already highly aroused organism to prevent further arousal and excessive excitation from further arousing
the organism to the point of producing a catastrophic reaction.

Thus the hypothesis of Hutt and Hutt, that early infantile autistic
behavior is a function of a chronically high and inflexible state of
arousal, rests on the primary premise that electrocortical activity as recorded in an EEG is at least a reasonably acceptable reflection of arousal;
and on the secondary, derivative, premises that (1) behavior withdrawal
and stereotypy are associated with states of high arousal, and (2) that
chronically high states of arousal produce blocking of sensory pathways.

The following comments and questions are raised regarding the Hutt
and Hutt formulation.

1. There is a noticeable failure to deal with the major pathognomonic
feature of early infantile autism: lack of affective contact. If it is in-

tended to be subsumed under the phrase "behavior withdrawal," it still remains inadequately discussed.

2. Electroencephalographic recordings are currently undergoing considerable criticism as poor measures of arousal. (See, for example, Routtenberg, 1966, for a recent review and discussion of this problem.) Further, EEG recordings on normal young children are quite unreliable and show great variation.

3. Sensory deprivation studies on animals and humans have shown that both behavioral withdrawal and continued performance of stereotyped behaviors are also characteristic behaviors pursuant to prolonged sensory deprivation or isolation in young as well as adult organisms (Reisen, 1961; Schultz, 1965).

4. Increase in frequency of stereotypic responses in the face of new, novel, and complex environmental situations, in children with typically severely limited (retarded) behavioral repertoires, could just as easily be interpreted as a simple display of the extent of the dearth in their behavioral repertoire. Likewise, because of this limited repertoire they possess no adequate response. Therefore they resort to an obsessive repetition of the only responses available to them. Viewed in this way, the "warding off" effect of stereotypy becomes secondary to a primary response deficit and could be construed as an attempt on the part of the child to maintain some structure, however primitive, by way of the few limited responses available to him. That is, the stereotypies occur in the absence of any other available, more meaningful, coping responses to a new, novel, or complex stimulus situation.

5. In the context of the neurophysiological hypothesis to be proposed later, we have observed at least two varieties of early infantile autistic children on the dimension of activity. Running, in a sense parallel to this activity dimension, is what might be referred to as a sensory threshold dimension. That is, some of the children are extremely hypoactive, displaying what one might call "quiet stereotypies," the frequency and occurrence of which seem unaffected by anything but the most exaggerated and gross environmental intrusions, alterations, or complexities. These same hypoactive autistic children manifest most strikingly the apparent invulnerability or unawareness (in any humanly apparent way) of pain, and what is often decribed as apparent deafness. In sharp contrast are those autistic youngsters who display various degrees of hyperactivity (interspersed with periods of quiet absorption) and whose stereotypies are much more vigorous;

and the occurrence and frequency of these stereotypies seem to correlate, as Hutt and Hutt have suggested, with increasingly more novel and more complex environmental stimulus situations. These same hyperactive autistic children are generally more irritable, do not display the above-mentioned high pain threshold, and are less likely to appear deaf, though they still retain, especially during their quiescent periods, the apparent ability to shut out (or the temporary inability to receive) external stimulations.

In summary, then, we are essentially in agreement with the observations of Hutt and Hutt (though questioning the efficacy of the EEG as a measure of arousal) and the view that stereotypy and behavioral withdrawal are behavioral phenomena exclusively or primarily indicative of high arousal states. That the ascending reticular formation involvement is a major factor in the etiology of early infantile autism will be discussed and elaborated on in more detail in a later section.

We next turn our attention to an article by Schain and Yannet (1960) purporting to deal with 50 cases of early infantile autism at the Southbury Training School. That these 50 cases represent "pure" examples of the syndrome of early infantile autism in the Kannerian sense—as opposed to a mixture of primary autism, secondary autism, and brain damage with autistic adaptation—has already been thoroughly and adequately questioned by Rimland, not only on the basis of the authors' (Schain and Yannet) stated diagnostic criterion, but upon the basis of the reported finding that 42 percent of these cases had a history of seizures. However, what is of particular interest and pertinence to the present discussion is their primary concern, in contrast to the two previously discussed investigations, with the disturbance in affective contact which characterizes all these children. This concern, in conjunction with their findings of high incidence of seizure history (in their population), leads them to interesting theoretical speculations regarding the possible primary involvement of the limbic system in the disorder. Their speculations are based on two factors. First, the structures within the limbic system have long been thought to provide the anatomical substratum of emotional behavior. And, second, experimental seizures are far more readily induced in this area, particularly in the hippocampus and amygdala, than in the neocortex. Thus, in view of the primary affective deficit in these children, Schain and Yannet cautiously suggest, with little elaboration, the limbic system as a potential site of dysfunction in the central nervous system of these children.

Chapter IV

The Sleeping Child

*the two arousal systems —
a neurophysiological model*

Viewing the behavior of the autistic child in the light of the preceding discussion, how can what is currently known about the neurophysiological functions and anatomical connections within the mammalian brain lead to a potential explanation of this behavior short of accusing the parents of such children of having deprived them sensorily and emotionally from the beginning of life?

In a recent article on the neural mechanisms of sleep, Routtenberg (1966) was led to postulate the existence of two arousal systems as potentially more adequate to explain the mechanism of consciousness and sleep. In subsequent presentations (1966; 1968), based primarily on the self-stimulation literature, an attempt was made to apply this two arousal system hypothesis to such concepts as motivation, drive, incentive, memory, and learning. If this new look at arousal phenomena and consciousness, especially as they relate to motivation, incentive, reward, reinforcement, memory, and learning, has sufficient validity, it may be possible to give greater understanding to certain heretofore poorly understood behavioral abnormalities through an attempted application of this two arousal system model.*

* We wish to express special thanks to Dr. Aryeh Routtenberg for his helpful suggestions and critical comments in our application of his two arousal system hypothesis to the behavioral syndrome of early infantile autism.

49

The following section will include a general summary of the two arousal system, its anatomical connections, and its hypothesized integrated functioning under normal conditions, internal and external, to the organism. Potential imbalances leading to malfunction, maladaptive behavior, and retarded learning processes will be discussed. Finally, a detailed attempt will be made to apply this two arousal hypothesis to the understanding of the syndrome of early infantile autism, characterized, as noted earlier, by a grossly retarded ability to learn, and an almost total inability to relate to other human beings.

The two arousal system hypothesis

Figure 1 represents a simplified diagram of the two arousal systems as envisioned by Routtenberg, illustrating certain functional relation-

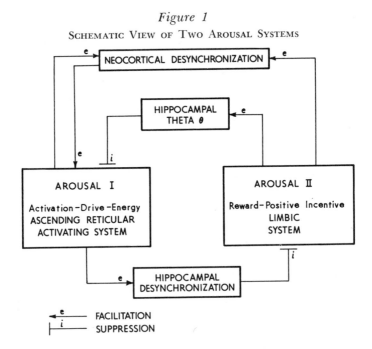

Figure 1

SCHEMATIC VIEW OF TWO AROUSAL SYSTEMS

ships of the two systems, and the hypothesized facilitatory and inhibitory relationships between them.

The following points serve to summarize the essential features and interactions of the systems as postulated by Routtenberg:

1. Arousal System I is essentially the classical arousal system originally described by Moruzzi and Magoun (1949). This system is associated physiologically with EEG desynchronization.

2. Arousal System II is part of the limbic-midbrain system anatomically described by Nauta (1959) in the cat. This system is associated with the self-stimulation phenomenon. That is, those regions within the brain stem which have been found upon stimulation via microelectrode implants in animals to yield powerful reward (positive or negative) responses on the part of the implanted animal are anatomically situated within the limbic-midbrain system described by Nauta. Implants in positive areas may be so rewarding as to cause the animal to forgo food, water, and sleep as he bar-presses for stimulation to the point of exhaustion. That implants in other areas are negatively reinforcing is shown in the behavioral attempts of these animals to escape, avoid, or shut off the stimulation. Thus, there is good reason to assume that these areas are somehow basic to the neural mechanisms of reward, incentive, motivation, and affects (pleasure, pain, etc.).

3. Both System I and II are capable of bringing about neocortical desynchronization. However, System I is more critical. System I desynchrony can be differentiated from System II desynchrony by way of hippocampal electrical activity and by way of lesion studies. System II neocortical desynchrony is associated with hippocampal theta activity.

4. Hippocampal theta tends to dampen the activity of System I (Grastyan, 1959).

5. A positive-feedback loop exists between System I and the neocortex.

6. At low or intermediate levels of activity, System II will predominate over System I since the suppressing effect of hippocampal theta will tend to diminish the positive-feedback effect between System I and the neocortex. At high levels of activation, System I will predominate since the feedback system will be in too great a state of activity to be suppressed by hippocampal theta.

7. Arousal I has a more sustaining (tonic: Sharpless & Jasper, 1956) influence with respect to neocortical desynchronization.

8. Arousal II, on the other hand, appears to be more critical than Arousal I for the maintenance of basic vegetative activities, including such phenomena as wakefulness, reward, incentive, and motivation.

9. Input to both systems is a function of collaterals from the direct sensory pathways leading from the sensory receptors to the neocortex.

Regulation of the two systems

Thus it can be seen (Figure 1) that if the two systems are functioning in an integrated fashion, there necessarily exists between the two, at all times, a kind of balance. Arousal I and Arousal II are arranged in such a fashion that each suppresses the activity of the other. This reciprocal inhibition allows for the two systems to be in a state of dynamic equilibrium. The appropriate reversals of ascendency may be visualized as in Figure 2.

Figure 2

BALANCED FUNCTIONING; DYNAMIC EQUILIBRIUM;
APPROPRIATE REVERSAL OF SYSTEM ASCENDENCY

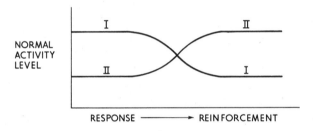

In addition, it seems necessary to postulate the existence of a *level* at and around which this balance operates. Lindsley (1961), in attempting to explain the behavioral disturbances which result when organisms are exposed to conditions of sensory distortion, deprivation, or overload, suggested the existence within the ascending reticular activating system (here: Arousal System I*) of a kind of physiological barometer. He suggested that this barometer, or thermostat, adjusts or regulates input-output relations, and, further, that this barometer or thermostat has an *adaptation level*. He also proposed that under conditions of sensory deprivation, overload, or distortion, the balance of this regulator is upset with the result that perception and attention are disrupted, and be-

---

* Note: It should be pointed out here that Lindsley subsumes all the functions, separated and delegated in this discussion to either System I or System II, under a single system, the ascending reticular activating system. He says: "The role of the ARAS, the ascending recticular activating system, is particularly important not only for the understanding it supplies of the sleep-wakefulness transition, but equally for its applicability to a number of psychological problems, including perception, attention, learning, drive, motivation, and, to some extent, emotion." (p. 178)

havioral performance is either held in abeyance, or becomes highly stereotyped and not adaptive. Extending Lindsley's model of an adaptation level, or barometric setting, within a single arousal system to Routtenberg's two arousal system hypothesis would suggest that under normal conditions (internal and external to the organism) of growth, development, and behavior, the two arousal systems exhibit a normal balance pattern of reciprocal inhibition-disinhibition which is operative at a level correctly adapted to internal and external environmental conditions (see Figure 2). Thus, if both conditions, (1) balanced equilibrium between the two systems, and (2) adaptive level setting appropriate to normal internal and external environmental conditions are met, normal behavior, perception, attention, learning, drive, reward, motivation, incentive, and affect should be observable in, or available to, the organism.

Potential malfunctions in regulation

The above formulation immediately suggests the possibility of unadaptive level settings for both arousal systems (the Lindsley "barometer" model); that is, for some reason, internal or external, inborn or acquired, both arousal systems are set too high or too low. This would coincide, for example, with what Lindsley suggests happens in sensory distortion, deprivation, and overload experiments. When the response to such conditions (distortion, deprivation, or overload) is to hold all behavior in abeyance, the adaptation level of both systems has dropped too low, with a resulting functional, at least, and more or less temporary (or permanent) hyposensitivity. On the other hand, when the behavioral response to sensory distortion, deprivation, or overload is of a stereotyped, repetitive, and nonadaptive type, the adaptive setting of the barometer, or level, has jumped too high. Under this condition, it is suggested that the organism is at least temporarily functioning at a hypersensitive level. It should be pointed out that the levels of hyper- or hyposensitivity alluded to here are extremely aberrant or divergent from the normal setting, and interfere grossly with any possibility of normal adaptive functioning. Whether or not a given organism responds to such extreme conditions by a drastic fall or rise in the adaptation setting may be simply a matter of the somatic-compliance of the given organism. The possible implications of these unadaptive level settings, as they relate to learning, will be pursued in a later section.

The second obvious malfunction which appears to be possible relates to the hypothesized balance in functioning existing between Arousal System I and Arousal System II. Numerous possibilities aside from normal balance can immediately be envisioned. It appears useful, at least initially, to categorize them under two major headings:

1. An imbalance in which System I is set higher than System II and therefore constantly exerting an inhibiting influence on System II, such that System II is for all practical purposes immobilized. That is, arousal is exclusively a reflection of the activity of System I.

2. An imbalance in which System II is set higher than System I and therefore exerting an inhibitory influence on System I, with System I thereby being essentially immobilized. Arousal in this situation would be exclusively a reflection of the activity of System II.

Once one has considered the idea of an imbalance between the two systems, regardless of the direction of the imbalance, it is possible to combine this with the previously discussed concept of level settings. The following further ramifications then suggest themselves:

1. Both Systems abnormally low, but out of balance; therefore any activity which is manifested is still primarily the reflection of only one system.

2. Both Systems abnormally high, but out of balance; therefore manifest activity is still primarily the reflection of only one system.

3. Systems out of balance, with the system in ascendency at hypo-normal or hypernormal setting vis-à-vis the other system whose setting is at a hypo-normal level. That is, the axis of the imbalance could have almost any conceivable gradient, such axis gradient being a function of how disparate are the settings of each respective System.

It is suggested here that should any of the above outlined abnormalities in level and/or balance setting occur and persist, abnormal behavior would result.

Lindsley has already pointed to the possible dire effects of the extreme external environmental conditions of sensory deprivation, distortion, or overload on the postulated adaptation level in an otherwise normally functioning organism. A word should be said concerning possible internal origins of unadaptive level settings and/or disequilibrated functioning of the two arousal systems. Such speculations would necessarily involve two general areas: first, that of transmitter substances, either too much or too little of either a facilitatory or an inhibitory substance; second, the question of cell sensitivity, either hypersensitivity or hyposensitivity to facilitatory or inhibitory substances. Presumably, such deviations could be inborn or acquired. Further discussion of the model at this biochemical level is beyond the intended scope of the current endeavor.

Integrated function—memory and learning

The possible answer as to a more precise definition of what specific behavioral abnormalities might be in evidence—or, stated conversely, what specific behavioral abnormalities might be a reflection of what specific type of imbalance—requires a closer look at postulated integrated functions of the two systems (as opposed to anatomical connections) as manifested in behavior such as learning, memory, and motivation, briefly alluded to earlier.

In addition to the various anatomical-neurophysiological connections and implications of the two arousal system hypothesis summarized earlier, Routtenberg (1966) made a tentative application of this system to the process of memory and learning.

At this point it becomes necessary to state, in terms more closely related to behavior, Routtenberg's postulated functions of each of the arousal systems. These are expressed primarily in conservative animal learning language.

1. Arousal I system has, as one important function, the activation of responses necessary for reinforcement. "In a more general sense, Arousal I must be active for the production and the selection of the appropriate responses: Thus, one might formulate the view that, *response occurrence*, whether approach or withdrawal, *is more probable when Arousal I is active and less probable when Arousal I is inactive.*" Arousal I system is thus predominately concerned with drive or energy for response.

2. Arousal II system is primarily concerned with incentive, reward, or positive reinforcement—with increasing the probability that that particular response will occur *again*. It seems not only necessary, but valid, in attempting to apply this two arousal system hypothesis to human learning, to postulate that, in humans, what are referred to as affects and emotions have their primary roots in the midbrain-limbic system; i.e., Arousal System II. That is, that motivation, incentive, reward, and so forth, on a human level, are inextricable from affects and emotions, though certainly all are subject to greater refine-

ment, elaboration, and awareness by way of the more highly developed human nervous system (see Gellhorn and Loofbourrow, 1963; also Pribram 1967).

3. "In the present view, reward or positive incentive stimuli predominantly excite Arousal System II which normally leads to certain consequences, here called reinforcement. Thus, reinforcement is not viewed as rewarding, but rather as the consequence of the positive incentive leading to the enhanced probability of response reoccurrence. Therefore, reward does not necessarily lead to reinforcement, and reinforcement does not necessarily arise from reward. The latter case may arise when Arousal System II is activated, or Arousal System I suppressed in the absence of reward; the former when, upon presentation of reward, Arousal System I activity is in some way not reduced." (Routtenberg, 1968, p. 74.)

It was stated earlier that under normal circumstances the two systems are in a constant state of activity, and that the reciprocal suppression allows for Arousal I, Arousal II to be in a dynamic equilibrium; first one active, then the other; i.e., the organism regulates its behavior such that there exists a balance of activity between these two systems.

On the basis of studies of the activity of these two systems during animal learning experiments, their integrated functioning exhibits the following sequence. When the organism is first presented with a new or novel stimulus, Arousal I is active, responses are emitted, and the occurrence of a reward stimulates the activation of Arousal II as a consequence. Activation of Arousal II dampens or reduces Arousal I activity (see Figure 2). "Therefore, in a typical animal learning situation, a rewarded response is learned because the drive that produced the response is suppressed by the effects of the reward. One could then define reinforcement as that which suppresses the system which gives energy to the response." (Routtenberg, 1966.)

Grastyan (1959), working with cats having recording electrodes in the hippocampus, has experimental evidence which suggests that the relation between System I and System II is such that in the process of learning, System I predominates during exposure to new, novel, unfamiliar stimuli, as well as during exposure to stimuli so familiar as to call forth automatic learned responses. Conversely, System II is in ascendency during that part of the learning process when associative links between familiar stimuli are forming and consolidating. Thus, while System I is vital in terms of activating or alerting the organism to attend to stimuli and emit responses, it is System II which predominates during the actual learning process.

Routtenberg, in applying his two arousal hypothesis to memory processes—particularly the relationship between short, intermediate, and long term memory—has stressed the importance of the inhibitory effect of System II on System I following reinforcement. He suggests that this drive inhibition would permit the recirculation of impulses that were previously made in a situation where reward occurred. Whether any or all three stages of memory would occur would depend upon the extent of the perseveration, and the number of trials in which some form of the reinforcement was presented. He is extremely cautious as to the extension of this model to the level of human learning. He suggests that "... in such a situation there may be more interplay between the arousal systems and lateral-frontal and orbital-frontal cortex," but proposes "... that the basic mechanism is the same, but that other re-representational structures (in the Jacksonian sense) may play a more prominent role than the basic brainstem structures" (1966).

Thus, the learning process, as it involves the appropriate functioning of these two arousal systems in the brainstem, suggests that System I is active during attention and alert to new and novel stimuli; and, as a drive energy system, is responsible for the emission of responses. Following this response emission, System II, the reward system, suppresses System I in such a way as to allow for the consolidation of the response-reward association thereby facilitating the learning and memory processes. This integrated functioning, this reciprocal suppression, requires that Systems I and II be appropriately balanced so as to allow reciprocal suppression to proceed smoothly. It further necessitates that the balance exist at, and around, a level appropriate to external and internal incoming stimuli. It should also be noted that this level setting and, consequently, the two systems in balance, have a range within which to operate; in other words, using the barometric model, the setting encompasses a number of degrees within which the balance can fluctuate, as opposed to a rigid single degree setting which would prohibit adequate flexibility in the variation of responses to environmental conditions (see Figure 3a).

Therefore, under normal conditions, with both systems in balance, their ranges of operation are identical, and this range within which reciprocal inhibition can take place can be referred to diagrammatically as the *area of learning*. To anticipate the discussion of malfunctioning

Figure 3

HYPOTHETICAL SCHEMATA OF BALANCE, LEVEL
SETTING, RANGE, AND AREA OF LEARNING
(*a*) Normal Balance, Normal Level Setting,
Normal Area of Learning; (*b*) Normal Balance,
Slightly Subnormal (Hypoactive, Hyposensitive)
Level Setting, Somewhat Limited Area of Learning

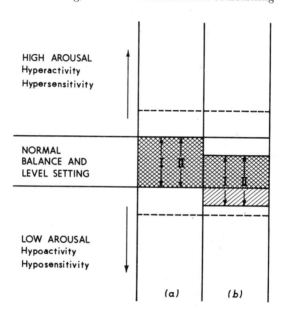

to follow, this would mean that, even if the two systems were mildly out of balance, as long as there exists some area of overlap of the ranges of the two respective systems, some learning, though limited, should still occur, although the "size" of the *area of learning* would be limited accordingly (see Figure 3b). Even level settings mildly divergent from normal, as long as there exists some overlap of ranges of the two systems, might be expected to produce some limited learning though this would probably occur with some difficulty and appear "retarded" or slow.

Malfunctions—the marasmic child

Observation of the behavior of newborn and very young infants, which has such a dramatic reward-pleasure seeking or open affective quality, coupled with a primarily diffuse and reflex response quality, suggests it is probable that in the human infant, at least initially, the relationship between the two systems is one in the direction of predominance of System II. This could be seen within the present context as due, not to an excessive inhibition of I by II, but rather due to the fact that the level and balance settings, by definition adaptive mechanisms, are in the very process of making or establishing that adaptation. That is, in the newborn and very young infant, the condition of the two systems is viewed as being in the process of establishing a balance and setting a level adaptive to the environmental stimulations (internal and external) with System II being initially the most active system. These adaptive mechanisms of the balance between the two systems, and the level of the balance, become established during the first few weeks of life (paralleling or following the rapidly maturing neuromuscular and other physiological maturations of the organism). Under normal conditions, as this adaptation proceeds, System I gains in strength, in the process of which the dynamic equilibrium quality, the balance, the reciprocal inhibition function of the two systems, become established. And it becomes established at a level (within a range) appropriate to the overall (normal) environmental stimulus input, in a word, to the "mothering" environment. For it is the "mothering" environment which primarily composes the early environment to which the child is exposed and upon which, under normal circumstances, his adaptation is built.

We have tentatively suggested that the initially higher rate of activity in System II in the newborn and young infant, under normal circumstances, leads to an adaptive balanced equilibrium between the two systems given sufficient environmental, mothering stimulus conditions. What, then, would be expected to happen to such an initially normal infant, if the environment were not an adequately stimulating, mothering one? To take the extreme case, what would happen if a normal infant were placed in an institution, comprised of environmental conditions such as those described by Spitz (1965) to exist in the foundling homes which he studied; that is, in an environment which lacked not only the affective stimulations comprising maternal loving care and attention, but one which also deprived the infant to a severe degree of nearly all kinds of stimulation, human and inhuman, by virtue of his existence with custodial care in a crib, in a cubicle—the sides of the crib often being covered by sheets, and the walls and ceiling of the cubicle being of a single, monotonous, unvarying institutional coloring? Spitz describes the behavioral progression which ensues as follows:

1. "The children become weepy, demanding, and tend to cling to the observer when he succeeds in making contact with them." [p. 270]
2. "The weeping often changes into wails. Weight loss sets in. There is an arrest of the developmental quotient."
3. "The children refuse contact. They lie prone in their cots most of the time, a pathognomonic sign. Insomnia sets in; loss of weight continues. There is a tendency to contract intercurrent diseases; motor retardation becomes generalized. Inception of facial rigidity." [p. 271]
4. "Facial rigidity (wide-open expressionless eyes, frozen immobile face, and a faraway look, as if in a daze, apparently not seeing what went on around them [p. 269]) becomes firmly established. Weeping ceases and is replaced by whimpering. Motor retardation increases and is replaced by lethargy. The developmental quotient begins to decrease." At this point, the behavior is considered that of an anaclitic depression, and with intervention might possibly be reversible.
5. (After three months' deprivation, at approximately six months of age) ". . . motor retardation became fully evident; the children became completely passive; they lay supine on their cots. They did not achieve the stage of motor control necessary to turn into the prone position. The face became vacuous, eye coordination defective, and the expression often imbecile. When mobility reappeared after a while, it took the form of spasmus nutans in some of the children; others showed bizarre finger movements reminiscent of decerebrate or athetotic movements." [p. 278]
6. ". . . by that (four years of age) time, with few exceptions, these children cannot sit, stand, walk, or talk. . . . We have seen that this (deprivation, affective and sensory) leads to a progressive deterioration engulfing the child's whole person. Such deterioration is manifested first in an arrest of the child's psychological development; then psychological dysfunctions set in, paralleled by somatic changes. In the next stage this leads to increased infection liability and eventually, when the emotional deprivation continues into the second year of life, to a spectacularly increased rate of mortality (30%)." [p. 281]

The final stage which may culminate in the death of the organism is referred to as *marasmus*. The affective picture leading to this marasmus is one of increasing sadness, languorous forlornness, and finally apathy. From the standpoint of attention, alertness, and responsiveness, the picture is one of general and increasing motor retardation leading, finally, to complete passivity and lethargy; and it becomes increasingly difficult, if not finally impossible, to alert the attention of the child.

Within the framework of the current two arousal system hypothesis, the beginning and end of the behavioral process or syndrome development in marasmus can be dramatically illustrated by comparing Figure 4a and 4b. Due to the almost total lack of environmental stimulation of any kind, no balance is established between the two systems, and no level is set since, as an adaptive mechanism, there exists for all intents and purposes nothing to which it can adapt. Yet to the end, which may

Figure 4

HYPOTHETICAL SCHEMATA: NEWBORN OR YOUNG
INFANT AND MARASMIC OLDER INFANT
(*a*) Normal Newborn or Very Young Infant,
Balance Level, and Ranges in Process of
Adaptation with System II Predominating Initially;
(*b*) Marasmic Older Infant with Failure of
Normal Adaptive Processes to Occur.

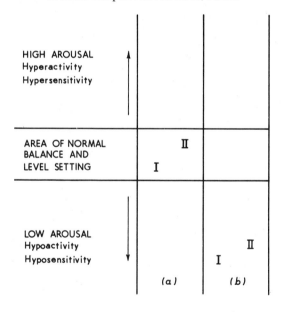

be the literal end of death, what is communicated by the infant to the observer is an affective quality of deep despair, in a completely passive organism.

It is on the basis of this behavioral data that the hypothetical diagram (Figure 4b) of the state of the two systems is constructed. Thus, then, the marasmic child is suggested as an example of one of the earlier postulated potential malfunctionings of the balance and level settings within the two arousal hypothesis. That is, a situation in which the condition of ascendency of System II over System I, characteristic of the normal infant prior to establishing the adaptive balance and level setting, persists due to environmental conditions of extreme deprivation, sensory and affective, and in fact deteriorates under such conditions. What had started as a *normal condition for proper development (System II in ascendency)* becomes critically inoperative when the environment fails to present it with the affective and sensory support, or response, that would ensure its proper adaptive setting and functioning.

Malfunctions—the early infantile autistic child

In contrast to the normal developmental condition in the child who, due to deprivation, eventually becomes marasmic, the problem presented by the behavior of the early infantile autistic child is markedly different. Here, from the beginning, the behavior of the child strongly suggests that the ascendency of the two systems is reversed (I higher than II). Therefore, we should not look primarily to the environment as an obstacle to his proper development, but rather to an inborn condition of "imbalance."

In the earlier discussion of potential malfunctions, i.e., imbalances and nonadaptive level settings, it was pointed out that an imbalance could exist or become established in the direction of sustained ascendency of System I over System II; that is, of sustained inhibition of II by I. Within the framework of the suggested functions of these individual systems, this would mean that when System I was predominantly in ascendency, not only would arousal be primarily a function of that system, but it would mean that the organism, while capable of alerting and attending to new novel stimuli, and while capable of emitting responses, would be severely limited in (if not almost incapable of) establishing any associations between responses and rewards, since System II would be for all practical purposes incapable of suppressing the drive energy system (I) long enough for such association to become established or consolidated. Further, this would suggest that the vast majority of all impinging stimuli would remain forever new and novel to the organism. That is, since no, or very few, associations between response and reward contingencies would be established, thereby causing them to become familiar or "learned" in any effective way, these environmental stimuli would continue, even on successive presentations to the organism, to appear as unfamiliar, new, and novel.

It was pointed out in an earlier discussion, that there are at least two circumstances or conditions under which autistic children do learn, or acquire, the very limited associations which comprise their behavioral repertoire (aside from the purely self-stimulating and stereotypic activities in which they engage). Both circumstances are considered situations where sensory experience reached the child under conditions of high stimulus strength, either (1) because of excessive repetition (reinforcement) of the stimulus constellation (as in routines), or (2) because the stimulus constellation was characterized (reinforced) by impact of an unusually strong affective or emotional climate. This is consistent with the current hypothesis which would allow, under conditions of high stimulus strength (and perhaps only under these conditions), for either the gradual buildup or sudden surge of input to System II to allow it, under these circumstances, to suppress System I sufficiently enough to enable this occasional, but very limited, learning to take place.

But finally, and most important, this two arousal hypothesis, embodying the possibility of sustained suppression of System II, offers a potential explanation for that characteristic which Kanner first described as the pathognomonic symptom of early infantile autism, the "disturbance in affective contact present from the very beginning of life." For it is this limbic-midbrain system which is concerned at a very basic level with the functions of emotional behavior, reward, motivation, and incentive—or in a word, affects. Given sustained suppression of this system, an individual would be expected to appear out of affective contact, or affectless—and this once again is the most striking characteristic of the early infantile autistic child.

Such a child, in contrast to the marasmic child, would not appear depressed or languorous, because he has not lost, or been deprived of, affective contact, rather he has never experienced affective contact. He has never experienced it, because he has never had the capacity to experience it. It is, therefore, not surprising that his behavior is described as indifferent, aloof, detached, isolated, disinterested, and/or preoccupied; that he has been described as living in a "glass ball," "a circle of silence," and most recently, "an empty fortress," where, apparently, nothing is capable of reaching him, and where practically all of the influences of the outer environment, especially the parental, stimulating concerns and interests, fail to reach him.

By the same token, the suppression of arousal System II in the autistic child leaves the response energy system (System I) in a condition of useless (to the development of the child) and ineffectual (in the process of communication) ascendency reflecting only the basic biological need for stimulation. Under such circumstances, the behavioral responses given, lacking any reward, would be expected to be repetitive, stereotyped, empty, goal-less, aimless, and completely unadaptive. And again, is this not another pathognomonic behavioral feature of the autistic child who expends his energies in such activities as rocking endlessly, scratching the wall, mouthing or fingering objects, flickering his fingers in front of lights, or spinning tiny objects?

Thus, by assuming an imbalance between the two arousal systems as described, not only does the behavior of the autistic child become more understandable, but this understanding is no longer in terms of a reaction to a rejecting or depriving environment. Rather, it is understood in terms of an inborn organic deficiency in functioning. And to restate: The imbalance is in the direction of sustained ascendency of System I over System II; i.e., sustained suppression or inhibition of System II by System I. The result of this purported imbalance is a severe disturbance of affect; severe limitation of learning, or ability to establish meaningful associations; and goal-less, aimless, repetitive, and stereotyped behavior, without any apparent adaptive value aside from pure stimulus input.

But there is yet another aspect of this imbalance: the axis of the gradient of the imbalance. System II, in its state of suppression by System I, is always grossly hyponormal. In the context of the earlier discussion of the Hutt and Hutt neurophysiological hypothesis regarding the possible etiology of early infantile autism, it was mentioned that at least two varieties of early infantile autistic children have been observed along what, at that juncture, was referred to as the "activity dimension." Thus some autistic children appear to be extremely *hypoactive*, and others, *hyperactive*. Within the context of the proposed imbalance, with System I (the drive energy system) in ascendency, the activity level of the child is seen as a function of the gradient of the axis of this imbalance and is related to the previously discussed concept of level settings. In the hypoactive autistic child, System I is in ascendency, but both systems are functioning at a hyponormal level (see Figure 5a). In the hyperactive autistic child, System I is not only in ascendency, vis-à-vis System II, but is seen as operating at a normal or hypernormal level. That is, in the hyperactive autistic child, the gradient of the axis of the imbalance is much steeper (see Figure 5b).

Figure 5

HYPOTHETICAL SCHEMATA OF AUTISTIC CHILDREN
(a) Hypoactive, Hyposensitive Autistic Child;
(b) Hyperactive, Hypersensitive Autistic Child.

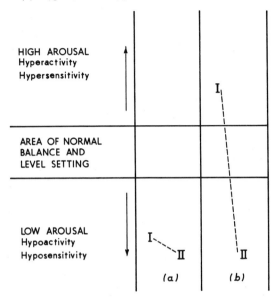

Considering the purported functions of System I (attention and alerting to stimuli; emission of responses) this variance in gradient has specific behavioral manifestations. Thus, the hypoactive autistic child usually is historically (i.e., in his early developmental history) described as being an extraordinarily "good" baby, who is quiet, undemanding of attention, a good eater, and a good sleeper. Later, as it becomes more and more evident that there is something "wrong" with him, he begins to display what might be called "quiet stereotypies." If he rocks, it is persistent but quiet. He may stand at the wall quietly scratching for long periods of time. Only the most gross and exaggerated environmental intrusions, alterations, or complexities, are likely to come close to disturbing him. In this sense he is both hypoactive and hyposensitive.

The hyperactive autistic child, on the other hand, presents on close observation a quite different picture. His developmental history is usually that of an "irritable" baby; he may from the beginning have problems or irregularities in the area of eating and/or sleeping. Later, the stereotypies he develops are vigorous in execution and frequency, and appear, in quality and quantity, to vary much more strikingly with environmental intrusions, alterations, and complexities. This child appears to be hypersensitive to new, novel, and/or complex environmental stimuli; yet because of the previously discussed inability to learn or associate them in any meaningful way, he responds to them in the only limited and unadaptive way available to him; i.e., by increase in activity (response emission) and with increasingly vigorous stereotypies. (See Escalona and Bergman, 1949; and Escalona, 1963.)

We now turn to the relationship between the postulated imbalance in the two arousal systems, and how it functions to internally impose a state of sensory deprivation on the early infantile autistic child. We have spoken of two different varieties of autistic children, the hyperactive and the hypoactive. However, regardless of whether the autistic child is hyperactive or hypoactive (level of System I), System II, that system which would enable environmental stimuli to accrue meaning, is grossly suppressed. The difference between the two types is analogous to the two approaches, discussed earlier, used in animal and human experiments for imposing conditions of sensory deprivation. One approach is to reduce all stimulus input to a minimum. This would be analogous to the condition of the hypoactive, hyposensitive autistic child; that is, he is relatively unresponsive to the normal levels of environmental stimulation (both systems hyponormal) and therefore receives only a minimum of such stimulations, and even these, due to the suppression of System II, remain meaningless and senseless. The other method of producing sensory deprivation is to reduce patterning and meaningful organization to a minimum, while maintaining a somewhat normal level of input (e.g., white noise). This situation would be analogous to the condition of the hyperactive, hypersensitive autistic child; that is, he may be more susceptible, due to the high setting of System I to the environmental stimuli, but due to the suppression of System II, these stimuli remain senseless and meaningless. Thus, both types of autistic children are sensorily deprived since few meaningful stimuli reach either of them.

However, the distinction between the hyperactive, hypersensitive autistic child versus the hypoactive, hyposensitive autistic child becomes extremely important when one attempts to derive a rationale for methods of treatment from this theoretical understanding of early infantile autism. Within this theoretical framework, in all children with early infantile autism, there exists a gross hyposensitivity, a barrier, if you wish, to normal environmental levels of affective stimulation due to the suppression of System II. Therefore, to overcome this affective barrier, or imbalance, requires high-impact, affective stimulation of a consistent, persistent, and well-structured nature. With the hyperactive, hypersensitive autistic child, other types of stimulation—i.e., tactile, proprioceptive, kinesthetic stimulation, which will in fact be the "vehicles" of the high affective quality—need not exceed normal levels, indeed, *should not* exceed normal levels. In the case of the hypoactive, hyposensitive autistic child, however, not only must he be "bombarded" with high affective stimulation, but all other types of stimulation, again primarily tactile, proprioceptive, and kinesthetic, which serve as the vehicles of the affective stimulation must *also* be of high impact—either by virtue of initial strength or excessive repetition. The full therapeutic implications of the neurophysiological model outlined in the preceding pages will be discussed in detail in Chapter V.

Part II

. . . and taking the child by the hand He said unto her: Arise . . .

Mark V : 42

A Child of Reality or a Child of Fantasy

developmental arrest versus psychosis

It may have seemed a somewhat useless pursuit, as Escalona suggested (1963), to attempt to define clearly the possible barrier to communication in the autistic child since, autistic or not, any child needs interaction with the parental environment in order to insure some degree of personality growth and development as a human being. The usefulness of determining where the core obstacle to communication may reside, as far as the autistic child is concerned, stems from the necessity of knowing in what direction the emphasis should be placed were one to attempt to influence and change the situation created between the child and his parents by the infantile autistic condition. That parent-child interaction and communication are needed for development of the child is conceded; but with the autistic child, how can one insure that some interaction and communication will take place without knowing what the specific obstacles to the communication and, therefore, to the personality growth of the child are?

Attempts to treat autistic children have, in general, been notably without success. Most of the early treatment efforts were almost ex-

71

clusively along psychoanalytic lines (Eveloff, 1960; Mahler, 1955). The resulting failures to ameliorate, to any significant degree, the autistic condition have led to increasingly poor prognostic opinions for such children, and hence to recommendations for early institutionalization in the face of total lack of other available treatment approaches. An exception to this gloomy picture of therapeutic failure with autistic children might be found in recent years with the introduction of "operant-conditioning" methods as a means of behavioral modification in the autistic child. Such techniques began first with the use of automatic vending machines (Ferster, 1964) as reinforcing instruments in modifying specific behavioral reactions in the autistic child, and have subsequently run the gamut, primarily under Lovaas and his group (1966) in California, of using electric shock (negative reinforcement), candy and food (positive and negative), and social reinforcement (positive and negative). Although these methods have been found useful in modifying, to some extent, the autistic behavior, and in adding a number of new responses to the child's behavioral repertoire, they have had the major limitation of failing to make these modifications or new behaviors generalize (transfer) outside of the experimental situation except to a very limited extent.

In spite of its relative successes, or possibly because of them, the operant conditioning approach continues to lack any basic conceptual framework through which to understand the behavioral syndrome of early infantile autism. This does not mean that there is no rationale to this approach; but it does mean that the rationale that is used here is one of direct application of the principles of animal conditioning and learning. Such wholesale transfer of animal techniques to a human child, without due consideration being given to what might be called the human condition, that is, the basic requirements of human growth and development, could not but lead to an overall failure in modifying to any significant degree the behavior of the autistic child. To the extent, however, that other types of treatment approaches have failed even more and led to a hopeless view of the autistic condition, the application of operant-conditioning techniques is possibly justifiable simply on a "what can we lose" basis.

To say that other treatment approaches have failed even more than operant-conditioning is not meant as a wholesale indictment of these approaches. This is said merely to emphasize the strong necessity of distinguishing as clearly as possible the etiological basis of the various forms

of autistic behavior in children, because much of the treatment failures may be directly consequent to the existing confusions in understanding the autistic condition.

When Kanner (1943) circumscribed early infantile autism as a specific and unique behavioral syndrome in young children, he referred
to it as a "disturbance in affective contact," without indicating whether
or not he viewed this syndrome as a form of developmental deficiency,
or as a psychosis to be subsumed under the general category of childhood schizophrenia. Eventually, according to his most recent article
(1965), he agreed with Despert, Mahler, Anthony, et al., that the condition of early infantile autism should probably be considered a psychosis, representing the earliest form of childhood schizophrenia.

It is important in this regard to weigh the contradictory implications
of such a position. As the earliest form of childhood schizophrenia, early
infantile autism precedes, in the classification hierarchy of childhood
mental disturbances, Mahler's various forms of symbiotic psychoses or
other "atypical" kinds of childhood behavior, commonly referred to as
"secondary autism" or "autistic adaptations." However, what distin-
guishes early infantile autism from these other disturbances is that, in
the latter cases, one usually observes two or three years of apparent normal development, which subsequently, for a variety of external reasons, becomes arrested and is then followed by a regression to an autistic form of behavior. In such cases of "secondary autism" there are good
reasons to believe that the child's developing ego, confronted by unbearable environmental circumstances, collapsed in its functioning as an
integrated unit. The existing ego functions of perception, emotion, affect, and motoric behavior then, were seen to operate not only in a dis-
organized way, but in a regressive autistic way.

This is not the case for early infantile autism. This behavioral condition is always reported as being present in the early months of the
child's life and never described as happening after two or three years
of normal development in the child. In this condition, there is no collapse in organized behavior, no regression to an ego-less state of functioning. As far as can be ascertained, the autistic infant from the very
beginning of his life is abnormal. He does not respond in a normal
fashion to environmental (maternal) stimuli; his behavior at no point
shows any manifestations consistent with a normal process of development. From the beginning, there is no organizing or integrating ego
function, and therefore there is no place, psychologically speaking, to

regress to, because there is so little psychological development to begin
with.

If such is the case, the early infantile autistic behavior cannot be considered as a psychosis of childhood in the usual sense of the word. In a
psychosis, the disturbed behavior appears consequent and reactive to
environmental conditions and circumstances which affect the child in
such a manner that he turns away from the environment, his development arrested and his communication seriously impaired. What had
been normal for two or three years becomes, in these cases, oddly abnormal and regressive. In the early infantile autistic child the development from the beginning is stymied, and it is only through far-fetched
and specious reasonings that one could claim that the very early developmental arrest, evident here, is consequent to the infant's "sensing,"
in the early hours after birth, that his mother wished him dead thereby
causing him to turn away from her. Thus, it would seem much closer to
the observed and reported history of the autistic infant's behavior to
clearly distinguish this syndrome from those childhood disturbances
which are reactive to environmental stress and are forms of psychotic
behavior.

Early infantile autism is probably better understood as an extreme
developmental deviation from what would otherwise be a normal developmental process. This extreme deviation, it is suggested, is consequent to an inborn functional neurophysiological imbalance, such as
described earlier, and as such, cannot be viewed as involving, on the
part of the parental environment, a traumatic or unfavorable quality.
The parents of the autistic infant need not, therefore, be viewed with
misgivings as far as their parental role toward the infant is concerned.
Their deficiencies in this role stem from the absence in their autistic infant of any real capacity to send out signals or cues to which the parents could appropriately respond. Because their child is not "with them"
they do not learn to be "with him," and eventually, especially if they are
told that the child's condition is hopeless, they may become discouraged,
and finally withdraw and separate from the child. At such times, they
may be considered distant, cold, rejecting, and it would be easy to conclude that they were that way from the beginning of the child's life!

Our position is that these parents are reacting rather normally to an
abnormal situation and that, conditions of normal interaction and communication between parent and child being absent, they are waiting
while their child is developmentally asleep. If and when the child can

be made to wake up, we would expect these parents to find once again in their transactions with their child, the parental potential to be normally adequate in helping their child develop normally. How to awaken the autistic infant, and how to bring about a normal developmental process in which his parents can normally participate and share, is the topic to be presented in the following pages of this book.

Chapter V

How Can Kathy Wake Up?

*the therapeutic implications of the
neurophysiological model*

The early infantile autistic child is not a product of a death wish; nor do his behavioral deficiencies result from an impoverished environment, lacking in sensory stimulating qualities, or from a rejecting environment, offering little affective and emotional gratifications. We now understand the condition of early infantile autism in a child as the expression and manifestation of a severe developmental deviation, or arrest, consequent to a functional imbalance between two intimately related arousal mechanisms in the brainstem of the central nervous system (see preceding chapter). We have made no attempt to explain how this imbalance came about in the first place, except to suggest that, since the number of early infantile autistic children is such a small percentage of the total normal population of children, their condition probably represents, within statistical expectations, the most severely defective end of the normal developmental curve in children.

The behavioral deficiencies of the autistic child seem to reflect a basic arrest in his total human growth. All areas of development, physical, intellectual, emotional, and social, are in various ways affected, so

that the autistic child's behavior is like the expression of a series of unrelated, discrete, and unintegrated functions in an organism surviving
in this world without being part of it. The most striking aspect of this
severe developmental deficiency is the child's affective isolation and
lack of emotional responsiveness. It is this affective defect which the
neurophysiological model described earlier wanted to account for, since
this affective imbalance appears to be the source of the developmental
arrest in the child. The value of this model, however, would be of little
consequence if it did not contain, intrinsic to its comprehensive structure, the implications for a method for reversing the imbalance and providing, for the autistic child, the totality of those experiences needed for
instating a normal developmental growth process in his life. These implications will be discussed in detail in this chapter and will serve as
the foundations for a therapeutic rationale in dealing with the early
infantile autistic child.

The affective threshold

The functional imbalance which we postulated to exist between the
two arousal systems in the autistic child is always in the direction of
suppression of System II, that is, that System which mediates affective
input, reward, incentives, and motivation. In this regard, it can be said
that the autistic child has a high threshold of arousal for those components of a stimulating situation which give affective value in pleasure,
pain, satisfaction, and gratification or displeasure, to the child's response to the situation. It is not, in fact, that the child is totally devoid
of such affective experience, since the endless repetition of stereotyped
behaviors (rocking, finger twiddling, and so forth) appears to have an
autoerotic importance for him, and since there is evidence, in the clinical
descriptions given by Kanner (1946), of traumatic-like affective responses
in some autistic infants. But rather the high threshold of affective responsiveness characterizes the autistic infant's behavior to such a degree that, under ordinary conditions of stimulation, whatever stimulus,
object, person, or activity would carry an affective value of pleasure or
displeasure for a normal child, leaves the autistic infant unaffected, disinterested, indifferent, and unaware. Understandably, such a child finds
no motivating incentive to attend to, or seek repetition of, most sensory-
stimulating circumstances, since for him there is no meaningful quality
to them, and no personal advantage or profit. By the same token, there

can hardly be any reinforcing value to the continued presence of these stimulating circumstances, as long as their stimulating impact remains too low to transgress the barrier created, in the child, by the high threshold of affective arousal. Therefore, unless stimulating conditions are created which would carry a high intensity of affective components for the autistic infant, there is little chance that his behavior would reflect awareness of the impinging stimuli, or a meaningful and attentive response to them.

Furthermore, unless the high threshold of affective responsiveness can be overcome, the autistic infant cannot relate, or meaningfully associate, one stimulating event to another. He cannot remember and profit from his experiences; thus he cannot learn. The central influence of affects on the various aspects of learning has always been recognized by students of behaviors involved in attentional, perceptual, memorative, and intentional activities. But it is only recently that experimental investigations have systematically brought forth that the gratifying, or rewarding, components of a sensory stimulating situation determine whether that situation as a whole, or any part of it, will influence the quality of the response to it, or the probability that such a response will be given again (retained-conserved) when the same situation is repeated. (For a comprehensive discussion of the relationship of affective values to perceptual and cognitive activities, see Kidd & Rivoire, 1966, especially chapters by C. M. Solley and Dorothea McCarthy.) This is especially evident in the development of intelligent behavior in the child—that is, behavior appropriately responsive to the stimulating situation and reflective of the needful state of the child—whose responses to environmental circumstances are always determined by the degree of sensory-motor activities with which the child has had contact, or which have been involved with such environmental circumstances. (Piaget, 1952)

The pleasure, or displeasure, which accompany the sensory experiences which the child obtains in actively engaging himself with parts of his own body, or objects and people in the environment, influences the child's behavior in seeking further pleasure or avoiding further displeasure. Not only do the affective values of a stimulating situation lead to the establishment of associative links between the various aspects of the situation, but also to an organization of the responses in terms of their affective capacity to bring about more and more pleasure, or eliminate more and more displeasure. Once the child has learned to associate certain types of situations with certain types of gratifications or rewards, his own need for such gratification and reward will drive him to initiate those activities and responses which will stimulate, or provoke, from the environment, responsive behavior of a rewarding and gratifying quality to the child. Thus is a communicative pattern established between the child and his environment in which the affective values of the stimulating environmental situation, on the one hand, help bring about a stable set of meaningful appropriate responses to the situation, and, on the other hand, determine in the child a need to direct his activity and behavior toward eliciting gratifying and affectively rewarding responses from his environment.

Such intentional and purposeful activities are impossible to the autistic infant whose high threshold of affective arousal constitutes a barrier to any meaningful and stable association links between external stimulating events and the response he gives to them. The autistic child has no way of knowing what's good or bad. Every response he gives to a situation is discrete, and unrelated to any other response, because the affective qualities which would serve to bind the relationship of stimulus to response, or to organize responses together, never truly reach him. It is as if every situation were novel and alerting only to the extent of eliciting from the autistic child an unending series of automatic, stereotyped, disconnected responses, without meaning or goal, without reward or satisfaction. Thus, he never *needs* the environment because he hardly ever knows what he can get out of it; he ignores it, stands outside or beyond it, and never initiates activities aimed at eliciting from it gratifying responses. He has almost no communication with the environment.

There is one other aspect of the learning process, through which new and changing behavioral responses are stabilized and organized, on which the affective components of sensory stimulation exert a central influence. This reference is to those aspects of learning concerned with remembering and forgetting. Perhaps no one has done more to focus the attention of psychologists on the importance of affects in remembering or forgetting certain situations or events than Freud, whose "free association" technique demonstrated unequivocally that forgotten experiences could be recovered if the affects related to these experiences could be reinstated. It would seem that experiences (responses given to certain circumstances) are easily forgotten when the affective components surrounding these circumstances are removed. (For a complete discussion of the relationship of affects to memory see Rapaport, 1950; Katona, 1940; Bartlett, 1932.)

But what if such affective components were never made part of a sensory stimulating situation? In such a case, no event could be retained, no series of events could be made part of a stimulating sensory pattern, and, therefore, no predictable, appropriate, and meaningful set of responses could be called upon to meet novel or different conditions in the environment. The autistic infant, deprived of affective stimulation, cannot rely on affective links to hold together patterns or sets of responses. In a minimal sort of way his "memory" depends completely on the stability, not of the affects connected with a situation, but of the objects in the situation. These must remain forever the same so that his responses, mostly unrelated to these objects, can have the sterile stability of sameness. It is indeed paradoxical that the "preservation of sameness," which is of diagnostic importance in the syndrome of early infantile autism, has no other value than to restrict and isolate the autistic child. It is a mechanical, robot-like repetition of an activity which, though it may have some autoerotic value, remains meaningless and goal-less, and therefore never triggers off any behavior motivated by a need for more or different forms of gratifications. The autistic child demonstrates in his behavior that he has hardly any awareness of what comes before, or what follows, any one of his stereotyped activities. These are seemingly automatic and empty. The autistic child finds no profit in any new experience, because the affective quality of this experience remains beyond his awareness (his arousal); therefore, he never seeks to repeat it, nor does he remember it ever existed for him. It is interesting in this respect that an exception is found in those situations which appear to have a highly charged affective value—considered traumatic—and which even the autistic child endlessly seeks to repeat (see Kanner, 1943; and Bosch, 1962). Thus the absence of affective responsiveness (the high threshold of affective arousal) prohibits the retention of responses and their adaptation in any meaningful and purposeful pattern appropriate to environmental situations or conditions.

The sensory environment

There is more to early infantile autism than a condition of high affective threshold. Observation of the various expressions of this syndrome in a number of infants led us to differentiate those infants whose behavior, though affectively low, appeared nevertheless to be hyperactive and hyperresponsive to the variations in environmental conditions from those who, affectively apathetic, behaved also in a hyporesponsive way to any environmental circumstance. In noting this difference, which our neurophysiological model attempted to account for, we are nevertheless faced with two different kinds of problems. In one, the hyperactive and hyperresponsive child can be thought of as having a low threshold of sensory responsivity, even though his affective intake remains at a minimum. In the other, the hypoactive and insensitive child can be viewed as having both "systems," the affective and the drive-response systems, at a below-normal level of arousal. This duality of situations imposes practical implications which may have important bearing on the developmental and learning process of autistic infants.

In the one case, where the child, affectively insensitive, appears nevertheless to be overly stimulated by, or overly responsive to, environmental conditions, developmental conditions and learning possibilities could be established only if those stimulating events were allowed and pursued which brought on an affective response of interest and attention rather than a diffuse, undifferentiated, and somewhat global form of behavior. This would mean that a great deal of structure and limits would be attached to any effort at stimulating such a child, while constantly allowing the child's own awareness of his affective experience to incite and motivate him to seek repetition of the stimulating condition to which he was exposed.

In the other case, where the child, affectively insensitive, seems also unresponsive to normal levels of sensory stimulations in the environment, it would be important, in order to create conditions of normal development and instigate possibilities of learning, not only to provide highly affective stimulating events, but also to insure that the sensory events, charged with affective quality, be of a forceful and impactful nature, through insistent repetition and careful attention to the degree of awareness that the child demonstrates of the stimulations given. This implies that the stimulating environment must be intrusive upon the child, not waiting, so to say, for the child to bump into the environment, but rather making sure that something always intrudes upon him to alert and awaken him.

In either case, whether the autistic child be hypersensitive or hyposensitive, the quality of the sensory environment must be structured (defined and differentiated) as a human environment, since the developmental and learning process to be achieved is directed at a human individual.

The human environment

What we wish to emphasize in this section is that whatever therapeutic implications our neurophysiological model may have with regard to the low affectivity level of the autistic child, or to the consequent difficulties that may exist in regard to his learning capabilities, or to the quality of his responsivity to environmental stimulations, any attempt at correcting these deviations, or at meeting these difficulties, has to include what we choose to call the "human component," because the development that we are concerned with is that of a human individual, and not that of any other animal. This human component has to define and differentiate those means that can serve either to overcome the high threshold of affectivity in the autistic infant, or to provide him with that quality of sensory stimulation appropriate to his level of responsivity. Thus what we refer to here as the human component is the *structure* which must be maintained if we are to achieve, with the autistic child, any degree of normal human development.

How are we to define this human component and differentiate its stimulating effect upon the autistic child from any other environmental stimulation? This question can be answered if the circumstances and events involved in the ego (personality) development of a normal child are clearly kept in mind. The normal child, affectively "open" from birth to the care and attentive ministrations of his mother—who, biologically, is best equipped to "correspond" to his need at this early stage (see Introduction)—appears to thrive as long as an atmosphere of pleasure, acceptance, and of "welcome to this world" is maintained. What the mother does, besides feeding, changing, comforting, or pacifying the baby, is to respond naturally and spontaneously to him in such a way that somehow he is constantly given to understand—that is, the communication is made to him—that it is quite all right that he be around, and that it is real pleasure and fun to have him around. This communication is made by surrounding the child with an affective climate which accompanies every experience he has, and which supports every response he gives. In the interactional process between the child and his mother, what the child seeks is to be a human individual, and the task

of bringing up the baby is one of humanization. The reciprocal movements and activities between the child and his human environment insure that the initiative of the child, in establishing and maintaining an
identity as a human being, will neither be thwarted by a lack of responsive acceptance from the parental environment, or choked (suffocated)
or overwhelmed by an undisciplined and uncontrolled take-over by the
parents of every move the child makes.

Consequently, whatever therapeutic intervention may be derived
from the neurophysiological functional model we have presented to understand and explain the behavioral syndrome of early infantile autism,
we must still view the process of growth and development of the autistic
infant as a human process aimed at more than awakening the child to
attend to certain objects, or people, in the environment, or to help him
learn certain responses to certain environmental circumstances. Like the
normal child, the autistic infant's awakening to the world must include
the affective human quality of pleasurable satisfaction at being a human,
surrounded by humans, and responding to this discovery within an affective climate that reflects the child's awareness that he is welcome to
this human world.

Thus, the stimulating effort that must be made to overcome, in this
child, the affective imbalance, and to provide him with that appropriate
degree of sensory stimulation which will trigger off a growth initiative
and allow learning to take place, must be done in a human fashion. The
autistic child is a human being and must be treated as such. The stimulating agent to his own experience of growth must be another human
being; and this agent must use himself fully in creating for the autistic
child the specific conditions (as described earlier) for a normal growth
process. To repeat, what is being sought here is the beginning of a reciprocal transaction between the autistic infant and his human environment, to the end of instigating in the infant that form of human initiative, found and observed in any normal child, which leads him to seek
human contacts; and in the actuality of affectively experiencing such
contacts, to progressively make the discovery of himself as a human
being, and of the environment as human.

The interactions and transactions through which an individual communicates his human presence to the child, in such a way that the child
is made clearly aware of this presence, constitute what we choose to refer to here as the structural aspects of the therapeutic-educational effort
derived from our understanding of the autistic condition. We call it

structural because its intended effect (or referent) is the emergence, in the child, of a psychological structure, an ego, a personality. Like any other dynamic or life structure, the human structure can be defined only by its functions; so that to characterize a structure as specifically human, we must insure that the functions through which it is expressed have a specific human character. This human character in functioning cannot emerge, in the development of the child's functions (perception, feelings, emotions, needs, and so forth) without the presence of another human being stimulating and fostering this emergence. Perhaps we could say here, in the light of the theoretical views presented in the Introduction, that the human "imprint" on the child requires, as Scott suggested with regard to any form of imprinting (see Scott, 1963), the felt physical presence of another human being, actively engaged in making his presence felt. However, with reference to autistic children, and to the neurophysiological model we have suggested to explain the autistic condition, we must add that the human presence can effectively imprint on the autistic infant only if this presence is communicated with a highly affective component of pleasurable and gratifying quality.

Furthermore, the importance of a felt human presence in fostering in the child the emergence of a human "structure" (ego-personality) rests on the fact that only such a presence can provide for the child those stimulating, sensory, and affective forms of behavior which are specifically human; that is, which cannot be provided, in terms of quality, spontaneity, tempo, degree of impact, and so forth, by any other non-human presence. When the child, through his crying, alerts the mother to some need he has of her presence, she responds with a variety of activities that can only be defined as maternal; these activities are all dominated by certain qualities of feelings, certain degrees of spontaneity, imagination, selectivity, and unpredictability. But usually they are dominated by the reflexive consciousness of the mother, which not only enables her to observe whether her activities have the beneficial effect she seeks to achieve with her child, but also allows her to deliberately and systematically reproduce, in a constantly more modulated and responsive way, the same effect in the child. That is, whatever response the child gives to her ministration—he stops crying for instance, and smiles at her—she can arouse over and over again, reinforcing through the spontaneity and enjoyment of her own behavior toward the child, the child's own behavioral spontaneity and initiative in his awareness of her presence to him.

This "human fashion" of being with a child must remain the central focus of any effort at helping the autistic infant emerge from his isolation and begin to function like a human being. The human presence of the therapist has to be emphatic, impactful, and assertive; yet it must be modulated to the child's behavior in such a way that what is constantly reinforced in the behavioral responses of the child are those aspects which reflect initiative, spontaneity, awareness of the other's presence, and awareness of the gratifying qualities of this presence.

In this regard, it is important that the earliest forms of natural stimulating situations be emphatically provided to the autistic child by the human stimulating agent. By earliest forms of sensory-affective experiences, we mean those which are not only first chronologically as far as postnatal conditions are concerned, but also first as far as what is known of the development of the central nervous system. Thus tactile, kinesthetic, and proprioceptive sensory-affective stimulations should be focused upon from the beginning. This means that the human stimulus must intrude himself upon the child, first using tactile, kinesthetic, and proprioceptive stimulating opportunities; and he must insure that such stimulations be pleasurable, gratifying, and fun for the child. Distant sensory receptors, such as hearing and sight, are not neglected, of course, but they must be used and understood as if they were modalities of the wide array of tactile stimulations to be provided (see Introduction). Repeatedly, insistently, and yet wisely and appropriately, the human affective climate must be established through these intrusive stimulations, so that the child can be made to discover and experience his own "humanity" in these contacts with another human being. As soon as the child demonstrates, by his responsive behavior, that the stimulating contact has reached him, this beginning of the human communicative process must be built upon, enlarging and intensifying the affective climate, while broadening the area of sensory stimulations. The important point here is that the response of the child to the totality of the human stimulating agent reflects the increasing need in him for such human stimulation. It is less important, from the beginning, to use the child's responses to help him learn how to be and communicate with another human being, than to bring him to need and want, more and more, to be, and communicate, with a human environment.

Once this reciprocal communicative process is established, in the climate of a high affective stimulating human environment, it would be expected that the capacity to learn and remember, to relate one experi-

ence to another and profit from the variety of experienced situations,
would appear in the autistic child. The emergence of this learning capacity would have to be capitalized upon and exploited, but always
within the demands of "humanizing" this infant. Such is the meaning of
the human structure in which the child must develop that his discovery
of himself, and of the world about him, must constantly be directed by
the humanizing end to be achieved in the development of the child.
Thus, there would be no developmental benefit to arouse the attention
and interest of the child in reaching for a candy, or in rattling a spoon
in a cup, if such responses would only lead to an absorption of the entire conscious life of this child in such inane activities. The task of
arousing the autistic child to a level where his development as a human
being can proceed along "normal" lines requires, therefore, that human
conditions of growth be maintained in any interaction with him. The
question cannot be: How can this child be made to learn this or that
form of behavioral response? or through what sort of conditioning can
his behavior be brought to acceptable norms of social living? The personality growth of a child is not made out of the successive additions in
his life of discrete bits of behavior which make him more or less acceptable to his social environment. When a child is accepted by his parents, the communication given him of such acceptance is basically unconditional. The child is not loved only because he manages to do this
or that which his parents consider required for proper social living. The
love communicated to a child appears rather as the catalytic agent, the
climate which constantly supports and reinforces the child's own need
to reach out for a wider discovery of the world, a greater mastery of his
own body and of his own environment, and a deeper involvement with
the important human beings surrounding him. Thus, to create for the
autistic child conditions of human growth cannot possibly be an effort at
conditioning certain discrete aspects of his behavior, but rather it must
be to create through a climate of warm, affective, and stimulating acceptance, the fundamental condition and climate of normal human personality development.

What is basically implied, then, in our theoretical position, with regard to autistic infant's developmental arrest, as this is reflected in a
behavior of affective isolation and of severe learning deficit, is that the
conditions of human development in this child are the same as in any
other child, except that these conditions have to be systematically and
relentlessly created and imposed on him. If, to grow as a human being,

the child needs the felt and responsive presence of another human (the mother), then the autistic child's awareness of this presence and arousal to this presence must be the only contingency of any interaction or trans-action with him. The child's behavior must constantly reflect his felt experience of the presence of the other; his awakened consciousness of this presence and his effort at maintaining this presence of the other to him. If, to grow and learn as a human being, a child requires the uncon-ditional love and acceptance of his mother who, rejoicing that he is with her, communicates her pleasure to him in a wide variety of attentive, caring, loving, ministrations and activities, then it should be most im-portant that any activity or response given to the autistic child's behav-ior be just as communicative of unconditional love and acceptance. If, to grow and develop human functions characteristic of human beings, a child requires that the "human structure," as defined, be constantly manifested in the spontaneity and freedom of responses given by the mother to every initiative at mastery and growth of which the child's behavior gives evidence, then, with the autistic child, it will be crucial that the same type of spontaneity and freedom be retained in every re-sponse given to him. Thus, the presence of the therapist, in an atmo-sphere of unconditional acceptance and love, will constantly permit the reinforcement, in the child, of every behavior which might show initia-tive, curiosity, and mastery of himself and his environment. In summary, the autistic child should first be given the conditions of human growth and learning. The stimulating instrument of his growth and learning must be sought in the active presence of another human who utilizes in a normal way, but forcefully and emphatically, his own behavior to arouse in the child the need to be with, and seek the presence of, this other. Only under such conditions could we expect any learned behav-ioral response acquired in the presence of the therapist to become easily generalized to any other situation, where the presence of another human, similarly accepting of the child, will evoke in him behaviors of initiative, curiosity, and mastery. In other words, whatever the situation, the au-tistic child, alerted and aroused by the felt presence of a human being who unconditionally accepts him, and spontaneously reacts to him, should find in communication with this person an increasingly wider and more varied set of circumstances and events to arouse his curiosity and challenge his efforts at mastery.

Thus, as an indirect but logical inference from our theoretical under-standing of the autistic condition in infancy, any attempt at insuring normal patterns of growth and development in the autistic infant should involve his parents as central agents of the "human condition." In the communication and relationship with the human environment, which is an essential and basic factor in the personality development of a child, the most normal human environment is constituted by the child's parents and family. The reciprocity of influences on each other, between a child and his parents, depends on the quality and effectiveness of the communication that can be established between them. Such communication (indicated in the Introduction) becomes active and growth producing only to the extent that the child can send appropriate messages to the parents to which they can respond; and that the messages sent by the parents can be meaningfully (affectively) received by the child. The normal development of the child takes place in such a mutual and reciprocal interaction, because only if the child "tells" his parents what he needs can they truly be parents to him and stimulate his development. Thus, having defined the autistic infant as one who cannot receive human messages sent out by the parents, and who cannot himself give information from which the parents can derive appropriate behavior responsive to his needs, it is clear that to include the parents as central educational agents in the development of their autistic infant will first require that they be made attuned to the types of messages which the autistic infant can send, and second, that they modify the quality of the messages they communicate to their child in such a way that the probability will be greatly increased of the infant's receiving such messages. Assuming that such requirements can be met, we could then expect that a reciprocal pattern of communication and influences would develop between the autistic child and his parents which would have the double consequence of (1) insuring the normal ego development of the child—that is, the child would start a progressive growth in which all functions, affective, cognitive, motoric, and conative, would find expression in an integrated and object-related way—and of (2) helping the parents change and modify their behavior in the direction of being more effective and responsive parents in their care and education of their child.

In summary, the implications of our neurophysiological model of understanding the early infantile autistic behavior carry direct practical consequences that can be translated into an action program aimed at awakening the autistic infant from his long sleep; and at offering him, through his parents, an ever increasing response to his needs for growth as a normal human being. In the following paragraphs, we will outline those practical steps which we took in designing the "awakening" of a group of autistic infants, and in insuring that their parents learned how to be parents to their respective autistic child.

Chapter VI

Designing Kathy's Awakening

the research hypotheses
and the methodological design

The research hypotheses

We designed the awakening of Kathy as an experiment to test two major hypotheses derived from our understanding of the autistic condition in infants:

Hypothesis No. 1: If we could provide the autistic infant with a highly charged affective climate of human interaction in which a wide amount and variety of sensory messages are communicated through stimulations, especially of a tactile, kinesthetic, and proprioceptive nature, the probability is great that the child's affective "barrier" can be transgressed and that the sensory messages can be received by him in such a way that his behavior in response will demonstrate an increasing capacity in him for appropriate affective reactions, for intelligent and adaptive behavior, for goal-directed and meaningful action, in the context of a normal family life.

Hypothesis No. 2: If the autistic child's parents can be exposed long enough to a normal quality and level of responses (messages-communica-

91

tion) from their autistic infant, the probability is great that their behavior toward their child will change and become responsive to his needs for growth and development; that is, the parents will learn to be effective and normal parents to this child.

The first hypothesis is based on our view that the autistic condition in infancy represents a condition of affective and sensory deprivation consequent to a neurophysiological imbalance between two Arousal Systems (Reticular Formation and Limbic). To test out this hypothesis required, therefore, that we set up a situation for the autistic child which would be structured in reverse of the experimental situations utilized in studying the effects of sensory and affective deprivation. To achieve this, we chose a clinical setting to which the subjects in the experiment would be brought from home at regular intervals two or three times each week for one hour. In its essential structure the clinical setting had the following features:

1. A relatively well defined physical space—a small room, with a sink, a table, two chairs, and a toy cabinet—but with very few toys available; one wall of the room had a one-way vision mirror, so that observations could be made from an adjoining room.
2. In this well-defined space where very few distractions were available, the therapist would be, for the autistic child, the focal point; that is, the activities of the therapist would be constantly and relentlessly directed at the child in such a way that the child could not escape the presence of the therapist.
3. These activities of the therapist would deliberately be all of a highly stimulating quality to the autistic child, especially through a wide variety of tactile contacts, a great deal of motoric activities, and a constant effort at making sure that the child had demonstrated, through his behavior, that he had actually experienced the stimulation given.
4. All interactions between the therapist and the child would be transacted in an atmosphere charged with spontaneity, with pleasurable or gratifying qualities, so that all activities not only would communicate a sensory message, but each message would be accompanied by an affective experience in the child of pleasure and satisfaction.

By making the therapist the focal point of the child's experience in the room, it was hoped to intensify the human quality of whatever stimulations would be given to the child, while providing a consistent and impactful affective component to these stimulations. The child, in this setting, would not be allowed to isolate himself; the therapist would force his stimulating presence on him and alert the child to this presence in its rich sensory and affective impact. Thus, no special efforts would be made at teaching anything to the child of a specific nature (such, for instance, as orienting himself in space, recognizing any special object, using words to express his needs, and so forth) but rather the therapist, using himself as a focal point of reference, would allow the development of the child's own initiative and spontaneity in the expression of his perceptual, cognitive, motoric, and affective functions, in the actuality of the pleasurable and gratifying contacts of his therapist with him. To create this highly charged affective climate, a spontaneous and genuine "fun" quality for both the child and the therapist should be maintained in all interactions in the experimental setting. A child normally likes to play; the autistic child, left to himself, never does. The setting, therefore, should provide an intensely playful atmosphere, so that each sensory message given might be associated, related, and integrated to a felt experience of pleasure in the child, in the presence of the therapist.

It should be clear from the foregoing that none of the interactions between the child and the therapist could be planned or programmed ahead of time, except in this general way that the strategy, in this experiment, should be aimed at alerting and awakening the autistic child, and that the tactics to achieve this should always be the communication of sensory-motor messages in a context of play, pleasure, and spontaneity. What would be constantly reinforced in the child would be the initiative he would show in his behavior at reaching out of his isolation toward more and more human contacts of an affective and meaningful quality to him. Each session with the child would be structured within such a context (for details of the Therapeutic and Educational Process, see Chapter VIII), so that whatever developmental gains the child might demonstrate would reflect characteristics of a truly human development.

The methodological design

To measure these developmental gains, we decided to use as a baseline the developmental level and condition which each child had reached just prior to being included as a subject in our program. Thus, in this experiment, each child was to be his own control.* Prior to treatment, each subject would undergo extensive physical, neurological, psychiatric, and psychological examinations, the results of which would serve to determine the developmental baseline from which the child's subsequent growth could be measured. Once treatment began, the following types of data would be collected at specified intervals, both within the clinical experimental setting and outside the setting.

a) Within the clinical experimental situation, observational notes of each treatment session would be made by an observer, an experienced child psychologist, who through the one-way vision mirror would observe the therapist and the child in their interactions. Every six months the observer and the therapist would fill out a selected number of the Fels Behavior Rating Scales on the basis of the child's behavior within the therapy situation. Furthermore, sound movies would be taken, as frequently as possible, of the child-therapist interactions.

b) Outside the treatment situation the following psychological tests and rating scales were to be administered at the indicated intervals:
1. Developmental scales (yielding a mental age or an I.Q.) to be administered by an experienced child psychologist every three months, as long as the items of each scale remained age-appropriate: Cattell Infant Intelligence Scale; Merrill-Palmer Scale of Mental Tests; Stanford-Binet Intelligence Scale, Form L-M; Leiter International Performance Scale.
2. Vineland Social Maturity Scale, evaluating in the child such areas of functioning as self-help, locomotion, occupation, communication, self-direction, and socialization; to be administered to the child's mother every three months.
3. Fels Child Behavior Rating Scales which measure such personality traits as affectionateness, negativism, curiosity, aggressiveness, etc.,

---

* All prognostic and follow-up reports in the literature regarding autistic children (Kanner and Lesser, 1958; Eisenberg, 1956; Mahler, 1952; Rimland, 1964) indicated at best minimal and/or transitory improvement in the autistic condition with or without therapeutic intervention. Further, children who could be accurately diagnosed as being cases of Early Infantile Autism are very difficult to obtain in any large numbers, especially within the restricted age range of two to six years. Thus, on the basis of the widely accepted irreversibility of this condition and the very realistic consideration of the rarity of its occurrence, the investigators believed that it was both scientifically and realistically feasible to deal with the problem of control in this study by having each subject serve as his own control. That is, each child who qualified as a subject was evaluated prior to the application of the treatment procedure in order to establish a developmental baseline. Subsequent progress was then evaluated for each child against his own baseline at periodic intervals during the treatment.

and which would be rated at intervals of six months both by the home observer and by the mother (these ratings would be in addition to the two ratings made, at the Clinic, by the therapy observer and by the therapist). Additional anecdotal information from outside the treatment situation would be provided by weekly notes from the child's parents regarding the home situation and stressing both progressive and regressive behaviors on the part of their child.

As stated earlier, each child was used as his own control and was evaluated on an individual basis. Therefore separate statistical analyses were made for each child on each of the scales involved. This was possible because each child was rated several times (at specific intervals) during the course of treatment; and most of the scales, as administered, were divisible into several subscores corresponding to the several functions or areas of functioning encompassed by the total scale score. The notes of the therapy observer, the home observer, and the mother are of special value with regard to the question of generalization of treatment gains outside the clinic situation. This question is of particular importance in view of the fact that the widely popularized use of "operant conditioning" techniques with autistic children has met with notable failure in this area (Lovass, 1966; Ferster & DeMyer, 1961); that is, in achieving any marked degree of generalization outside the experimental situation.

All the scales to be used met the criteria of ordinal scales; none reach the criteria of interval scales. No assumptions could be made about randomness or normal distribution. Therefore, the data were ranked and two nonparametric statistics served as the primary statistical tools: (1) the Friedman Two-way Analysis of Variance, and (2) the Kendall Coefficient of Concordance.

The Friedman Test was used to test whether, for a given child within a given scale or set of scales (i.e., the Vineland Social Maturity Scale or the Fels Scales), there is no change in behavior skills between successive three month (Vineland) or six month (Fels) ratings. The Kendall test was used to test whether, for a given child within a given scale (i.e., the Vineland), there was no change in the *relation* (pattern) among the several rankings of the subscales at successive three month intervals. The Kendall test was also used to check interrater reliability among the individuals rating the child on the Fels Scales; i.e., the home observer, the mother, the clinic observer, and the therapist.

Since the development and performance of autistic children has been traditionally reported as notoriously uneven, a single score (such as a developmental, intellectual, social, etc. age or quotient) is of limited informational value in assessing the evenness, or unevenness, of progress in any of these areas when it occurs. Therefore, where it was possible, an effort was made to look at and compare, either statistically or qualitatively, the specific areas of functioning measured within a scale—rather than attend simply to a single overall developmental or social quotient. That is, the interest here was not only in whether developmental, social, or other changes took place, but also in whether changes in patterns in specific areas of change took place. This was felt to be particularly important in regard to the question of whether, once they began to emerge out of their autistic condition, these children would display consistent, normal, or fluctuating patterns of development.

Thus, for example, the Vineland, which yields a single social age, is designed so as to be readily amenable also to closer scrutiny of the more specific areas of communication, socialization, locomotion, occupation, self-help general, self-help eating, and self-help dressing.

Of the 30 Fels Child Rating Scales, 15 were chosen by discussion and agreement between the therapist and the two observers (clinic and home), according to the criterion of potential reflection of change in specific behaviors characteristic of the syndrome of Early Infantile Autism. That is, it was agreed that these 15 scales were apt to reflect more directly (over the period of treatment) any changes in behavior specifically relevant to Early Infantile Autism. For example, since, as was discussed earlier, lack of affective contact is considered to be the central symptom of Early Infantile Autism, the Affectionateness scale (1.1) was selected on the basis that it describes a continuum ranging from a description of a child as avoiding affection, cold, impersonal at one extreme to, at the other extreme, a child who is "fond of affection" and spends much time in pursuit of it. Similarly, the Sense of Humor Scale (7.1), which involves not only awareness of being with somebody else but also an affective sensitivity to the pleasurable qualities involved in the relationship, has definite value in assessing the autistic child's movement from uninvolvement with others to meaningful involvement with others. (See Table 1, Chapter X, for a list of these scales and their relationship to emergence from characteristically autistic symptoms.) These 15 scales were subjected to the Friedman test in the same manner as were the subtests of the Vineland. That is, for each of the four raters the three ratings (initial, six months, one year) on each of the 15 scales were ranked and the Friedman test applied. The Kendall was used to check inter-rater reliability. In order not to burden the text unduly, the detailed data of these statistical analyses are carried in the Appendix.

These, then, were our plans and procedures to test out our first hypothesis (see p. 91). Some modifications had to be made as the program developed, such as, for instance, the inclusion of two therapists together at various times in the treatment sessions, or allowance made for sickness or indisposition in the child which might force postponement of testing at the stated intervals. Other modifications will be pointed out as we report the results (Chapter X).

Our second hypothesis (see p. 91) was predicated on the assumption of a "mutual correspondence" between the child and his mother which permits a communication between them without which the child's development cannot take place. The autistic child cannot communicate and, therefore, the parent cannot provide the appropriate responses to his developmental needs as a human being. As a consequence, the parent cannot truly be a parent to him. But would such a parent learn to modify her pattern of parental responses to the autistic child were the child to give her messages, or were she taught to "hear" her child's communication to her? Our second hypothesis states that she probably would.

To test this hypothesis, our design included introducing the parents to the experimental situation from the beginning. A complete diagnostic personality assessment was made on both the mother and the father before treatment of the child started. Furthermore, each parent's pattern of relationship and interaction with the autistic child was carefully assessed by observing each parent in the therapy room with the child and filming their activities. During the course of treatment, the parents were asked to observe their child's sessions with the therapist, and the active and affective quality of therapeutic interactions was discussed with them afterwards. At various intervals, each parent was observed again in the therapy room where he or she was allowed to do whatever they wanted with their child. At the end of six months, and again at the end of one year, another complete diagnostic study was made of each parent. Additionally, the home observer was asked to note the parents' behavior toward the autistic child as part of her periodic (every six months) visits to the home. These data, we hoped, would begin to give us some information on the questions which our second hypothesis raised.

The designing of this entire program could not take into account the infinite number of variables which any study of the complexities of human lives entails. The subjects, five autistic children and their families, will be described in the next chapter; the detailed steps of our interactions with each child will be outlined afterwards (Chapter VIII); and finally, the participation of the parents in the program will be fully discussed in Chapter IX.

Chapter VII

Kathy, Her Friends, and Their Families

the subjects in the project

The subjects in the treatment program, described in the previous chapter, were five children, between the ages of 2 and 6 years, who had been diagnosed at the Pediatric Evaluation Center, independently of the therapists, as having the Kannerian syndrome of Early Infantile Autism. These children and their ages at the outset of treatment were: Kathy, 2 years, 8 months; Connie, 5 years, 2 months; Elizabeth, 3 years, 3 months; Tommy, 2 years, 3 months; and June, 4 years, 10 months. For each of them, individually, the initial comprehensive evaluation and condition at the outset of treatment will be described below.

Kathy

Kathy was brought to the Evaluation Center with the following presenting problems as reported by the social worker: "Kathryn doesn't say anything at all. She's afraid of anything new—people, food, even toys. She's afraid to ride in the family car, covers her head in strange places (which she's been doing since she was a year old). She's still on baby food because she won't try any new foods. She won't feed herself and has never made any attempt to. She sucks her thumb almost constantly but has never put anything else in her mouth—not even a cookie. She uses her feet as much as her hands to explore, and puts her face down to things too. She kicks everything, never plays with toys other than to carry a piece of a toy, shake it, and then to drop and kick it. Her coordination seems to be clumsy although she can pick up tiny objects easily. She doesn't seem to understand directions at all, but reacts with fright to a scolding if the tone is harsh. Mother's concern began when, after pulling up at 8½ months to a standing position, and walking holding on to furniture before age one, Kathryn was still afraid to let go and walk at 15 months and didn't walk until 17½ months. Mother's concern was around the child's fear of trying to walk (without holding on) rather than the act itself."

The family constellation is as follows: "Kathy is the younger in a sibship of two, her brother is 5½ years old. Her father, age 31, is a chemist. Her mother, age 26½, is not employed (has completed three years of college). Kathy has her own room in a suburban three-bedroom home. Mother is an only child. Maternal grandmother lives [out of state]; maternal grandfather died in 1946. Paternal grandparents are both living [out of state], and father is only boy in sibship of four."

The early developmental history records the following information: "Mother didn't feel that there was anything unusual about her pregnancy. Kathy was full term. Labor was slow for 12 hours, but was suddenly very rapid and Kathy was born within an hour. Birth weight was 7 pounds, 14 ounces; and as far as parents know there were no problems in the nursery.

"Kathy was discharged with mother after six days and was a very good baby. The only problem around feeding was that she was never a hungry baby, and still never fusses for food. She was on three meals a day at 3 months, but never cried from hunger. She took her bottle easily, but didn't open her mouth readily for a spoon. She never seemed to like food, and completely refused some baby foods.

"After she started to crawl (at 7 months) she no longer wanted to be picked up or cuddled. Mother at first didn't force the child to be held, but when this behavior continued she felt she'd have to pick her up and hold her, or the child wouldn't even know she was her mother. After a while, Kathy tolerated this without resistance. Kathy still does not seek affection, but accepts it when mother comes to her. She never goes looking for mother, but seems happy to see her when mother comes into the room. Mother feels Kathy prefers to be left alone. Kathy doesn't seek out father or brother either, but seems happy when they come to her. Mother says she has the feeling, when she enters Kathy's room, that she is 'penetrating the child's world.' Mother became more aware of Kathy's strange behavior mostly around the time she showed fear of walking. Mother feels that there has been no real change, or progress, other than walking, since Kathy was 10 months old.

"From the time Kathy was a year old, she couldn't be taken anywhere without crying—until a year ago when, as long as she was held, she wouldn't cry. The first time she could be set down without crying was in spring 1964. Now she can be left in the church nursery while parents attend church services, although they don't think she socializes at all with the other children.

"Kathy cried the first time she was put on the toilet, but since then doesn't resist—instead she waits to be taken off. Would continue to sit if she weren't taken off. Mother began training recently. Kathy is dry all night, but floods in the morning.

"Kathy was afraid of the big tub, when mother tried to put her in it, and attempted to climb out. Mother bathed her in the kitchen sink after that until Kathy was nearly 2 (spring 1964). She is no longer afraid of the big tub.

"Kathy will allow anyone to dress and undress her, but won't allow anyone, including father, to feed her. Mother attempted to make Thanksgiving dinner food into the texture of baby food for Kathy, as she wanted her to be able to share the Thanksgiving meal, but Kathy wouldn't take any of it.

"Kathy banged her head, while sitting, when she was a baby. Parents said she'd laugh, and seemed to enjoy the noise of it. She didn't hit her head hard. She has always been a crib rocker however, and rocks so hard she's moved a twin bed across the room.

"Parental concern is primarily around Kathy's fearfulness, as they are worried that it will interfere with her ability to learn. Son had been slow to talk, so this didn't concern them, as he is a normal child."

The final impressions and recommendations of the social worker were as follows: "Kathryn's parents are attractive, intelligent people. They seemed genuinely concerned about Kathryn, and quite bewildered by her behavior. Mother had observed very early that the child put nothing into her mouth, not even when teething (at which time she bent to crib to bite on it), and seemed related to child's fears sufficiently to cope with them as they were encountered. I did not feel parents were infantilizing the child, nor did they seem to be rejecting. They related easily and comfortably to me, and to each other. Their concern seemed to be for the child rather than around their problems with her, and they seem to have felt shut out by her. They don't know how to enter her world."

After Kathy had received the entire battery of diagnostic evaluations (detailed in Chapter VI, on methodology) the Evaluation Conference Summary carried the following information on the various aspects of her functioning.

The pediatric history reads as follows: "Mother, 26, and father, 31, both in good health. One brother, 5½, in good health. Family history noncontributory. This was mother's second pregnancy. No miscarriages. Except for two bouts of urinary infection during the fourth and fifth months respectively, treated with antibiotics, pregnancy was uneventful. The baby was delivered after 12-hour labor in cephalic presentation. Mother was awake and states that baby cried immediately. . . ." [What is omitted here is essentially a repetition of material supplied above in social worker's report.] "Mother thinks that the child sees and hears well. Child does not mind being wet and soiled. Held head, date unknown. Rolled over at 4 months. Sat at 7 months, pulled up at 8½ months, stood alone at 15 months, could have done it before, but was afraid. Walked without support at 17½ months, walked upstairs and downstairs holding on at 2. Will not do it without holding on. Except for frequent mild URI's [upper respiratory infection] and German measles at 1½, no other illnesses. Fully immunized."

The results of the pediatric examination were essentially normal. "Kathy is a well-proportioned little girl weighing 27 pounds (below 25th percentile) and measuring 36 inches (at the 50th percentile). Head circumference is 19½ inches and chest circumference 21 inches. In the nursery, she was walking around showing little interest in toys. Her gait, coordination, and strength appeared normal. When brought into the examining room, she became very frightened and irritable.

"Pediatric examination was essentially normal except for presence of mild URI (mildly infected throat and nasal discharge). Neurological examination: Reflexes are physiological, Babinskis seem to be negative, but this is not very reliable in view of child's uncooperation. In observing the child, she grasps objects like an infant, raking them with her fingers; even very small objects were picked up in this manner. Coordination in fine motion was not good, was more like that of a much younger child rather than true incoordination. What she did with toys was practically nil. They were all thrown on the floor."

The Physical Medicine evaluation noted no abnormalities except in Kathy's behavior and response to people. "This child shows no abnormal motor patterns in gait and reach and grasp. Muscles are flexible and strong. The area of aberration is in behavior and response to people. Mother's history of motor development indicates a fairly normal curve and, therefore, we are not dealing with a global mental retardation, but rather with abnormal adaptation."

The Ophthalmologic evaluation was also essentially normal although Kathy was described as "very uncooperative and difficult to examine."

The Audiological examination raised the rather interesting speculation. of auditory agnosia. "Hearing for speech and pure tones entirely within normal limits. This child demonstrates only sporadic attempts to localize sound and these are, for the most part, inaccurate. It appears that she has a receptive language problem, and the problem may not be limited to language at all, but rather to something more general in nature—such as an auditory agnosia. This is speculative."

The Neurological evaluation, although complicated by her near-panic state, could uncover no defect. "Neurological examination on this extremely frightened, crying, uncooperative youngster is entirely within normal limits. Although she does have a history of delayed physical development, the history is odd in that the delay would appear to be the result of a fear reaction rather than a real delay in maturation. Although there is no doubt that the child is functioning at a retarded level, one would wonder whether we are not dealing with a severe emotional reaction, or even an autistic reaction, as the primary pathology."

Urinalysis found Kathy to be "negative for PKU." However her EEG was considered to be borderline ". . . because of paroxysmal nonfocal slowing awake." The X-rays of Kathy's skull and wrists showed her ". . . bone age as normal" for her chronological age.

Kathy's speech evaluation underlined her severe deficit in her communicative abilities. "Kathy exhibited no awareness of language or gesture language. After she adjusted to the change of coming to my room, she engaged gayly in a give-and-take game with my hand. According to her mother she communicates very little, but does wave toward her crib when she wants to go to bed. She babbles a few sounds, says ma-ma-ma when angry. She uses oral musculature for feeding at a minimum of her ability and reacts to changes in this area as she does in every other."

Her Physical Therapy evaluation found no gross motor impairment, only retardation. "Upon examination this child does not demonstrate any impairment of her gross motor function. She appears to be severely retarded. Adaptive behavior appears to be at approximately a 7-month-old level. No therapy is indicated." This was further substantiated in Kathy's Occupational Therapy examination which covers both gross and fine motor coordination. "No motor dysfunction was noted for gross or fine coordination. Motor development was within normal limits. Kathy has very little meaningful contact with her environment. Eye contact is minimal. Child occasionally covers up her eyes with left arm. Her activity consists of walking around the room occasionally, picking up a toy which she holds rather than regards or manipulates. Often she heaves a deep sigh as if severely depressed. Child is not regulated for toileting during the day; however, she remains dry at night. She is disinterested in food and must be fed; and she cooperates when being dressed."

Because of Kathy's pervasive fear, evaluation of her on standardized tests proved impossible; thus the Psychological evaluation was based on three successive play observations which yielded the following diagnostic picture: "On the basis of the scanty observations (formal examination was not possible), one cannot make any estimate of this child's intellectual capacity. One obtains the impression, both from a history which shows she was alienated from the world from the first few days of life and from these clinical observations, that one is dealing with a child who shows classical behavioral features of primary autism with anaclitic, phobic, and counterphobic features. In view of the unusually large collection of fears this child displays, one would do well to be certain that her sensory capacities are fully appreciated, for it is possible that her fears could stem from a defective or distorting sensori-perceptual apparatus."

Kathy's last evaluation was in the form of a Psychiatric consultation which yielded the following comments: "Kathryn is a 2½-year-old white girl who was seen with her parents and 5-year-old brother. She seemed quite oblivious to her surroundings, was in incessant motion, crawling, walking with an atypical gait, or running from place to place. She made no sounds except for crying when frustrated in her wishes. To examiner's surprise, however, she allowed him to hold her in a tender, affectionate manner for 30–45 seconds and further was able to use both mother and father as effective tension-reducing systems."

After carefully considering all evaluative information gathered, the final diagnosis arrived at by Evaluation Conference was: Infantile Autism.

Thus it came about that beautiful, brown-haired, brown-eyed Kathy was referred to us and became the first subject in our treatment program. In view of our neurophysiological theory, we were immediately interested in determining for ourselves, within the conceptual framework of hyperactive versus hypoactive autistic infants, just where Kathy might fall, since this would have definite, direct implications on our approach to her in the therapy situation. This proved to be relatively obvious; she was not at all hyperactive, given as she was to spending hours in her room, undisturbed, scratching at the wall, or flickering her hands in front of the lights; she slept long and well (12 hours on the average). She was not hypersensitive; indeed, as well as showing no evidence of hunger, she showed, initially, no response to pain; and as was indicated in her audiological evaluation, it appeared as though she might have receptive agnosia. Thus, we saw Kathy as a hypoactive and hyposensitive autistic child.

Connie

For Connie, coming to the Evaluation Center was one more name to add to the already long list of clinics and hospitals where her parents had taken her, dating back to 10 months of age, in search of some explanation of her increasingly apparent aberrant development, and in hope of finding help. The following Developmental and Social History tells the painful story.

"Connie is a 5-year, 2-month-old white girl referred for complete evaluation. Mother, 30, in good health. [Mother] is a college graduate and has taught physical education. She has been employed as a regular, and as a substitute, teacher in the public schools; but more recently she has been assisting at the day nursery which Connie is attending. She underwent surgery a few years ago for the removal of cysts and a suspension of the uterus, in hopes of becoming pregnant. Connie is her only child and only pregnancy. Father, 36, in good health. In our contact with [father] we found him to be a ruddy-complexioned man of fine physical appearance, very unrestrained in manner. He has a Bachelor of

Science degree in education and some additional hours toward a Master's degree in counseling and guidance. He is a physical education instructor also, in the public schools, and has a realty business on the side.

"During the second trimester Connie's mother complained of extreme tiredness. Anemia was diagnosed (type unknown). She was treated with shots of B_{12} and liver extracts, with good response after six weeks of treatment. She also took one grain of thyroid throughout her pregnancy (this had been prescribed previously to help her become pregnant). After her pregnancy, she was found to have a low PBI and is now on three grains of thyroid a day. The baby was delivered at a hospital by forceps (reason unknown, hospital did not forward birth record). Child was delivered under general anesthesia. Mother does not know if she cried immediately. Birth weight was 7 pounds, 15 ounces. Parents were not informed of any difficulties in the nursery. Discharged with mother after five days. During her first 8 months of life, Connie was very irritable, crying much, and sleeping so little that mother found it a treat if she had peace for one hour. There were no feeding problems. Early motor development has been normal. Mother states that the child could maintain a sitting position with support very early (4–5 months?); however, she failed to be able to pull herself to a sitting position until she was 13 months of age. She crawled late at 14 months and walked only at 2½ years. At 10 months, she could repeat words with the proper intonation (four or five words), but has regressed since then, having no words now. At 10 months of age mother noticed that Connie's eyes started to cross. She consulted an ophthalmologist who advised putting atropine drops in the good eye to stimulate the bad one. On the day when the drops were put in, the child became extremely restless (no illness, trauma, or pica at the time). Mother stopped putting in the drops, thinking that they were the causative factor. Irritability persisted, getting progressively worse. At 17 months of age, the child was seen at a university in the orthopedic clinic for evaluation of failure to stand, irritability, and speech retardation. No conclusions reached because mother did not bring the child back for follow-up. Shortly afterwards, the family consulted another pediatrician. Around that time, Connie had stopped saying the few words she knew. She was so restless that her mother one day, having reached the breaking point, brought her to a nearby hospital where she was hospitalized for one month. The only reports we have on this hospitalization are of EEG and skull X-ray—both normal. Child was discharged on phenobarbital (¼ grain every four hours).

Mother states that she was getting worse, withdrawing steadily. She lost complete interest in her toys, for example, and stopped going to the window to look outside. At the age of 2½, a third pediatrician was consulted and hospitalized the child for three days. He felt that she had suffered phenobarbital intoxication. Connie has not been on medication since that time.

"In September of 1963, when she was one month short of her second birthday, Connie was admitted to a children's hospital for a thorough workup. An EEG showed a 6/sec activity in all areas and sharp spike seizures in the left parietal area. Amino acids, spinal tap, and skull X-rays were reported as negative to the mother. Audiologist thought that the child might be deaf. Parents were informed that the child was suffering from a degenerative disease of the nervous system, a diagnosis they refused to accept. Parents then consulted a pediatric neurologist who told them, after having read the birth record, that Connie was brain damaged and, in addition, had severe psychiatric problems. He advised residential treatment. Since then Connie has been seen at a speech clinic by a psychologist and at the mental health center by a psychiatrist. At present, the child is completely withdrawn. She does not play with toys, does not establish contact with people except for physical contact (will put her head against anyone). She has no words. She is completely indifferent at being wet or dirty. She does not help in her dressing and has to be fed. Connie is now on the waiting list for a state institution for the retarded. In giving the pediatric history, [mother] was repeatedly on the verge of breaking down. She seems to realize fully how sick her little girl is."

The summary of the Evaluation Center Conference on Connie carried the following diagnostic information:

The Pediatric examination stated that: "Connie is a sturdy, healthy-looking girl with shining blue eyes and pink cheeks. She weighs 38 pounds, and measures 42 inches (both at around the 25th percentile). Her face is large with round cheeks. Chest circumference 56 centimeters. EENT: Completely normal findings. Eyes were straight when examined. Chest, abdomen, and genitalia all normal except for mild diaper rash. Extremities: Arms have a mild degree of cubitus valgus. Legs are slightly rotated externally from the hip. The child walks on a wide base with her feet turned out and rather stiff knees. On neurological examination reflexes are all physiological. Throughout interview with mother, the child kept prancing around the room, smacking her lips, wringing her hands, or gazing at her finger, which she would move in front of her eyes. From time to time, she would come and rest her head on doctor's arm, stopping all activities. She did not look at or pick up one toy, ignored mother, and did not speak a word. No eye contact at any time. Mother handled her gently and with a great deal of patience."

Connie's eyes were essentially normal except for a slight tendency toward farsightedness: "External structures are normal. Extraocular muscles are straight. Visual acuity is not obtainable. Under cycloplegia the net retinoscopy reveals a small amount of hyperopia. Media and fundi are normal."

Connie's Neurological examination was essentially negative: "It is obvious that this youngster is functioning at a psychotic level of adaptation. She sits relatively quietly with some rolling or rocking in a constant hand-wringing movement. However, at least with this examiner, she looked at examiner's eyes and maintained eye contact for long periods of time. At one point, she pulled the examiner's face toward her to give the examiner a kiss and then wanted to be held. At no time did she refuse physical contact with the examiner. Neurological examination revealed that she does hear a 126-cycle tuning fork. She follows objects with her eyes. Her deep tendon reflexes are equal and hypoactive bilaterally, and there are no pathological reflexes. She walks with a wide gait, with the feet in external rotation, but this is probably related to a bilateral pes planus."

The Orthopedic evaluation failed to reveal any neuromuscular deficit: "Child walks with moderate degree of out-toeing. There is moderate pes planus, slight external tibial torsion, and slight excess of external rotation at hips (ER 70 degrees, IR 43 degrees). No apparent neuromuscular deficit."

Connie's Physical Medicine evaluation found her musculature to be somewhat of an infantile type and of low strength: "Child is constantly grimacing her face and gesticulating with hands. No attention or cooperation during examination. She cried easily, no speech—only angry noises and mumbling. She seems to be hypotonic and hyperreflexic. No apparent pathological neurological reflexes; abdominal reflexes superficial. Muscles feel rubber-like, flabby, infantile type. No definite segmental weakness, however, and general impression is that muscle strength is generally down. There is bilateral external rotation of both thighs. However, no subluxation or other striking hip pathology. Walks on wide base with knee hyperextended, and thighs abducted and externally rotated, and flat-footed on the ground. She is able to climb stairs with mother's help, not able to get off the floor without support. Uses for grasp only the left hand according to mother and our observation."

Her blood workup was within normal limits and the X-rays of Connie's skull were negative. Her "bone age on wrist X-ray was compatible with the chronological age."

Connie's EEG was labeled as abnormal: "Abnormal EEG because of a small negative spike seizure focus in left parietal area spreading to left frontal as was apparently previously seen. This is compatible with development of a seizure disorder and is occasionally seen as residual of encephalitis. Repeat EEG is suggested in one year."

The Occupational Therapy evaluation noted Connie's delayed motor development: "Motor development was delayed, child not walking until 2 years, 9 months. Child moved continually, spinning and turning in circles in a propelled wide-based gait. Occasionally she appeared to drag her right foot. It was also noted that she avoids using her right hand. Child could not be involved in activity. Self-stimulating activity predominated throughout her performance; however, she did establish eye contact."

Evaluation of Connie's language development placed her at no more than a 12-month level, and no receptive language could be detected: "Although history reveals a cessation of imitation and babbling, there is no indication that she has ever achieved more than a 12-month level of language development. Presently, she has no words and utters unusual noises. Although therapist could detect no understanding, the mother is sure she understands a few simple words. The child is not imitating sounds nor gestures (although she has just learned to imitate a clap). She engaged in no play with toys, mouths all objects, and seems to differentiate little between humans and objects. Peripheral speech mechanism appeared to be normal."

Connie's Physical Therapy evaluation stressed her marked delay in gross motor development: "Child, upon examination, demonstrates only mild impairment of her gross motor function, but she demonstrates a marked delay in her gross motor development. At the age of 5 she functions motorically like an 18–24-month-old child."

The Psychological examination of Connie stresses the handicaps imposed by her lack of awareness and responsiveness to the environment, as well as stressing her retardation: "On the Cattell, Connie scores at 5.2

months of mental age. However, it must be very carefully stated and understood, that these are gross underestimates of optimal intelligence. Any intelligence test assumes an awareness and responsiveness to the environment. Once this awareness was present, the ability to grasp, to reach persistently, and many other failed responses, could be easily passed since they are within her maturational sphere. Connie achieves at present a mental age of approximately 5 months. Diagnostic impression is Early Infantile Autism, with concomitant mental retardation."

The Psychiatric evaluation supported the impressions of the Psychological examination: "The clinical picture appears to be that of an autistic child with totally inadequate object relationships and the self-stimulating behavior frequently found in autistic children as substitutes for environmental stimulation."

The final diagnostic impression arrived at in the Evaluation conference was "Psychosis of childhood, or Early Infantile Autism" with the recommendation that the EEG be repeated one year hence.

Thus, at 5 years, 2 months of age, Connie, with her sparkling blue eyes and her long blond pony tail became the second subject in our treatment program.

Descriptively, from the standpoint of our neurophysiological hypotheses, we viewed Connie as definitely hyperactive because of her constant and vigorous hand motions, and her state of continual motion involving prancing and turning in circles. Her extreme irritability and erratic sleeping patterns (few hours and early awakenings) support characterizing her as hypersensitive. Though obviously hypoaffective, she was in some ways less so than the other children in that she would occasionally approach other humans, though it was difficult to tell if she truly differentiated them from objects; and she would occasionally establish eye contact. In terms of the gradient of the axis of imbalance between the two arousal systems (see Chapter IV), we saw Connie as having the steepest gradient of imbalance of all the children in the program. Expressed diagrammatically, she would most closely resemble the illustration in Figure 5b, p. 65.

Elizabeth

Elizabeth, according to the social worker's report, was referred to the Evaluation Center by the family pediatrician because of her very delayed development during the first two years of life and her failure to make any progress between the ages of 2 and 2½. Elizabeth's mother had become seriously concerned about Elizabeth when she was 14 months old. The family constellation was described as follows: "Elizabeth is a 2-year, 10-month-old, white, Catholic child, the third in a sibship of three children born to [father] age 35 and [mother] age 35. The other children are Mark, 4 years old, and David, 6 years old and in first grade." The family owns a suburban, seven-room, split-level home. "Elizabeth has her own bedroom, the boys share a room, and there is a family room where the TV and toys are. Father works as a systems analyst. Mother worked for about 15 months after marriage . . . but has not worked since having children."

The parents see the main presenting problem as Elizabeth's inability to talk. "They feel that she is able to communicate with them but she is unable to verbalize this communication. However, in discussing this with them, it would seem more likely that they anticipate her needs. Elizabeth does not point and lead them in any way to get what she wants; rather, they offer her, for example, a drink of water, and if she smiles, they know that she will accept the water. Another problem area is seen in Elizabeth's walking: 'She walks like a toddler.' She does not run and often appears to lose her balance. She falls infrequently because she is extremely cautious, though she climbs well. She doesn't have much opportunity to take walks with mother, but when mother does walk to a friend's house, Elizabeth will sit down and refuse to walk. However, in returning home, she will walk back. At the present time, Elizabeth will eat table foods if they are mashed or cut up in very small pieces, and if they are offered on a spoon. In August, 1965, mother tried to teach Elizabeth to feed herself. She resisted a great deal but finally took the spoon as long as mother held her hand to guide it to Elizabeth's mouth. She still insists that mother hold her hand during feeding, and will refuse the food if she does not. She goes through a ritual each time she eats, of properly placing the spoon in her hand in a particular spot, with her mother holding her hand with a particular amount of pressure, and in a particular position. She does not insist upon this with everyone else. However, she will not even hold her own spoon with anyone else—she simply allows herself to be spoon-fed (for example by her father or paternal grandmother). She does not eat cookies or lollipops. She has been drinking milk from cup since age 11 months, as long as someone else will hold the cup.

"Elizabeth goes to sleep easily, and has never had any nightmares.

She sleeps in her crib and sucks her two fingers to put herself to sleep. She has no object that she is particularly fond of, or that she wishes to sleep with. Toilet training has not yet been attempted.

"Elizabeth has a few words—'Daddy,' 'Hi,' though mother isn't certain she knows *who* Daddy is. If she cannot reach an object she wants, and no one will get it for her, she walks away from it and goes on to something else rather than to communicate her wish in any way. [Mother] feels that Elizabeth is much more fond of her father, and that she responds to him with greater depth. [Father] feels that when she becomes overly excited her eyes roll outward, but that Elizabeth can control this at will. [Mother] does not feel that it is very noticeable or very important. [Mother] feels that Elizabeth never becomes excited in response to her. When Elizabeth hasn't seen mother for a few hours, she simply smiles at her return; she never spontaneously hugs and kisses her.

"Elizabeth's favorite pastime is rocking either on her hands and knees, or in a sitting position. She started rocking when she was 9 months old. She banged her head frequently starting at age 8 months, but this stopped when Elizabeth was 2½ years old. However, she will still do it on occasion. Elizabeth looks at the TV, but the parents do not really feel that she sees anything. She prefers playing by herself, either in the water or in the toilet bowl, emptying out ashtrays, taking utensils out of the kitchen cabinets, or poking at the eyes of dolls. Elizabeth is reported to be able to play by herself for hours—'she is too good a child.'

"Elizabeth will often remove herself from the rest of the family. If the family is all downstairs in the family room, she will go and sit by herself in a corner of the dining room. If she is brought back down, she will stay for a while and then leave again. Elizabeth will also attempt to do this sort of thing when taken visiting. She will usually stay in the same room, but remove herself to the farthest corner, and sit and rock facing the wall. She will also sit and rock while scratching the walls, the heating vents, or the grill on the bottom of the refrigerator to the point that she has almost no nails, and often to such an extent that they are bleeding. She shows no evidence that this is painful to her."

Early developmental history: "Elizabeth was born by Caesarian section and had a birth weight of 6 pounds, 2 ounces. She was two weeks premature, and the parents believe she was placed in an incubator for one day. All of [the mother's] deliveries were by Caesarian section. She had difficulty in becoming pregnant initially and was given 'hormone' treatments. Her second child was five weeks premature, and she was therefore given 'shots' to help her to carry full term when she was pregnant with Elizabeth. She took medication when pregnant with both Mark and Elizabeth because of an elevated blood pressure.

"Elizabeth began to vomit when she was two days old, and she was switched to glucose and water. She then had her stomach cleaned out because of an accumulation of mucous. When she was taken home from the hospital, she was a sleepy baby and she had to be awakened to be fed. She frequently gagged and vomited. She was found to have a murmur of the heart which disappeared at age 2 months and appeared again at age 5 months. The parents have been told that it now can no longer be heard. She sat up at 9 months, crawled at 18 months and walked at 2 years. Though mother first noticed Elizabeth's problems at age 14 months in that 'she wasn't doing anything,' father felt that he thought something was wrong with Elizabeth when she was 8 or 9 months old because of her lack of response.

"[Elizabeth's father and mother] met when he was in the service some 13 years ago. After corresponding for several years, [she] came to the United States and they were married eight years ago. [Elizabeth's mother] is a small, attractive, and well-groomed woman of 35 years, who presents a pleasing appearance. [Elizabeth's father] is a tall, good-looking, quiet man of 35 years. During the interview, he let his wife do all the talking, though he did respond when asked something directly. The maternal grandmother is living (age 58 years) and in good health. The maternal grandfather died in 1954 of hypertension. [Elizabeth's mother] has 3 siblings (sisters). The paternal grandparents are both living: Grandfather is 63 years of age and in good health, except for an ulcer; grandmother is 59 years of age and in good health. [Elizabeth's father] is an only child. Both [parents] state that they are in good health. The [father] is a high school graduate and studied 2½ years at a technical institute. The [mother] is a high school graduate, and has worked as a secretary and general office clerk."

The Pediatric History in the Evaluation Conference Summary seems to summarize much of information contained in the Social and Developmental History given above: "Father, 35, and mother, 35, both living and well. Brother, 6, and brother, 4, both living and well. No miscarriages. No familial diseases. Mother had elevated blood pressure, albumin in urine at about the seventh month. She had Lutein regularly all throughout her pregnancy. Caesarian section two weeks before due date was performed, as the two previous siblings had been delivered by section. Birth weight was 6 pounds, 2 ounces. No pathology. There were feeding difficulties in infancy starting on the second day and lasting three to four days. Child was discharged on eighth day, doing well. The child was started on Olac and then given regular milk at 6 months; put on solids at 5 weeks. She now has a regular diet, but all foods, including cookies, have to be mashed. She is on vitamins. Habits: Bowels okay; appetite good; sleeps well; rocks frequently, though this appears to be diminishing; head banging has disappeared; and finger sucking. Development: Date not known when she held head. Sat up at about 9½ months. Stood with support at 16 months, stood alone at 18 months, and walked at 21 months. Very few words, not understandable. She is not at all toilet trained, all efforts are unsuccessful. She does not chew foods, eats only mashed ones, and does not feed herself. She will play with only very simple toys (pull toys). She does not know how to use blocks.

"The referring pediatrician advises that when the child was 2 months of age, she was first noted to have a systolic murmur along the left sternal border that was interpreted as a septal defect. The murmur gradually decreased in intensity over the next several months and had finally completely disappeared at the age of 2 years. A chest X-ray taken at 7 months did not show any cardiomegaly or apparent increase in pulmonary vasculature. No other cardiac investigation was done. At 10 months of age the child weighed 19 pounds, 6 ounces and measured 28½ inches. She sat weakly by herself and did not crawl. At 14 months she had not gained or grown, and her development had not changed appreciably. At 17 months of age she weighed 19½ pounds and measured 30 inches. She was crawling and walking with support, but was not speaking. At 2 years she was able to walk well, climb stairs, and say a few words. Intermittent divergent strabismus was noted bilaterally and child was seen by an ophthalmologist who found no other ocular pathology. Child was seen again at age 2½ and at that time had made no further progress in either growth or development. It was at this point that the child was referred to the Center. Of the childhood diseases, she has had chicken pox at age 2. She is completely immunized."

The results of the Pediatric examination record that: "Child weighs 26 pounds (at tenth percentile for 28 months) and measures 33 inches (at third percentile for 28 months). Head circumference is 21½ inches and chest circumference is 21 inches. Attractive child, but is much younger in both looks and actions for her age. She spoke no words, was playful. She had an alternating squint. There is a soft systolic murmur at the apex and along the left border. Neurological examination is negative."

The results of the Neurological examination revealed only intermittent external strabismus and the presence of bilateral flat feet: "Neurological examination reveals a pudgy youngster who did not say any intelligible words, and seemed to function at a level appreciably below the 3-year level. Deep tendon reflexes were active and equal bilaterally. No pathological reflexes and no abnormalities of movement were noted. She had an intermittent external strabismus. The only positive finding is a bilateral pes planus."

Examination of Elizabeth's hearing "revealed hearing for speech and pure tones, entirely within normal limits. Sound localization is present and accurate." Likewise her blood workup was "within normal limits."

Elizabeth's X-rays showed her to have a bone age approximately one year less than her chronological age. "X-rays of skull reveal multiple sutural bones. No evidence of increased intracranial pressure. Chest negative. Wrists for bone age reveal a bone age of approximately 2 years as compared to chronologic age of 3 years."

Her EEG was entirely normal: "Both a waking and a sleeping record were obtained and results were within normal limits."

Elizabeth's motoric functioning was estimated to be retarded approximately one year by the Occupational Therapist. "Elizabeth is a chubby sad-eyed cherub of 3 years who functioned at an observed 18–21 month level motorically. She approaches toys by methodically exploring them tactually before she discovers their further possibilities. All play was largely tactile exploration. Child is not toilet trained, but will occasionally go when put on the potty chair. She neither finger feeds nor eats with a spoon, relying on her mother to feed her. She cooperates when dressed, but does none of it herself."

The Physical Therapy evaluation also noted a marked delay in her gross motor functioning: "Child, upon examination, demonstrates a marked delay in her gross motor development. She functions motorically like a 12-month old infant at the age of 3. She is an independent walker. Gait is wide-based and she has flat feet. Gait is reminiscent of a child who has just learned to walk."

Although Elizabeth's peripheral oral mechanism functions well enough to support speech, no elements of language behavior were observed. "Not even rudiments of language behavior were observed in this child. The fleeting auditory attention and lack of imitative ability are probably basic to the problem. Visual and tactical avenues of perception may be more highly evolved but perhaps one cannot make such comparisons. Peripheral oral mechanism functions well enough to support speech."

Her Psychological evaluation highlighted her lack of language, her advanced visuomotor and visuoperceptual skills, and the severe disturbance in her interpersonal relationships. "On the basis of the score obtained, Elizabeth would appear to be functioning within the range of moderate mental retardation. However, the pattern which she presents is rather unusual, not only because of her lack of performance on the language items, but also because of her clearly more advanced visuomotor and visuoperceptual skills. The manner in which she related to the testing situation in general, and to the examiner in particular, especially during the second session, suggests that this child has some severe disturbance in her interpersonal relationships. As a matter of fact, it seems fair on the basis of the observations made here to suspect that this child may actually show symptoms of some form of childhood psychosis. Accordingly, the chief recommendation which we have at the present time is for psychiatric evaluation."

The psychiatric consultant was unable to ascertain the cause of Elizabeth's apparent retardation: "Elizabeth was seen for a psychiatric diagnostic evaluation and the psychiatric consultant felt that there was not enough evidence at this time to ascertain whether her retardation was primarily on an emotional basis or primarily on an organic basis. It was recommended that she be followed at the Evaluation Center for further observation."

The final Evaluation Conference stressed Elizabeth's global retardation (speech, bone age, motoric, and intellectual) and arrived at the diagnostic formulation of psychotic adaptation or Early Infantile Autism. Elizabeth was then referred to our treatment program to become the third member of our group of subjects. With respect to our neurophysiological hypotheses, we saw Elizabeth as very similar to Kathy. She was hypoactive, spending most of her time rocking, scratching at walls, and tactually exploring objects in her environment; she slept long and well. She displayed no apparent discomfort at pain, made no attempts to communicate her needs (i.e., hunger or thirst) and often "appeared deaf" to the parents, all indicating a severe degree of hyposensitivity.

Tommy

"Thomas was referred to the Evaluation Center by his pediatrician for evaluation of delay in development and the possibility of psychomotor retardation. [Tommy's father and mother] came together for social evaluation; they impress one as an extremely young couple, appearing even younger than their stated ages of 26 and 25 years respectively.

"Thomas is a 2-year-old, white, Catholic male, oldest in a sibship of two, with a younger sister who is 14 months old. [Father] works as an editor and writer of speeches, and other administrative publications in the public relations department at a university. [Mother] is a housewife. Both parents are college graduates, and have been married for three and a half years. The presenting problem with Tommy is his retarded development; mother observed that she had sensed that he was slow, developmentally, from the beginning. Of special concern was his inability to walk prior to second birthday, and lack of any comprehensible speech. The birth of a sibling in 1965 made Tommy's early retardation even more dramatically clear.

"Mother was quite unsure of most of the developmental landmarks, but she made the following approximations: Held head at 2 months; sat at 10–11 months; crept at 9–10 months; pulled up at 12 months. He could stand alone for only a few seconds at 14 months, and would walk only when hanging onto mother, although at times he walked with his head and feet on the floor. However, Tommy had begun to walk, unsteadily but independently, just prior to our interview in February, and father felt strongly that now other developmental milestones would probably follow closely, since walking had been their major concern.

"Tommy has no distinguishable words, and though he does appear to understand some simple words and commands, he is unable to reproduce them himself, and only hums and makes guttural noises. He still requires baby foods, or food with a 'mushy' consistency, and refuses solids of any kind, other than cookies and toast. He cannot drink from a cup, and is unable to hold a cup at all, although mother has not attempted to teach him to do this.

"Parents did relate that Tommy was a 'self-contained' baby, who did not enjoy cuddling or physical contact, and has just recently reached the place where he seems to enjoy being picked up and held. He also gets so deeply engrossed in a particular object, or repetitive activity, that he cannot be distracted, and often gets involved in this type of activity. Another idiosyncracy which concerned parents is Tommy's fear of certain rooms in the house; he will not enter parents' bedroom, the living room, and one half of the dining room.

"It is to be noted that the [parents] spent many months in the Peace Corps prior to Tommy's birth, and were stationed [abroad] during the early months of pregnancy with Tommy. (She had one miscarriage earlier in their stay there.) Due to the diet of starches and little or no protein, [mother] was anemic and became progressively more run down physically; due to her physical condition, and the lack of medical care, they returned to the States in order that she might receive more adequate and consistent medical attention. In the early months of Tommy's life he had anemia, a heart murmur, and failure to gain; however, this was never classified as any particular disease entity or syndrome."

Tommy's Pediatric History elaborated on some of the aspects already recorded in the social evaluation. "Thomas is a 2-year-old white boy referred by family pediatrician for evaluation of motor and speech retardation. Mother, 25, and father, 26, both in good health. One sister, Susan, 1, in good health. Remainder of family history noncontributory. This was mother's second pregnancy. She had one miscarriage (at six weeks) before Thomas. Mother states that except for anemia (Hb around 9 gm.) responding well to medication (Vitron C), her pregnancy was uneventful. The baby was delivered after a short and easy labor of four and a half hours by low forceps under general anesthesia. He breathed immediately. Birth weight 6 pounds, 10 ounces; length 21 inches and head 12¼ inches. Baby's record mentions enlarged thoracic A-P diameter (no workup). The baby was discharged with his mother. At home the parents encountered no special problems except for some crying spells in the late afternoon, which lasted for three months. The baby was breast fed for three months; at the end of this period mother thinks that he was not getting enough milk as he gained only 4 ounces in one month. Good gain was resumed on artificial feeding. Around the age of 2 months a heart murmur was discovered which disappeared subsequently (no workup) after receiving iron for moderate anemia, hematocrit 30 percent. Motor development has been delayed. Thomas sat late and walked only five weeks ago (two weeks before his second birthday). Speech is also slow. The child has no words yet, babbling still like a one-year-old. Mother thinks that he may understand a few words (cookie, juice, eat, and so on). In his play with toys, he enjoys poking and fitting different things into each other. Mother is worried about strange habits that Thomas has developed. Around 14 months he started to be afraid of parts of the house, being panicky when mother would put him there even when she stayed with him. It got so bad that he would stay only in one room and half of another, at times dashing quickly to retrieve a toy from the "dangerous parts." He also refused to sit on mother's lap except when she would be on the floor, and would resist sitting in the bathtub, being very willing, however, to lay in shallow water. Around that time, mother also ran into feeding problems, the baby getting less hungry and tired of his baby food, and mother getting increasingly frustrated and focused on his intake. At present he refuses most of the baby food, and is not on table food yet, eating mainly starches (cereals, crackers, cookies), milk, and fruits, with vitamin supplement (Tri-vi-sol, 0.6 q.d.). In giving the history, mother is quite anxious and worried about her little boy. It is quite clear that she has been quite overprotective, watching his every move. At age 10 months, he had otitis media with no complications. Is fully immunized."

According to the Pediatric examination: "Thomas is a healthy looking, well-developed blonde boy. He weighs 26 pounds (below the 25th percentile) and measures 34½ inches (above the 50th percentile). His head is somewhat large, measuring 20¼ inches. Chest circumference 20 inches. EENT: No abnormal findings. Teeth are well developed. No dysplasia or discoloration. Chest, abdomen and genitalia: Normal. Extremities: Wrists look somewhat enlarged. No bowing of the legs. Neurological examination discloses very brisk reflexes in the lower extremities compared to the upper ones. Babinskis are in flexion. There also is a minimal degree of hypotonia in the legs. When sitting, the child keeps them mostly stretched and abducted. He walks like a beginner on a wide, unsteady gait with his legs and feet in valgus."

An additional Pediatric consultation supported the above findings: "Mother states that she early noted that her son was different than other children. He seemed to be fascinated by his hands and would lie looking at them for a long period of time. She also states that she has noted that he ignores people and she thinks that he reacts to her as though she were a person to be ignored. She has noted his fascination with lights. She states that as an infant, when she went to pick him up, he would assume the anticipatory position, but that he did not really respond with a good hug or affection. Thomas was observed through a one-way mirror. He walked about the playroom on a broad-based gait mouthing a cookie. At times he did make eye contact with his mother. His attention span was very short, and he was only briefly with a variety of objects in his environment. When examiner came in to play with him he did not respond in any overt way; he would not take examiner's hand. He did not respond to sounds. He did not engage in any kind of by-play with examiner."

Physical examination revealed a completely uncooperative toddler who resisted all attempts at examination. "His head seemed large for his body. Brief look at fundi revealed no gross abnormality. It was not possible to check his reflexes. His knees jerked, did not seem to be hyperactive. There were no other gross physical abnormalities."

Examination of Tommy's eyes revealed only a small hyperopia (farsightedness). "Extraocular structures are normal. Extraocular muscles grossly straight. Net retinoscopy under cycloplegia reveals a small hyperopia which is not significant at this age. Ocular media are clear. Fundi normal."

"The objective Neurological findings on Tommy are essentially within physiologic limits." The Physical Medicine evaluation stated that Tommy "presents no neuro-musculo-skeletal abnormalities."

Evaluation of Tommy's hearing, despite his lack of cooperation, concluded that he probably heard well enough to support speech and language development. "This child cried intermittently throughout the entire examination. Despite this behavior, we observed what we judge to be relatively fleeting listening behavior to the sound of a bell, horn, squeeze toy, and voice presented at an intensity level of 30 dB. Although his behavior and responsiveness to sound stimuli was certainly not typical of what would be expected of a 26-month-old child, he did display some awareness to fairly faint and moderate levels of sound, and he did show some rudimentary attempts at searching for a toy emitting a sound. It is the clinical impression that this child probably hears well enough to support speech and language development, all other things being equal." Speech evaluation of Tommy supported this and further stated that his current language age was 6 months. "A history of delay of all areas of development including speech was reported by [mother]. Presently, Tommy hears and understands language inconsistently. He ignores, or is oppositional to, verbal directions. Expressively, he has no words, babbles in an infantile fashion, and may be beginning to imitate sounds. Some autistic mannerisms were displayed. According to

Mecham Verbal Language Development Scale, his language age is 6 months."

Tommy's gross motor development, as stated by the Physical Therapist: "Child functions below age level in his gross motor development. At the age of 26 months, gross motor activity is like that of a 12 to 15 month old infant, who has just learned to walk."

The Occupational Therapist reported similar findings: "Tommy began walking two weeks short of his second birthday. He is unsteady on his feet. Eye contact was established with the child for three to four seconds after extensive active physical play (i.e., twirling and tossing him in the air). Tommy was usually irritable when approached by the therapist. When left alone, he wandered out to the old X-ray room where he gazed upwards at the lights in the ceiling. Mother stated that he gazed at lights through his fingers as early as 3 months. Child also engaged in running his hands up and down the textured walls, and rocking behavior. Involvement with presented toys was usually avoided; therefore, developmental assessment could not be considered as valid. Motor development was between 15 and 18 months. Tommy is not toilet trained, feeds himself using a spoon, and cooperates when being dressed."

The Psychological evaluation clearly saw Tommy as a child with Early Infantile Autism. "On the basis of the test results alone, one would safely say that Thomas is functioning within the range of moderate mental retardation. However, it becomes quite clear in observing this child that his perfunctory performance on a test could not possibly be considered as typical, since this result is not representative of his abilities. The manner in which this child interacts with his environment, namely, his preferring to deal with objects rather than with people; his peculiar approach to objects in terms of being only interested in details; his unusual interest in such things as texture; and his unexplained periods of apprehensiveness suggest quite strongly that we are dealing with a child who is in all probability psychotic. It is also quite apparent that this child is engaged in functioning at a stage of primary narcissism. For example, his behavior with his hands, as well as his verbal behavior, which does not seem to have any communicative value, but rather appears to be emitted for purposes of self-gratification, certainly suggests that this child has not moved beyond the stage of complete involvement with just himself. The main diagnostic impression which we have at the present time is that this child probably conforms to the picture of primary autism drawn by Rimland much more closely than any other non-verbal child seen in the Center thus far."

The diagnostic impression of autism was further confirmed by the Pediatric Consultation report. "From the diagnostic interview with Tommy and from the information available, there is no question but that he is an autistic child. The positive aspects that examiner can see are that there appears to be some object relatedness, although this results in a great deal of anxiety, and in moving away from the human person when he allows himself to momentarily become involved. The recommendation would be for intensive therapy for this boy; and while the mother was not seen diagnostically, it is assumed that concomitant therapy for her would be indicated. The conference discussion revealed that Dr. DesLauriers was going to see Tommy and that he may be accepted in the therapeutic program. If this is so, this is the best possibility available for him; but if not, then private therapy for Tommy should be recommended if funds are available; or intensive therapy in some clinic setting if at all available or possible."

The diagnostic consensus of the Evaluation Conference was Early Infantile Autism with delayed motor, speech, and intellectual development. Tommy was accepted as the fourth subject in our program. We saw Tommy, within the neurophysiological framework, as having relatively normal activity and sensitivity levels; that is he was neither constantly in motion like Connie, nor was he given to long periods of inactivity; rather, the amount and rate of his activity was normal though obviously aimless, goal-less, and purely of a self-stimulating nature. He was not unduly irritable; instead, one might say that his only available response to any intrusion was one of undifferentiated irritation. As is substantiated by the preceding descriptions, he was severely hypo-affective.

June

"June is a 4-year-old preschool girl* of a white, Catholic family. Her father, 28, is a salesman for a business computer firm. Her mother, 26, is in the second trimester of her fourth pregnancy. Brother, John, is 3.

* Note: This social and developmental history of June was taken 9 months prior to her entrance into the treatment program, by which time toilet training had been achieved except for enuresis.

Sister, Leslie, is 1," states the social history. "Both parents are college graduates, the father having had an additional year of graduate work.

"June was referred on the recommendation of her teachers at the Head Start program where it was noted that her speech was delayed, and that she failed to join in group activities. The pediatrician concurred with the recommendation. June has been evaluated at the Speech and Hearing Center on four occasions between the ages of 2 and 3. No definitive conclusion could be drawn at the time of the last evaluation. Further evaluation was recommended. A short frenulum was noted and surgical consultation advised; the surgeon did not recommend surgery. Her latest evaluation report makes note of June's lack of interest in human beings, and questions her object relatedness.

"The chief complaints as expressed by the parents were: (1) speech problem; (2) wandering; (3) sleep disturbance; (4) temper tantrums; (5) toilet-training delay; (6) poor social relationships.

"The [parents] first sought an evaluation for June when she was 3½ and still not speaking properly. They had changed pediatricians, as they became disillusioned with their first pediatrician who refused to commit himself as to whether June's speech difficulty presented a problem or not. The second pediatrician did see the speech and lack of toilet training as problems which required further investigation.

"Repeated over and over again throughout the diagnostic are references to June's improvement. She began speaking words at around 3½ but both her speech and her bowel control improved markedly on her fourth birthday (August, 1965), when June dramatically announced that she now wanted to use the toilet. Enuresis has continued. Bowel control has not been achieved.

"June attends preschool one time per week, (one and a half hours) and is found by the teacher to have a short attention span and to be an outsider as far as group activities are concerned. Later mother acknowledged that June's behavior and performance are not at an appropriate age level.

"Because the family was prepared for a diagnosis of brain damage or retardation, they seemed to give that kind of information in the beginning of the interview. The mother said that June was slower in everything. She sat up after six months—the mother could not elaborate on how long after 6 months. She was walking at 15 months. She never crawled. The mother's description of June's behavior as a baby made me suspect that the primary problem was not organicity or retardation. The mother said June did not laugh at too many things. She did not try to imitate others. As a baby, she was very restless. During the first year, the mother used to think that June had colic. There was much difficulty with her formula. As a baby, she used to hold her breath. The mother said that you could not play with June. [Mother] noted that you can distinguish between various cries that a baby has. With June she was unhappy if she saw you; she was unhappy if she did not see you. The mother said that June rejected kissing until she was 2 years old. Now she tolerates having others kiss her, but she is not an affectionate child. Toilet training was begun at 1 year.

"With regard to June's speech, the parents said that it started improving when she began playing with other youngsters. As far as speech is concerned, June does not use pronouns, and refers to herself as Junie in conversation.

"[Mother] became pregnant with June two weeks after her marriage. Both [parents] recalled that [mother] was depressed during the first three months of the pregnancy. She had some bleeding during the third month of pregnancy, and the doctor prescribed medication. Other than that, the physical part of the pregnancy was quite normal. June's father was with his wife during the delivery, and he remembered very clearly that the doctor told him that everything went very smoothly. [Mother] reported that June was bottle fed from the beginning. She said she never thought of breast feeding, and then thought a moment and said she had no desire to breast-feed June. During the first six months, June was always held when fed.

"From the beginning, June was 'unpleasant' and 'no fun.' She was always crying and fussing. 'It seems she resented being brought into the world.' She was very active but seemed to have no communication with anyone. 'You couldn't get her to respond to anything.' She seemed never to be happy in any position. Her only enjoyment seemed to be the bottle, but as soon as she would finish she would be unhappy again. June did very little sucking. She never sucked her thumb and refused the pacifier. [Mother] thought June had colic, but the pediatrician would never commit himself on this, and only recommended several formula changes. June, although occasionally drinking from a cup at age 1, continued to use the bottle primarily until 2½. She still occasionally asks for a bottle. As an infant, June seemed never to be content. She was not happy being played with. She did not respond to being picked up or cuddled. 'She would fuss if she didn't see you, or fuss if you came in.' Mother saw June as demanding and unsatisfiable. 'She ruled the house.' As an infant, June was 'not as sweet as she is now; she has come a long way.' Mother elaborated on her feelings about June as an infant. What she felt most intensely was a 'feeling of battle' between them. 'From the time of her infancy, I felt she hated me.'

"As to motor activity, June was always felt to be an active baby. She sat without support at 9 months, and was walking at 15 months, without an interval of crawling. There was some head banging associated with temper tantrums, but no rocking. There is no history of convulsions. As an infant, June would hold her breath while crying until she turned blue. June's favorite activity during infancy was that of violent jumping in a jump seat, an activity she would pursue for hours. Although 'not too graceful' June does not have coordination difficulty. Both parents mentioned her unusual manual dexterity. Although June can be very persistent, for example, in untying knots, in contrast to this is a short attention span seen both at home and at school. For example, she will not listen to a story. She cannot watch a television program, and will begin wandering after a few moments. In this area, too, there has been some improvement.

"June has always presented sleeping difficulties. There has not been a time in which she has not awakened at night or very early in the morning. She has been given tranquilizers and sedatives to no avail. The most difficult times were those of the first six months, and during a six-month period beginning a year ago during which June would awaken two or three times a night and scream. Mother could not explain this reaction but did say that it may have been related to the new baby. (Leslie was 3 months old.) This behavior stopped when the family moved to their own home last spring. Then June began her current patterns of waking at about four in the morning and wandering around. She seems perfectly content. She may get into bed between her parents, but then will wander off to crawl into bed with the baby. She may undress the baby or bring her a bottle. Often June wanders to the kitchen and prepares food for herself. In spite of talks, punishments, and so forth, June does not seem to understand that she is not to be in the kitchen during the night. Mother feels hopeless in helping June to reverse her sleep habits. She cannot keep June up after six. In fact, June often falls asleep at the table. June's bedroom is on the second floor. She will not fall asleep in her own bed, but instead insists on sleeping on the couch in the baby's room on the first floor. After she is asleep, the parents put her in her own bed. By morning, all the kids seem to be in the parents' bed.

"In discussing June's speech and communication developments, Mother described how June, as an infant, seemed unresponsive. She would not respond to parental smiles or laughter. It became kind of a bitter joke in the family that June would never smile more than once a day. She wouldn't respond to patticake except, perhaps, in a delayed fashion. June never seemed to listen or pay attention. She made sounds as an infant, but they were not imitations of parental speech. It was not until 3 that June began using recognizable words such as 'more,' 'Mommy' and 'Daddy.' Only in the past six months has she began to speak in sentences, but with some idiosyncrasies as noted above.

"Mother was asked about June's play activity. At first she denied anything unusual, describing how June likes best to imitate her own activities; for example, house work, and taking care of the baby. However, she then noted June's insistence on orderliness. For example, in building with blocks, each construction must be perfectly symmetrical. Similarly, she will notice things other children might not notice—that a picture is crooked. She will insist that it is broken and will become upset. June insists on using the same color cup and will fight with John if he takes her cup. June is ordinarily not destructive, but she will get John to join with her in destructive acts, such as throwing around the batch of mother's freshly ironed laundry. Mother reports that June says she is afraid of the stove, yet turns on the jets; is afraid of medicine, yet climbs up to the medicine cabinet; is afraid of dogs, yet approaches every dog she sees on the street; is afraid of trains, yet took John and wandered over to the tracks.

"It seems to mother that June has no fears. She could not understand why June behaved as she did in the clinic. She speculated that June may have been frightened by being cooped up in a small room without opportunity for activity. June has never been afraid of doctors. She doesn't mind shots at all (insensitivity to pain), and she has never had any serious medical illnesses.

"[Mother] does not think June is retarded. She thinks she is probably very smart but won't show it. Nor does [mother] think June has a speech impediment in the organic sense. She figures that a child with a speech impediment would at least try to imitate sounds, but June never would try."

June's Pediatric history summarizes much of what has already been detailed in the Social and Developmental history: "June is a 4-year-old little girl who is diagnosed as having infantile autism, probably at present emerging from this state. She is referred to the Evaluation Center mainly to rule out the possibility of organicity. Mother, 28, father, 28, both in good health. Siblings: John, 3, and Leslie Ann, 1½, both in good health. Mother has just given birth to a new baby, a boy. Family history noncontributory. This was the mother's first pregnancy; no miscarriages. During the first trimester she had one episode of mild spotting, treated by medication and bed rest (did not actually see obstetrician, prescribed by telephone). Mother felt well physically. She had no complications except for excessive weight gain. Emotionally, mother felt rather depressed during this pregnancy, as she had not anticipated pregnancy so early after her marriage. June was delivered spontaneously at [a hospital] in cephalic presentation after an uneventful labor. She cried at once. No complications in the nursery. Birth weight 8 pounds. As a baby, June was different from her siblings. She was restless, cried a lot, and would not be pacified when picked up. When she was a little older, she did not react appropriately; for example, she would have no smile for mother, but smiled at a dog or toy. She would not respond to cuddling, but would be happy to be held in a certain way and only if mother would pace the floor. Motor development has been about normal; sitting at 9 months and walking at 15 months. Speech has been quite delayed. She went through the regular stages of cooing and babbling, but failed to attempt repeating words around the age of 1. When she was around 3, she suddenly started to say words purposefully. One of her first words was 'more' to get more food. Afterwards, she started to put words together. Grammar has been (and still is) very incorrect, words are often distorted, and association of ideas is often odd. Coordination has always been good. June has ridden a tricycle since the age of 2½. Fine coordination is also more than adequate; she can undo a string with several knots. Training was quite difficult; the child now has used the bathroom since last December, but still has accidents and is not trained at night. June is practically self-sufficient in dressing and at the table. At present, assessing her child's behavior, the mother finds her quite different from her other children. She has all along been very unresponsive to her parents' display of affection, going her own little way without having much attention for them, even showing signs of dislike to their demonstrations of love. For the past two or three months, however, there is some improvement. She will at times climb on parents' laps and then tell them she loves them. In nursery school, mother observing children has made the remark that June seems to play in a parallel way with the children, rather than really with them. This summer at Head Start, she was never with the group. Mother finds June very distractible, although at times she can concentrate well on a task, like a puzzle. She has no judgment and does not learn by experience or through punishment. For instance, she often awakens very early and gets into all kinds of potential dangers, like lighting the stove and cooking at 4 A.M. She also has wandered away on many occasions; she would not give her name to strangers, and mother had to find her. Another fact mentioned is June's insistence on some unbearable rules; for instance, she will drink only out of a cup of a certain color, and will get into violent temper tantrums if her food is cut up. Mother thought that June was getting better since Christmas, relating more to people; but now for the past two or three weeks she is regressing again in her social adaptation and toilet training. The child has been essentially well and has had no childhood diseases. Developmentally, she sat alone at 9 months, crept at 11 months, and stood at 9 months, with support; stood without support at 12 months, walked at 15 months. Words at 3 and sentences at 3½. Trained for days in December, 1965. Not trained at night."

The general Pediatric examination of June was found to be entirely within normal limits: "June is a pretty little girl with short brown hair and blue eyes. She measures 41½ inches (above 25th percentile) and weighs 40 pounds (above 50th percentile). Her head is relatively large and round with a broad forehead measuring 20½ inches. Chest circumference is 23 inches. General pediatric examination is entirely within normal limits. Neurological findings are physiological. June did not want to let her mother go, so that the interview was carried on in the playroom. During this time, she busied herself on the slide and carried dolls from one place to the other. She did not pay any attention to doctor or mother, and totally ignored two bigger girls who came to get the dolls she was playing with. Her facial expression remained bland throughout, except on one occasion when she looked at herself in the mirror and patted her pixie hairdo with a faint smile. She let herself be examined as if she were a doll. She opened her mouth upon command and turned her head for ear examination without any change of expression. She said nothing except at the end when suddenly, with the same straight face, she asked to see the train (mother explained that she was referring to the trains passing close by where they live). In dressing, undressing, and playing, June displayed good coordination. No true hyper-activity was seen, but she had a short attention span, going from one toy to the other."

A Pediatric Consultation examination confirmed these findings: "June was observed in the playroom, and after a brief history from her mother was taken, a physical examination was performed. June responded to questions, and when examiner asked to be given a crayon, she did so. She did not appear to know the difference between the color of the crayons. She followed commands, and looked at examiner when spoken to and when she responded. Mother states she first became concerned over June's failure to speak or use words at age 2. She noted that she is 'immature' and responds with tantrums to frustration. She has been noted to 'ignore' her mother. She was fascinated by lights. She is described as being, not graceful, but having good coordination. Her mother has noted that there are times when she withdraws, and does not want to be part of the family. Most recently, mother has been concerned because of her early morning habits. She wakes at 3 or 4 o'clock, goes into the kitchen, puts a variety of pots and pans on the stove, and has burned some things. She also has been caught diapering the baby at this time. On one occasion she cut her finger attempting to open a bottle of aspirin with a knife. Mother thinks that despite her failure to talk and her negativism, she is smarter than she appears. She knows directions and often remembers things, to her mother's surprise. She is very much a creature of habit and will have a temper tantrum when something she is used to is displaced.

"On physical examination, June is a quiet, withdrawn child, who follows directions and will respond. She can talk, albeit in an immature way. She looks you in the eye, she does not have any unusual mannerisms, and she does not toe-walk. She cooperated well during a physical examination, although she required two lollipops. Her eyes are somewhat sunken."

Physical Medicine examination of June revealed "no abnormalities in the neuro-musculo-skeletal system." The Physical Therapy evaluation stated further that the "Child, upon examination, does not demonstrate any impairment of her gross motor function. She appears to have good strength, coordination, and balance for age; R.O.M. is good at all joints." To this is added the report of Occupational Therapy: "Coordination is well executed for age. June played at her own pace, approaching toys whenever she wanted; ignoring and/or resisting any suggestions made by the examiner. Child approached puzzles by trial and error, working persistently until she completed them. She attempted to copy form concepts, but gave up after several unsuccessful trials and traced around the circle. She appears to be a very controlled child who is exacting and meticulous."

Examination of June's eyes stated that: "Visual acuity with picture chart is at least 10/30 in each eye. External structures are normal, and extraocular muscles are straight. Under cycloplegia, the net retinoscopy is +1.50 = +1.50 × 90 in each eye. Media and fundi are normal."

Neurological examination of June revealed "findings to be essentially within normal limits." Her EEG "may be slightly slow, but probably within normal limits awake and asleep for age." X-rays of June's skull were "within normal limits; wrists for bone age reveal a bone age of 2 years, 6 months as opposed to a chronological age of 4 years, 6 months."

Evaluation of June's language development showed it to be somewhat delayed, and with somewhat unusual content: "June has a history of late development of speech and difficulty in communication. At the Center she demonstrated refusal to talk or respond initially, and gradual involvement with this examiner. When she spoke freely, there was no hint of a communication problem since she interacted verbally. Language usage was minimally disturbed, characterized by difficulty with verb tenses, and one pronoun substituting, her/she. These linguistic skills are normally achieved by 4 years of age. There was no difficulty observed in receptive language until an unusual resistance was encountered on picture vocabulary test. Articulation was within normal limits for age level, but there was an infantile quality to speech because of nonfluency, stress pattern, isolated mispronunciations such as her addition of 'oo' to all words ending with 'ool' (schooloo) and 'lisp' which may be related to short tongue frenulum. Content of verbalizations needs to be mentioned because this seems to be the best indication of some pathology. She verbalized as she played, and reiterated in sequence much of what we had already done, and this was said over and over. In the same way, she suddenly spoke of something that had happened before, but was no longer relevant, as if preoccupied or distracted by recurring ideas."

The Psychological examination stressed June's well-developed perceptual and visuo-motor abilities and her inconsistent verbal functioning: "Intellectual functioning in the borderline defective range of intelligence. Perceptual and visuo-motor coordination abilities are particularly well developed. Verbal functioning inconsistent. Results suggest an ego defect, reflected in (1) inability to use language for communication; and (2) an attention and memory impairment."

The Psychiatric summary suggested emergence from autistic behavior: "Shows marked withdrawal in defense against object cathexis. Autistic behavior and attitude shifting at present more toward normal development. Clinically, showed retreat into autism when offered an object. Poorly socialized, but improving."

The final diagnostic impression arrived at in the Evaluation Conference was: Severe developmental delay in a child now emerging from a primary autistic state. And so June became the fifth subject in our program. Although she was definitely hypoaffective, she was less so than any of the other four subjects. She could not be considered hyperactive, yet her extremely short attention span led her to a pattern of switching rapidly from one activity or toy to the next. Thus her activity level as well as her sensitivity could be considered to be within the normal range. In this sense she is more similar to Tommy than to any of the other children from the standpoint of our neurophysiological model.

Part III

*. . . and He commanded
that something be given
her to eat . . .*

Mark V : 43

Chapter VIII

Wake Up, Kathy!!

the psychotherapeutic process

Perhaps it is a misnomer to entitle this chapter: The Psychotherapeutic Process. In the light of the formulations advanced, in the preceding chapters, concerning the early infantile autistic condition, it would probably be more accurate to view the following descriptions as educational methods and techniques utilized to bring up, so to say, the autistic child. These educational steps are introduced in the life of this child in the form of varied and impactful experiences which are aimed at fostering and supporting a normal developmental process, rather than at correcting a psychopathological condition. The extreme lag in development which the behavior of the autistic child reflects, we do not view as a regression to an undifferentiated state, or as a defensive reaction in the face of unbearable dissatisfaction with the environment. Rather we see it as a developmental arrest or retardation, consequent to a neurophysiological functional imbalance. This imbalance, as was discussed in detail earlier, is between two arousal systems, and the techniques and methods to be described here find their rationale and foundation in this conceptual framework.

The emphasis we placed on the "affective imbalance" in behavior and sensory experience of the autistic child led us to give a prominent and focal position to the affective qualities of every educational or therapeutic technique in working with such a child. Furthermore, since we assumed that the retarded cognitive functions in the autistic condition were consequent to the affective imbalance and to a high threshold of sensory receptivity, a dominant characteristic of our work involved its high stimulating value and its complete reliance on the idea that the child would start learning, not by being taught anything special, but by being exposed, in an atmosphere of affective and sensory stimulation, to a wide variety of human experiences. Finally, if our theoretical views had good validity, we would expect, as the child's isolation and entrenchment in silence and void were overcome, that it would be possible to use ordinary teaching methods to widen his knowledge of his environment, and increase his skills at coping with it. The following paragraphs will make more explicit the details of our work in the light of our preceding discussion.

I. Overcoming the "affective imbalance"

The autistic child has been described as an "empty fortress" (Bettelheim, 1967), and his behavior depicted as a "circle of silence." To reach such a child, we had to assume, in practice, that the "fortress" was not impregnable or that the "silence" was not a form of death! But, trying to reach him meant making sure that the child became very much aware of the presence of the therapist in the playroom with him. This is the first important therapeutic step. It cannot be taken without sensitive consideration being given to what has been referred to earlier as the level of activity reflected in the child's behavior. An autistic child may be hyperactive or may be hypoactive; the approach must be different in each case. To Tommy, for instance, our 2½-year-old boy, whose behavior had the restless and constantly roaming qualities of a trapped and lost animal, we had to make our presence felt, not by moving forcefully on him and aggressively drawing his attention to us, but by allowing him to "bump" into us, so to say. This we did by placing ourselves on the floor in such a way that he had to move around us; and, secondly, by slowly making the area of restless roaming smaller and smaller, until the only thing he could move around and explore were our own bodies. It was like approaching an 8-month-old baby who does not know you; the most successful way is to back up on the baby and allow him to touch you first. By contrast, our approach to Kathy, whose typical early behavior consisted of standing quietly facing and scratching a wall, called for a more directly intrusive maneuver. As Kathy stood there, isolated in this quietly stereotyped, repetitive activity, the therapist placed herself beside her at the wall, and just as quietly began to scratch at the wall. After quite a while, Kathy heard the scratching noise made by the therapist and looked at her fingers. The therapist then moved her fingers toward Kathy's fingers and touched them, as if by accident. The fifth or sixth time that this happened, Kathy seemed to become aware of this and pulled her own fingers away. Insistently, the therapist repeated the maneuver until it was Kathy herself who moved her fingers toward the therapist's hand, and a small game of finger touching began. The initiative of the child, in both instances, has to be counted on and respected; but this initiative has to be exploited in the direction of alerting the attention of the child to the physical presence of the therapist.

Once the child knows that the therapist is there with him, every move is focused on keeping alive in the child this beginning awareness. This requires a great deal of patience, perseverance, and ingenuity. The "finger" game with Kathy, and the "bumping" game with Tommy had to be continued, with slight modifications, for the better part of an hour. These modifications always involve increased sensory stimulation within the context of the game: Making louder scratching noises with the fingers, covering Kathy's hand as the fingers touched, adding a few voice sounds to the play, and so forth; or, for Tommy, letting him step on our hand as he roamed around, putting our head in his way so that he would be tickled by the hair, or quietly patting his neck or his ear as he went by. Thus the child is not allowed to escape the presence of the therapist and isolate himself in autistic indifference. The therapist constantly and patiently renews the stimulating contact, to the end that the child will either actively seek such a contact, or actively fight it. In either case, the child's awareness of the physical presence of the therapist is kept very much alive.

Our experience has proven the unquestionable merit of such tactics in our overall therapeutic strategy. It creates very quickly an affective and "personal" atmosphere in the playroom. Nothing is really asked of the child, except what is assumed to be part of what he wants himself: a living, felt contact with a living and responsive human being—that he be aware of a therapist with him. This awareness is brought about by a variety of sensory stimulations provided in an insistent, and yet playful way, so that the child ends up by taking the initiative of seeking such pleasurable stimulations. The therapist must be alert to this initiative of the child and not misunderstand the child's apparent distressed or distancing behavior as an indication of rejection by the child of the therapist's presence. This may best be illustrated by referring again to the first sessions with Tommy and Kathy. As mentioned earlier, Tommy was allowed to bump into the therapist as he restlessly roamed around the room, and thus became aware of the therapist's physical presence with him there. Tommy was not always completely happy over having to walk around the therapist, and yet he kept coming back for more "bumping into." His initial distress was even more increased when, as he went by, the therapist deliberately touched his head, his neck, his ears, and so forth. Tommy would then back away, screaming and loudly protesting. But again this didn't seem to deter him from coming back for more "punishment." To the point that when after a while the therapist stopped touching him, it was Tommy himself who reached for the therapist's hand and smilingly placed it on his own ear as if to tickle himself. With Kathy, the distress took longer to come. After playing the finger game at the wall with the therapist for a long time, she suddenly stopped, as if she had realized that she was in a completely strange place. She stood looking at the room, immobile and overwhelmed. Then she started to cry, and the therapist quietly crouched in front of her, with arms extended, making reassuring sounds, and waiting for Kathy to come to her. Kathy kept looking at the therapist; she made a few moves to go to her, but then retreated. Finally she threw herself in the arms of the therapist, allowed herself to be held, lifted, and cuddled. She stopped crying and walked out of the playroom holding hands with the therapist. The apparently impregnable fortress of her aloof and indifferent behavior had obviously been shattered in this first therapeutic contact!

It is important to emphasize here that this "therapeutic contact" is primarily of an affective nature and is made in an atmosphere of play and fun. This means that the therapist, in this type of approach, has to be spontaneously capable of genuinely playful activity with the child. Clearly this requires a complete and unreserved commitment to the task of being with the child. In truth, it is a task, and a hard one, to avoid any forced, artificial, or phony responses in such a situation. There is no dignity to be maintained here save the dignity of the goal to be achieved in working with this aloof, indifferent, unresponsive autistic child. If, for instance, Elizabeth's affective isolation can be overcome by standing in a wastepaper basket with her, the therapist must be prepared to do so, and have genuine fun doing it. If, on the other hand, June's cold, distant, and frightened attitude can be penetrated by having the therapist jump off the table like some modern flying Batman, the therapist must do it, especially if, in the process, he falls in June's arms. There is nothing funnier than a therapist falling off a table, except possibly having the table collapse under the therapist.

The autistic child's high threshold of affective responsiveness yields rather quickly under the impact of such strong and persistent affectively laden experiences with the therapist. An evident shift in what we have called the "affective imbalance" takes place after a few weeks as if the child had been waiting all these years for just such experiences. More and more he seeks closeness and pleasurable sensations with the therapist. He discovers how to play, how to have fun, how to laugh; he even discovers how to cry when something really hurts him, and how to be comforted and soothed in the arms of the therapist. As this affectionate bond developed, and as this libidinal attachment was formed between the child and the therapist, we saw the possibility of a truly normal personality growth in a child who had been seen as an "empty fortress" or as living in a "glass ball." Yet, we were clearly aware also that this possibility of growth could be stymied, and the child's development could be arrested by the very strength of the affective life which was being mobilized in the child.

Mahler (1952), speaking to this point, had warned against what might be called the sandbar of symbiotic attachment of the child to the therapist. What might look so hopeful, she said, and so promising in the autistic child's early response to warm and accepting human contacts, turns out to be hopelessly disappointing as the child, in a parasitic sort of way, progressively becomes more and more clinging and glued to the therapist. All real development stops then, and the child appears contented to regressively relive the blissfulness of intrauterine life. The symbiotic foundering remains, according to Mahler, the fundamental source of failure in the treatment of the autistic child.

In overcoming the "affective imbalance" and lowering the child's threshold of affective responsiveness, we had also to avoid the pitfall of symbiotic attachment. We didn't do anything special to this end, and yet everything we did with the child worked against any symbiotic involvement. As was indicated in Chapter V, where we discussed the therapeutic implications of our understanding of the autistic condition, our therapeutic educational strategy would always have to be directed at fostering in the child the emergence of a human personality (human structure), by creating and imposing conditions of human growth and development. Assuming that such a growth and development is inherent in the natural organismic functioning of the human child, any condition which stimulates and arouses such functioning has to retain those human qualities, as we defined them earlier, which allow the child's development to proceed along natural lines of human maturation and growth. Normally, a child seeks, in his development, to go beyond the symbiotic level of affective attachment to his mother; and normally the mother, in responding freely and spontaneously to her child, modulates her responses and varies them in such a way that the child, never losing the experience of her presence to him, can easily use the security of this experience in him to widen his attachments to others and increase his sources of behavioral enrichment and learning.

With the autistic child, we expected, therefore, that if we created and maintained normal conditions of growth and development in our communications and interactions with him, there would exist a natural effort at going beyond the level of symbiotic attachment. This meant that we had to insure, first, that the behavior of the child always expressed a clear awareness of our presence to him, and a clear awareness of his own response to this presence; second, that our presence would always be communicated in a climate of unconditional acceptance and love, and that our activities with him would always have the spontaneous and unrehearsed quality which constantly would provide variety, novelty, excitement, and fun in the child's experience of himself and of us. The child's growth, we said, would be contingent on his experience of our presence and of his own behavior in our presence; however, the emergence of a truly human personality, through behavioral responses expressive of a variety of integrated and coordinated functions, would require that our stimulating and affectively rewarding presence to him not be contingent on any one specific transaction or interaction with him. Rather, the more initiative the child showed, the more spontaneous his activities, and the more assertive his discovery with us of new and novel stimulating occasions, circumstances, and events, the more we stayed with him./The child should never have to do anything we might arbitrarily decide we would like to see him do; but whatever he tried to do, we would support or teach him how to do better, or help him do it more easily, and so forth. If, for instance, we asked the child to go open the door of the playroom for us and he would decide rather to run to the sink and turn on the water, because this was so much more fun for him, we would not turn our backs on him, ignore him, or go away, leaving him to feel that his own initiative, his own playful assertion of himself, and/or his own choice of activity, was something we would not accept. On the contrary, in such a circumstance, we would cheer him on, help him recognize how effective his action was, and point out the hot and cold water, and so forth. Similarly, if the child became absorbed or obsessed with doing something which would tend to isolate him from us, that is from the awareness of our presence to him, we would increase the tempo and degree of our affective and stimulating intrusion on him, so that he had to respond to us either by involving himself with us or by actively fighting us off. Or again, if the child initiated an activity which was dangerous to him (like poking his fingers in an electrical outlet), or painfully destructive of himself or of others (such as pulling his own hair or scratching at somebody's face), or inappropriately attention-seeking (like a temper tantrum or wetting), we would never let such activity become more important than the child's enjoyment of our presence. We would never act as if our presence to the child was contingent on his ceasing such activity and desisting from such initiative. Clearly and emphatically, we would communicate to the child our displeasure at such activity on his part, but also we would immediately offer the child an opportunity for alternative expressions of activity and initiative. By not turning away from him at such times, we took the risk of reinforcing his dangerous, destructive, or inappropriate behavior; but we were also reinforcing his awareness of our presence to him, of our displeasure in response to his activity, and of the possibility open to him of alternate ways of expressing himself in a pleasurable way with us. In other words, the child's behavior never affected the intensity of our presence to him, but our response to his spontaneously initiated behavior always retained the flexible, varied, spontaneous, and common-sensical quality required in structuring the interactions in the direction of supporting the normal growth and development of those functions in the child through which he could progressively express in an adaptive, flexible, spontaneous, and free way, his pleasure at being a human being.

In such a context, therefore, the autistic child had little opportunity to remain stranded on the sandbar of symbiotic attachment to us. We were never trying to teach him anything special, except that it was fun to be a child, and that meant that all experiences available to him, all functions and skills appropriate to his development, were always fully accepted and responded to within the therapeutic interaction. Thus the child's experience of pleasure with the therapist was never limited to any one form of contact with the therapist. To be held and cuddled, to climb all over the therapist's body, to sit on her lap, or sensuously explore all parts of her face, may have been a source of great libidinal pleasure for the child, and the child might have wanted to leave it at just that, and forever have no other wish than to live by and through such a gratifying therapist. But the same quality of libidinal pleasure, and sometimes even of greater intensity, was also experienced in running after the therapist, and having the therapist run after him; in being thrown up in the air, or swinging, or playing hide-and-go-seek games, or singing "Old MacDonald Had a Farm," or wearing the therapist's bracelet or watch, or wondrously discovering his and the therapist's faces in the mirror, and so forth. Because we were convinced that the child needed us for his growth, and that this growth could take place under the impetus of affective and emotional gratification in his contacts with us, we also believed, having assumed the basic normality of the autistic child's developmental potential, that he would not wallow in the libidinal attachment to the therapist, but use this attachment as the anchorage point for his ego and personality growth.

Such an attitude and approach in our affective involvement with the autistic child had the beneficial effect of making all pleasurable experiences outside of the therapy room a source of renewed vitality and determination on the part of the child to seek these experiences and enjoy them. Thus at home, to the delight and deep satisfaction of the parents, the child sought and gave affection, but always within the context of various sorts of activities and games. The discovery of this affective response in himself seemed to have a contagious effect on the entire family. What was fun for the child became fun for all, and, as will be discussed more at length in a subsequent paragraph, this generalization of the affective response in the autistic child served as the foundation for the generalization in learning which he showed very quickly.

II. Widening the world of the child

The task of overcoming the affective imbalance in the autistic child is closely related to that of making the discovery of the self, and of the external world, a fascinating and rewarding adventure. To the extent that each experience with the therapist provides the child with a feeling of pleasure and aliveness, to the same extent will the child seek to renew the experience and the feeling, and thus maintain, with the therapist, a relationship that is worthwhile and meaningful. In such an effort, the child's own initiative comes to life: He seeks contact with the therapist, rather than always waiting to be intruded upon. Similarly, the child becomes less and less reluctant to be confronted with novelty, when each new object or new experience is associated with pleasure and good feelings. Thus the child's world progressively broadens, and it is the therapist's responsibility not only to encourage and support the child's initiative, or introduce him to more and more varied experiences, but also to prevent the child's inclination to stereotypy and sameness in the repetition of activities, as well as insure the possibility of a process of generalization in learning, from the playroom to the home situation. Some of the techniques useful in these respects are described in this section.

The autistic child's world is very narrow and limited as he first comes to us. His activities are few and stereotyped, involving a small number of self-stimulating actions (rocking, scratching, twiddling) or are of the restless and agitated kind, diffuse and aimless. Initiative in seeking new experiences does not exist, and confrontation with anything new or different in the objects of his world, or the pattern of his life, creates panic and flight for him. It is, therefore, a sign of obvious awakening to a new life, when such a child begins to show interest in seeking out a variety of experiences, or when he gives evidence of being less shaken by changes in his pattern of life. To this awakening, the therapist must be alert and responsive.

In Kathy, one of the first indications of initiative appeared after a few sessions of therapy, when she came towards the therapist, placed herself in front of her, turned around, and ran away from the therapist. Clearly, she wanted the therapist to run after her. This she repeated over and over, and the therapist made much ado about chasing her. For Tommy, the initiated behavior involved, as was described earlier, reaching for the therapist's hand and placing it on his ear, in order to experience the pleasurable feeling of having his ear touched and stroked. In Elizabeth who, from the beginning, enjoyed carefully placing large cardboard blocks in a precise way, the first sign of initiated relatedness on her part was when she pulled the therapist down in order to have her give her some more blocks to place in her block arrangement.

To encourage and support this emerging initiative in the child, the therapist must be flexible enough in her intrusive and structured approach to be ready to give up, in the service of the child's initiated activity, whatever was intended or planned at any one moment; she must be, on the other hand, insistent and persevering in demanding the attention of the child on her, so that the personal and pleasurable relationship with the child does not become lost in the endless repetition of any one activity demanded by the child/This means, for instance, that if the child immensely enjoys being swung through the air and thrown into the arms of the therapist, the child's insistence that this activity be repeated over and over must be respected. Not, however, in its stereotypic perseveration. The therapist will introduce new and different ways of swinging the child; she will make sure that the child becomes clearly aware that the pleasure he experiences is associated with a variety of activities, similar in some ways, but widely different in other ways. The real advantage of such a procedure rests in this: Not only does it help the child overcome his propensity to the "preservation of sameness," but it facilitates generalization, that is, transfering the experience from one situation (the playroom) to another (the home).

This factor of generalization is probably one of the most important to keep in mind, from a practical point of view, in this therapeutic approach. It would be of little value to the child that he be responsive and alive in the therapy room, or that he learned a variety of ways of enjoying himself, only to return home to his autistic isolation, indifference, and stereotypic behavior. The constant exploitation by the therapist of every situation and activity, in the direction of making it a pleasurable and highly affective experience *with the therapist*, arouses in the child such a level of drive toward reinstating this experience, that the child seeks and demands its repetition whenever there is a responsive adult in the environment, who might be ready to provide it. We have noticed this repeatedly with our subjects: *Whatever they experienced with us, they eagerly sought to re-experience at home, first, and later on, in nursery school.*

Kathy's mother, in the first month of therapy, reported in one of her notes that she had finally understood what she considered a strange (and certainly completely novel) behavior on the part of Kathy. Kathy, the mother said, would run up to her, stop, turn around, and run away from her. The mother had no idea what was up, except that Kathy was out of her room, and seemed intent on getting the mother interested in her. It was only after viewing through the observation room the antics of Kathy and the therapist (Kathy joyfully getting the therapist to chase her), that the mother caught on to Kathy's communication, and, then, eagerly, and just as joyfully, entered into the child's game.

For Elizabeth, the experience with the therapist generalized to her own backyard. One warm, summer morning, instead of working with her in the playroom, we decided to take her to a nearby children's playground on the Hospital campus. There, we introduced Elizabeth to the slides, the tunnels, the swings, and the monkey bars. It was fun and the movies we took of Elizabeth's behavior during that hour clearly illustrate how the pleasurable quality of the child's experience made her overcome very quickly her initial fear and anxiety in the face of novel and strange situations. But more striking is the mother's note about Elizabeth following this session: When the child got home, she insisted on going to the backyard to play. There, she went directly to the swing— she had been terrified before of this contraption—and made it clear that she wanted to be placed on it and swung. The factors which contribute to this easy capacity, on the part of the autistic child, to generalize (that is, in fact, to learn and profit from experience) appear to be inherent in the therapeutic approach we use, where the affective and experiential components are constantly in the forefront of the interaction with the therapist. This, for a young child, is the normal way of learning, and, given the opportunity, the autistic child gives evidence of his basic normality. New experiences are introduced in the context of, and associated with, ongoing pleasurable circumstances. As the child is confronted with a change in the situation, or a new object, or a different kind of activity, his natural tendency to retreat from it is overcome readily; first by the complete security he experiences with the therapist; and second by the curiosity he has about the change, the novel, the different; thus he takes then the initiative of seeking to maintain, or increase, his pleasure and good feelings by adding these new and different objects and activities to his discovery of the world. In describing this aspect of the process of the child's learning, Hunt (1961) paraphrases Piaget as follows: "As the infant's schemata have been accommodated to a wider and wider range of circumstances, variations in a wider and wider variety of circumstances acquire the capacity, through the discrepancy principle, to evoke his interest; he becomes curious about more things. With curiosity he develops what is commonly known as initiative" (p. 263).

The "discrepancy principle," to which Hunt refers above, and which was originally implied in Hebb's studies on the development of intelligence (Hebb, 1949, Ch. XI), conceptualizes many qualitative aspects of our interactions with the autistic child, which we have described above and which, as we pointed out, had a direct bearing on increasing the child's capacity to learn, and on helping him generalize his learning from one situation to the other. According to the "principle of discrepancy," the impact of any stimulation upon an organism has a greater probability of affecting and changing the response of that organism if it contains a degree of discrepancy from the preceding stimulating event or occasion; that is, if such a stimulation includes a certain amount of novelty, unexpectedness, or surprise. In the context of our approach to the autistic child, this means that the stimulation given must have an "arousing" quality in the childs' organism, both in terms of its affective impact and of the variety and novelty of its components. However, the discrepancy from an antecedent stimulating event, which is introduced in an on-going interactional process between the therapist and the child, must not include, it is important to note, such a degree of unusualness or unfamiliarity that the child is totally unprepared for it (that is, he possesses, in Piaget's words, no internalized scheme with which to accommodate to the stimulating situation); in such cases, the child would be totally overwhelmed by the new situation, or the situation would be so alien to his possible repertoire of responses, that he would remain wholly unaffected by it. We could expect the child, for instance, to be completely terrified when, in the course of interacting with us, a completely new set of variables were introduced. This occurred once, when Kathy, while running, hit the corner of her eye on a shelf. As a precautionary measure, she had to be X-rayed, which required not only the presence of a number of strange people, but also a very unfamiliar setting, and, as the most frightening condition, that she be tied down on the X-ray table. Even our presence, and that of her mother on such an occasion, could not prevent Kathy from responding with panic.

Thus, the introduction of variations and of novelty in a stimulating interactional process with a child can maintain the "arousing" effect only if such variations and novelty "fit" what might be called the accommodative range of the child in any one situation. The child will not be aroused in monotony and "white noise"; nor will he learn new behaviors or learn to generalize his behaviors to a variety of settings. Our approach, derived from the assumption of an existing sensory and affective deprivation in the autistic infant, had to reverse the conditions of sensory and affective restriction and deprivation. The constant, intrusive, and forceful introduction of new and varied stimulating events in our transactions with each child allowed for an element of "surprise," which would alert the child without frightening him too much, and thus keep "aroused" his attention and presence to us. It permitted also what might be called a noncontingent type of stimulating set to be established in the response patterns of the child; that is, he progressively expected variety, spontaneity, and diversity in a situation where, nevertheless, there existed, as a surrounding and reinforcing climate, the constancy, stability, and predictability of our consistent and immediately available presence. Finally, such variability in the stimulating circumstances within our interactions with the child enabled him to associate one event to the other, and enlarge the number of associative pathways through which any one event could be transmitted, thus giving the organism a wider range of potential responses, and fitting the child to meet more and more diverse circumstances and situations (Hebb, 1949). The "principle of discrepancy" would appear to be an intrinsic factor in learning and in generalizing learned behavior, by keeping alive in the child his attention, his interest, his curiosity, and his initiative (Hunt, 1961).

The principle of discrepancy is also essential in the child's discovery of his self through separation and differentiation from what is not himself. We will deal with this aspect of the child's development within the therapeutic process, in the following section, where first we will describe our methods in helping the child discover and master his body-self; and secondly, technical maneuvers in reinforcing the child's awareness of his separation and differentiation from others.

III. The discovery of the body-self and the child's need for separation and differentiation

For the autistic child, as much as for any normal infant, the most important discovery to be made—which is really the core of his development as a human being—is that of his own living, responsive, and active body; of its unity and integrated functioning; and of its separation and differentiation from others. One of the most striking features of the autistic child's behavior, when we first observe him and photograph his activities, is what might be called the disembodied quality of his bodily controls and functions. The child seems to walk, very often in a waddling gait, as if he had no idea that his legs belonged to him. His hands twitch and twirl, at times performing very complex or delicate maneuvers, and yet they seem to be operating outside of any willful or intentional direction. The eyes very rarely meet the eyes of another person; the ears never follow the direction of a sound; the child appears to be isolated and abstracted from whatever experience he has, or whatever activity he may be engaged in. His body does not belong to him any more than anything else in the environment. The endless repetition of the same behavior has the empty value of a wound-up mechanical toy, a robot. The sensory, tactile, kinesthetic, proprioceptive quality of the intrusive and forceful approach that we use in dealing with the autistic child, together with the sensuous and fun qualities with which we surround all of the child's experiences in the playroom, has an immediate and direct impact on the child's awareness of his own body. We make sure that this awareness includes the therapist as the transgressor of the child's body sensitivity. It is not just a question of touching, pushing, moving, or throwing the child. He must know that this happens because someone, the therapist, does something to him. And what is done to the child, early in the therapeutic process, needs to be done with enough emphasis, enough persistence, enough repetition, and enough insistence that the child cannot but sense, in the evidential meaning of this word (this is happening to me here and now), that whatever experience he has includes the presence of the therapist.

In terms of our theoretical understanding of the autistic condition, the focus we place on the direct, physical, face-to-face presence of the two human beings involved in an interactional relationship strongly gives support, not only to the pleasurable experience that accompanies the interaction, but also to what has been referred to earlier as the "principle of discrepancy." These two people facing each other are different. If they happen to physically bump into each other, the experience for each of them is different, even if, for both, it might be sufficiently pleasant that each of them seeks to repeat the experience. It is in this type of direct, physical, sensory interaction that the body ego of the child is born, saying, in effect: "Legs to walk with are not part of me, they are me; hands and arms to reach out with and feel, and hold, are not part of me; they are me. When my eyes smile and sparkle, I smile and sparkle. When my ears are alerted by a sound, I am alerted and interested and curious." The discovery of one's body is the discovery of one's self

in the actuality of being alive, responsive, happy or sad, acting and reacting, in relationship to stimulating events of a sensory and affective
experiential value.

The therapeutic approach we use with the autistic child envelops
and surrounds the child constantly with the physical and sensory, stimulating presence of the therapist. Though, except for one, none of our
subjects had any use of language, we talk to them, sing to them, and
make all kinds of noises and sounds, as we engage in play and pleasurable activities with them. As the child's attention increases, as he becomes more and more aware of the intruding presence of the therapist
in his life, we introduce more and more structure in the interaction.
The child may be interested in seeing a large ball roll and hit the wall,
and then bounce back when he happens to kick it accidentally with his
foot. We capitalize on this circumstance, bring the ball back to the
child, rub his leg and foot (we always take the child's shoes off, so that
he will feel the floor on his feet), and then we help him kick the ball
by lifting his leg, swinging it in front of the ball, and kicking it. This we
repeat as long as the child finds it pleasurable to see what happens to
the ball when he hits it. The child may get all joyfully excited and, as
Kathy, start jumping up and down, kicking in all directions haphaz-
ardly. We exploit the experience of fun the child is having by controlling the activity of the child sufficiently to increase the effectiveness of
this activity: The child will be even more happy if he can be made to
discover that he can move that leg and foot, kick the ball himself, run
after it, and so forth. But the freedom of emotional expression is not
allowed to lead to complete disorganization of behavior, loss of control,
purposeless and aimless activity. The child's exuberance—especially if
one considers how "affectless" the autistic infant behaved from the
start—should be kept up, but always in the direction of offering him the
opportunity to increase his mastery over his body, and over the activities of his body. To let a child go into an emotional frenzy has little
developmental value for him; but to exploit the released energies in
the child for effective, purposeful, goal-directed behavior can extend and
increase the exciting qualities of the child's own activities. In this connection, we refer again (see Chapter V) to the central importance in our
approach of "structure" and controls. The human structure (the self)
does not develop out of a chaotic exercise of a variety of functions, nor
is it defined by a set of unrelated and unintegrated functions. The innate direction of growth in the live human organism, as we can readily

assume from both common sense, and from the most recent biological studies on human evolution (Teilhard de Chardin: *The Phenomenon of Man*, p. 195), is toward the achievement of a human structure, a personality, an ego, a self. But it is only in contacts with, and in relationship to, his human environment that the human organism can maintain its innate direction, and achieve a human structure, a differentiated self. Through such contacts, a variety of functions are stimulated—cognitive, emotional, motoric, and so forth—and their effectiveness, as expressed in appropriate and adaptive behavioral responses, requires coordination and integration.

In the interactional process, for instance, between a child and his mother, whatever response is given by the child to the mother's stimulating contact has to be reacted to by the mother in such a way that the child's level of behavioral organizaion is not destroyed, or in such a way that the child is offered an opportunity for a more effective, adaptive, and organized behavioral response. This is what we mean by giving structure to the child's behavior, and, obviously, this requires imposing controls. It should be understood, however, that such controls are not primarily limiting of the child's behavior; they are channelizing, that is, instead of allowing a diffuse and haphazard and goal-less response, the intensity and effectiveness of the response is increased by insuring its target and focus. There is more pleasure for a child, in such a structured approach, if he uses his hands to grasp a bat and hit a ball (because all kinds of sensory and motoric experiences are then involved) than in just flailing his hands inanely. Furthermore, the controls are not imposed on the initiative or spontaneity of the child's activity, but rather on its direction and focus, so that whatever is effected through the child's response, the child can recognize as having been effected by his own response. This is the reward of mastery; it is not extrinsic to the behavior; it has an intrinsic stimulating value, which the mother, or the therapist, can support and sustain through their own pleasurable reaction to the child.

What we are stating here is that the child's discovery of his body and of the world around him must be a rewarding experience: rewarding in that the child becomes more and more aware that his behavior affects the environment, and that he can deliberately use it to affect it. In the process, he becomes "somebody" distinct and different than the environment he acts upon; and the more control and mastery he has of his actions, the more pleasure he experiences in his body, and the more effective his interactions with the environment. Connie's use of her hands, for instance, was limited to a ceaseless clasping and unclasping, accompanied by an intricate display of finger rubbing and pressing to the point that large callouses had developed on the palms of her hands and the fingertips. She would never stop this activity unless she was sleeping. But she enjoyed listening to songs, and her favorite was the "Incie Wincie Spider." Over and over we used this song with her, first to help her use her hands to beat to the rhythm of the song, by hitting her own lap with them, or clapping them together; then to communicate to us that she wanted to play the "Incie Wincie Spider" game. Thus, after many weeks, she was able to enter the playroom at the beginning of a session, look at us with a warm and friendly smile, lift her arms, and start clapping her hands so that "her song" would be placed on the agenda of activities right away. In the same vein we worked at getting her to feel and experience her legs in action by rhythmically moving them to the tune of the Anvil Chorus, which Connie enjoyed very much. Eventually she was able to push and pull her foot in and out of her shoe when asked to do so. It should be emphasized again that this sort of stimulation cannot be done mechanically, as if it were just a matter of body exercises. The child's attention must be obtained first, with patience and insistence, and the child must clearly show that he senses what is happening, and enjoys it.

In this connection, the question of eye contact with the child is of central importance. The autistic child never looks at a person: he looks "through," "beyond," and "away"; eye contact with another is so fleeting as to be nonexistent. This is so symptomatic that one can securely feel that real progress is being made in this child's development when he can hold, for even a short period of time, his gaze to another person's eyes and face, and clearly look at that person. Furthermore, in our work with the autistic child, eye contact becomes one of the most effective ways of knowing that the child is "with you" in any interactional circumstance. The following examples will illustrate this point. After bathing Kathy in the sink—this, by the way, is a wonderfully pleasurable activity in helping the child become aware of various parts of his body— she would be placed on the therapist's lap, facing the mirror (so the therapist might see her face, and so that possibly Kathy might suddenly become interested in seeing herself), and given a vigorous rubdown, involving a good amount of tickling and laughing. At the end of this, the therapist would introduce throwing the towel over the head of the child, who excitedly would pull it off. When this became a real fun game, the therapist would stand the child on the floor, and throw the towel over Kathy's head and crouch in front of her, so that every time the child would pull the towel down she would be looking straight at the therapist's smiling face. When, in the process of repeating the game many times, the child eventually initiates a new "angle" to the game by knocking the towel down before the therapist has time to throw it over the child's head, in order to look directly and laughingly into the therapist's eyes, then it is obvious that the child is very much "there," attentive and happy, aware that not only is something happening to her, but that she also is making something happen around or in front of her.

To achieve eye contact, we often had to restrain the child's head by placing both hands on the side of the head, physically forcing the child to look at the therapist's face. For Tommy, who never liked any form of physical restraint (we will discuss this form of behavior later on), this exercise was unpleasant. He would frantically fight his way out of the therapist's hands and, roaring and crying, walk away from this situation. It would be easy to interpret this behavior as clearly demonstrating that the autistic child actively and aggressively rejects the human contact, and turns his back on it (Bettelheim, 1967). This is not so, however. Tommy did not like to be restrained, and most small children normally feel the same way about being tied down. But he clearly was able to enjoy looking at a person's face, for, when the therapist would use a colorful plastic "doughnut," and look at Tommy through it, Tommy would look right back at the therapist and find so much pleasure doing so that he would himself pick up the "doughnut" and look through it at the therapist. Eventually, the human face became for Tommy such an intriguing and wondrous thing that, at home (according to the mother's notes) and in the playroom, he would take every opportunity to climb on the mother, or on the therapist, and with great delight explore in detail with his hands (like a blind child getting acquainted with the face of a friend) every part of the face—the eyes, the nose, the mouth, the hair. Obviously, Tommy did not want to reject, or turn his back on, his human environment; and it would be grossly inaccurate to interpret his behavior as implying this.

With Elizabeth, eye contact took a long time to achieve, because it was nearly impossible to keep her face from being buried in her bangs and in her chest. She quickly got interested in having us around, however, and her behavior reflected very clearly that she knew we were about, and that she enjoyed it. Always curious and interested in any of the situations we created to have her become very much involved with us, she managed, nevertheless, to keep her eyes on whatever object was at hand or whatever procedure was being developed. But she never looked directly at us. Yet she was so very much with us, pulling us in this or that direction, depending on whether she wanted to swing, be thrown around, have us work with her on building a tower of blocks, or have the therapist step in the wastepaper basket with her to play "rub a dub dub, three men in a tub"! It was only in the excitement and joy of jumping off a table into the arms of the therapist that she eventually discovered how good and pleasant it was to look straight into the eyes of the therapist. Then she allowed herself to completely surrender to the pleasure of being with somebody who truly enjoyed having her there. She would laugh then, and look into the eyes of the therapist.

Thus for the autistic child—and this is also true in the development of a normal child (see DesLauriers, 1962)—the discovery of his body, of its functions, of the space it occupies, and of the experiences it undergoes, as well as of the effects it has on the surrounding world, is so closely related to the discovery of another person acting on him, responding to him, and interacting with him, that it is in this very discovery that the child learns to separate and differentiate himself from the environment, that is, from what is not himself.

The possibility of a true and meaningful relationship to another person rests on two basic conditions: First, a person must be separated and differentiated from the other, and experience this separation in the actuality of being present to another person; second, a person must have the affective availability and drive to communicate one's self to the other, and experience the affective and stimulating presence of the other. Just as we worked very persistently at overcoming, in the autistic child, the affective imbalance and unavailability, just as persistently did we use every opportunity to underline and emphasize in the child's experience of himself, his separation and differentiation from us. Here again, our method—forceful, intrusive, and highly affectively laden—tended to exploit what we saw in the child's behavior as an expression of a basic human need to separate and differentiate himself from others.

Thus we chose to recognize in the original isolation, aloofness, and indifference of the autistic child, a pathetic, and somewhat minimal expression of separation, rather than a demonstration of his rejection of the world, and of his turning his back on it. For the autistic child, to resent at times our intrusions, to protest violently against our efforts at changing the isolated patterns of his life, represented in our view his own way of holding onto a minimum identity and a minimum of self, albeit rather empty and deficient. He was not rejecting us; he was trying very hard, with the few responses available to him, to maintain some rudiment of a self by asserting, in a somewhat global and undifferentiated way, his right to be "somebody" different and separated from others. When, therefore, it was possible to alert the child and awaken his awareness to the experience, pleasurable and stimulating, that the "somebody" he was so minimally could become more through his interaction with us, this form of so-called autistic rejection and isolation disappeared quickly.

IV. Phases of negativism

Yet, each movement the child made in giving up his isolation involved reluctance, fear, and anxiety on his part. And this became expressed in a variety of forms of negativism through which the child kept saying to us: I like very much to be with you, but don't push it to the point that I'll be everything you want me to be while losing what I really am, a person in my own rights. In the following paragraphs we will describe some of the techniques we used in overcoming the negativisms of the child while respecting his identity, his autonomy, his right to be a person separated and differentiated from any other.

The first form of negativistic behavior we encounter is directly related to the child's pattern of isolation and indifference to the environment. The autistic child, as we observed him from the beginning, may actively and aggressively resist the stimulating intrusion we imposed on him, and the structure within which we demand that his behavior conform. But to give up the intrusion, or eliminate any structure, by allowing the child to go his own way is not a proper solution to the autistic dilemma. What we have found that works is to keep up enough pressure on the child to insure his awareness of our presence, while allowing him to initiate, himself, moves towards us, seeking pleasurable stimulations. The example given earlier of Tommy himself reaching for the therapist's hand to place on his ear, and enjoying, thus, the pleasurably sensuous experience he had, illustrates this point. The same is true when we physically restrict the child's aimless or purposeless activities. The child usually resents this and fights off any such attempts.

Yet, if we restrict gently—that is, if we make sure that the restriction is not such that it closes off any other possibility of response in the child, and permits some degree of freedom or escape in the child—then the repeated awareness of such an experience in the child eventually brings him to the point that he himself seeks the restriction, the control, the structure. Again referring to Tommy, the youngest of our group of subjects, his intolerance for any physical restriction was such that one would have thought he was being manhandled, or subjected to unbearable pain, any time we tried to hold him. If, however, the affective and stimulating quality of the restraint was maintained, plus the possibility of escaping the restriction rather easily, then he, himself, would approach the therapist, sit on her lap, or allow himself to be held and hugged. But he needed to know somehow that he could always move away if he wanted to.

Closely related to this first form of defensive negativism is a second one which we have chosen to label: Negativism of fear. The strange, the novel, the different, evokes an immediate response of fear in the autistic child. This child's repertoire of responses or of adaptive behavior is so limited that, in a sense, any new or unexpected situation or circumstance arouses fear as if it were a danger or a threat to the child's life. He recoils from it, and refuses to approach it or stay with it. For this reason, in setting up the playroom situation at the beginning of treatment, we make sure that few objects are there that may frighten the child, or distract from the affective and reassuring presence of the therapist. It is only when the child shows very clearly in his behavior that he feels completely safe with the therapist that new objects and new situations are introduced in the interaction. The presentation of the novel or the unexpected is always "thrown in," so to say, in the very midst of an ongoing pleasurable and safe activity. For instance, it was in the process of swinging Kathy back and forth in front of the mirror, to her great enjoyment and delight, that we introduced a wooden seat on which she could swing, as on the real thing in a playground. And it was while Tommy was jumping off a chair into the arms of the therapist that we introduced a small wagon to ride on, and of which he had always been terrified at home. As soon as he was in the arms of the therapist, happy and cuddly, instead of depositing him on the floor so that he could run back and climb on the chair, we would sit him in the wagon. Of course, he would jump off immediately and run to the chair. Very quickly his good feelings helped him overcome his refusal to stay in the wagon; then he would get a short ride and to the exclamation: "Everybody get off!" (which was our way of anticipating that he might want to get off the wagon) we would make sure that he knew he could leave the wagon, run to the chair, climb on it, jump off into the arms of the therapist, and feel that life was great!

Thus, with the autistic child, the imposition of change in his stereotyped patterns of behavior, as well as of structure in his aimless and purposeless activities, requires also a certain respect for his need to maintain some separation and some minimal personal identity. In the affective climate of complete security and safety, which the child experiences with the therapist, the child eventually makes a point either of arbitrarily refusing to do anything that is asked of him, or of opposing any request, just to see what the therapist will do about it. These are what we might call two painful phases in our work with the autistic child; they tax to the limit the patience and endurance of the therapist, and demand of him imagination and ingenuity. In such circumstances, it is again of the utmost importance to capitalize on the child's own curiosity and need for affective stimulation. Recognizing in this behavior of the child a heroic assertion of his individuality, against and in spite of intruding influences, serves as a tension-relieving device for the therapist and, therefore, provides for the possibility of beating the child, so to say, at his own game.

The general strategy used here is neither uncommon, nor is it unknown to most mothers confronted with the *No, No* phase of their young child. It consists, essentially, either of demanding of the child the exact opposite of what one might actually want him to do, or of pretending convincingly that one doesn't really care one way or the other whether the child does what he is asked. In terms of tactics, this strategy can be applied variously. With June, who felt obliged, for instance, to refuse to do anything if she were asked directly, the most effective method of obtaining cooperation was to tell her we did not want her to do the very thing we hoped she would do. If we wanted her to sing with us, we would start singing, stop a moment to interject, "We don't want you to sing this song, June," and then go on with the song. This worked so well with June that it became a fun game expected and anticipated by the youngster. So much so, that if we forgot our part in the game, June would laughingly remind us by saying, for instance, "Tell me not to touch your drink!" (For other examples of this form of negativism see Chapter X, especially Kathy.)

Two points need to be made here with regard to the forms of negativisms just described. Intrinsic to the behavior illustrated above is, first of all, the obvious assertion of the child's beginning self, not by rejecting or turning away from another human being, but by making an even stronger attempt to maintain relationship and communication with the other. Secondly, in view of the autistic child's entrenched fear of unknown and novel experiences or objects, these negativistic forms of behavior appear to serve as a dampening and protective device which gives the child time to accommodate himself to the situation, assimilate it, and master it. The approach-avoidance paradigm, illustrated in so many animal learning experiments, is useful to keep in mind here. But more important, the personal affective support constantly given to the child in the form of play, fun, and games, as well as in warm affection, never allows the child's fears to turn into panic; and the intrinsic reward of experiencing something new, or discovering some novel function or object, enlarges the learning capacity of the child, and his mastery of himself and of his environment.

Truly, it is in this experience of mastery and competence that the emergence of the child's developing personality becomes best expressed, and it is to this end that the educational aspects of this therapeutic effort are geared. The assertion and communication of the child's self through various forms of negativistic behavior, as described above, represent normal phases of development, though in the autistic child these behaviors are chronologically delayed; and also, because the child's repertoire of activities is so limited, they appear so stubbornly prominent. But as the child's fears are overcome, as the threshold of his responsiveness to the affective experience of human contacts becomes lowered, and as he discovers in the playful and stimulating interactions with the therapist how good it is to feel alive and alert to so many new and different qualities in his environment, the child's own need to retain this aliveness and alertness drives him to seek more interactions, and more human contacts, without losing his separation and differentiation from others. His initiative increases. In every way he can he tries to communicate his desires and wishes; he does not wait for the therapist to structure the interaction, but becomes inventive and creative in his efforts at indicating what he wants and what he seeks to enjoy. In other words, the development of the child leads to more and more willfully determined and purposeful activities, and the therapist must be sensitive, at such times, not to confuse what appears to be negativism on the part of the child with what is, in fact, an expression and communication of his personal choice of what he wants from the therapist. This negativism of choice, as we might call it, is intrinsically different from any form of arbitrary or attention-seeking negativistic behavior. Here the child, confronted with a situation already set up for him by the therapist or the parent, refuses to go along with it, and chooses to do something else. His refusal does not involve rejecting the interacting person, or isolating himself in an absorbing task which eliminates anyone else. Rather, his refusal includes a communication to the other person that what is being asked then is not what the child wants, because he has something else on his mind. The following illustrations will make that point clear.

Elizabeth always found great pleasure in putting together the pieces of a variety of puzzles. She had her own way of solving these puzzle problems: She would take the pieces out first, and, with great attention and care, finger each piece as if to impress on her mind, through this tactile contact, the shape and texture of every piece; then, after replacing each piece in its appropriate place, would dump or break up the entire puzzle, and do it over without any further ritualistic ado. Truly, this was a pleasant experience for Elizabeth, and we exploited her talents in this regard by varying the puzzles, and systematically increasing their challenging difficulty. We could easily assume that we had a sure bet going, as far as pleasing Elizabeth, whenever we offered her a new puzzle. The wonderful surprise was to find Elizabeth with a somewhat different view of things! She came into the playroom, as usual, gleefully pleased to be with us again, and in a very good mood. We thought we would merely add to her enjoyment by giving her a brand new puzzle. Interested, Elizabeth went to the table where we had placed the puzzle, looked at it for a moment, dismantled it in one fell swoop, and pushed it away. This behavior did not dismay us, and we set up the puzzle again; but Elizabeth would have nothing to do with it. First she threw herself on the floor making whimpering sounds, as if she didn't quite know how to have a temper tantrum, but was going to give it a try anyway! Then she got up and ran to the other end of the room where she picked up the wastepaper basket, brought it to the therapist, placed the therapist's feet inside the basket, got in it herself, and with a large smile and a glint of triumph in her eyes made it clear that, right then and there, she was ready to play "rub a dub dub, three men in a tub"! Puzzles could wait! She had her own idea of fun for the moment!

An even stronger display of determination and choice was demonstrated by Kathy first at home, to her mother's amazement, and then in the playroom, to our own delight. After six months of therapy, Kathy was enrolled in a regular nursery school for normal children (this, in our view, was part of the treatment, and every child, except Tommy, went to school). Getting Kathy ready for school, putting her on the bus, and greeting her upon her return, quickly became a well established routine that both mother and child accepted as all in a day's work— until Kathy started putting up a fuss. It wasn't, as it turned out, that she didn't want to go to school. She just had her own ideas as to how she should be dressed to go there, and what she should wear. At first her mother reacted to Kathy's temper outbursts, during the dressing phase of school preparation, as to just another instance of arbitrary negativism, with which Kathy had so often tormented us and her parents. But this was no arbitrary opposition on the part of the child. She kept trying to let her mother know what she wanted to wear, and it was only when she finally took her mother by the hand to the clothes closet, and had her mother pull out what she considered a suitable and appropriate dress for school, that Kathy was appeased and happy.

With us, in the playroom, Kathy's assertions of self-determination and choice took on many forms. If we started a ball game, and Kathy wanted to swing, she would pick up the ball, throw it in the basket, and then come over to the therapist and place herself in one of her favorite swinging positions. If we had her engaged in stringing beads, and she had decided it would be more fun to be thrown up in the air, she would first sit on her hands, refusing any longer to touch those silly beads, then she would extend one hand in a pleading gesture to be picked up; if this was ignored, she would start scratching the back of her chair with a mournful look on her face as if to tell us: "You better watch it! See what you're doing, you're driving me right back to early infantile autism!" Finally, if we wanted Kathy to practice riding her tricycle and she had decided that she would prefer at that moment to have her "sound and speech" lesson, she would stubbornly sit on her tricycle and determinedly point to the earphones we used with her to amplify her own voice as she learned to say words with us. If her gesture was not convincing enough to achieve the desired result, she would get off her "horse," run to her small chair, and sit in her usual "word learning" position (her two hands on her feet, ready to have some sort of a "ride" after each well pronounced word). This had to be clear, as far as Kathy was concerned, and we were only too pleased to yield to her choice!

Thus the developmental movement in the child, which in Bettelheim's words, is a process of "humanizing" the young human being, progressively culminates in behavior which asserts the emergence of the self in self-determination, and in meaningful and purposeful activities. But whereas Bettelheim seems to expect that such a result can be achieved by leaving the child entirely to his own devices, to his whims and unchecked impulses, our educational-therapeutic approach remains dominated by the structural requirements of human personality growth. If the end of the process is to be a self, an individual, a functioning ego, through a transactional relationship with other human beings who respond, and are present to him as separated and differentiated "others," then structure, meaningfulness, clearly defined boundaries, must be established and maintained. But the joy of being alive must be discovered by the child in such structured relationships, and, therefore, the entire process of growth must be imbedded in, and surrounded by, an affective and emotional climate of play, fun, and gratifying rewards for initiative, competence, and mastery.

There are what have been called "critical periods" in this developmental process. They might be defined as those moments, in the child's growth, when all circumstances and conditions seem to be just right for a movement forward in affective responsiveness, in learning, in discovering, in initiative, self-expression, and determination. At such moments, real spurts take place in the child's progress, which attest to the fundamentally sound and normal potential of the autistic child. We have observed these throughout the months of treatment, and they seemed always to have been preceded by what appeared to us as interminable "plateaus" in the growth of the child. From our observations, and from the pattern of performance reflected in the measuring developmental and intelligence scales utilized in this project (see Chapter X), we were led to the conclusion that the readiness of the autistic child to move from one set of experiences to another, or from one level of activities to another, appears to be a function of the child's own awareness of his being "ready" for this new experience or this new activity. Until such awareness exists—which might be termed self-confidence or self-assurance—there is evident in the child's behavior an "inhibition of response" (response-inhibition) which, as long as it persists, gives a discrete and piecemeal quality to the efforts of the child learning or discovering novel aspects of himself and his environment. But as soon as the child is "ready," this response-inhibition gives way to the full and complete expression of the learned behavior in all its complexity, diversity, and meaningfulness. Thus the task of "bringing up" the autistic child is truly a labor of patience and endurance, but the ferment of growth, as in the normal development of any child, is the affectionate and playful quality which makes all these experiences that, as Escalona (1963) mentioned, are needed for growth, most human and humanizing. The therapeutic effort, twice or three times each week, for one hour in the playroom, could certainly not achieve this fully humanizing result in the autistic child, without involving the total human environment of the child. The parts played by the home, and by the school, remain central in our program. These will be discussed in detail in the following chapter.

V. Bettelheim and Lovaas

The preceding discussion of the therapeutic-educational process which we used with the autistic children in our program may be further clarified, at this point, by contrasting our approach with two of the more important current methods of treatment available for autistic children: Bettelheim's (1967) psychoanalytic approach, and Lovaas' (1968) behavior modification through operant conditioning.

We have referred, at various times, to Bettelheim's views on the etiology of the autistic condition in a child (see Chapter II). The autistic child, he says, represents an instance of "dehumanization" consequent to the unconscious (and possibly conscious, at times) wish of his mother that he not be alive and part of his human family. From such a starting point, Bettelheim logically follows to a central requirement in dealing with the child: He has to be removed from his family, from his mother. His next therapeutic steps are all geared toward "humanizing" the child; that is, giving him an "ego," a self, the possibility of truly being human and capable of exercising some amount of real autonomy and freedom. The child should be allowed to determine his destiny.

Let it be clear that, whereas we start on the assumption that the autistic condition is not a reaction to parental rejection (the parents are his most appropriate therapists, in our view), we do not differ with Bettelheim on the goals to be achieved with such a child; that is, helping him develop a self, and assert autonomy and choice in his behavior. We are critical, however, of the "method" through which Bettelheim expects to bring about in the "dehumanized" autistic infant the emergence of a self, of an ego. Bettelheim's psychoanalytic views lead him to give such preponderance to "instinctual strivings" and to the primacy of the "pleasure principle" that insufficient weight is given, in his therapeutic approach, to reality experiences and the requirements of the "reality principle," as they have been formulated in recent years by psychoanalysts concerned with "ego-psychology." (See DesLauriers 1962; 1967). In other words, Bettelheim seems to expect that an ego, a self, a human "structure" (see Chapter V) will eventually emerge in the developing child, if the child is allowed the full and complete satisfaction and gratification of giving in without restraint to the pleasures of his oral, anal, or genital instinctual strivings. By not restraining the behavioral expressions of such strivings or impulses, the foundations are laid for autonomy and freedom, because the child will begin then to experience that all autonomy or initiative has not been taken away from him; he can really do what he wants.

In contrast, our position holds that autonomy and freedom come through mastery of functions through which one adapts to, and copes with, the environment. The "ego," or self, is born in the interaction of the child with others from which he becomes separated and differentiated, and with whom he communicates with an ever widening repertoire of responses and actions through which he asserts his identity, his mastery, his autonomy, his choices, and his freedom. Structure, as we have defined it, creates in the child the conditions of a human development; it is in offering such a structure to the autistic child that we expect to "humanize" him. For instance, an autistic child may defecate on the floor; Bettelheim sees in such behavior an expression of the child's autonomy which the child should be allowed to enjoy fully, because the fecal matter may be a most cherished treasure belonging to the child, and he should be allowed to deposit it wherever, whenever, and as long as he pleases. We do not deny the possible pleasure the child may have in his own anal activities and the productions thereof. We simply assume that the child will have just as much pleasure, and just as intense a feeling for the importance of his actions and products, if he is made to feel that his own pleasure and own importance can be increased and shared, if he can master the sequence of behavior required to go to the toilet.

The autonomy of the child is not thwarted; it is given a direction which the child can always oppose, but only in clear awareness of his own intentional and deliberate opposition. Such an opposition is part of his assertion of his identity; but it is not all of it. A human being dies if totally isolated from others. Human identity develops through communication, in which the importance of the presence to each other of two people is deeply felt and accepted. A child does not need to go to the bathroom because it's the proper thing to do (it's socially acceptable) but simply because he finds, in doing so, the possibility of expressing his mastery of a rather complex set of activities and operations. When we spoke of imposing a "human structure" in our transactions with autistic children, we meant giving them an opportunity for mastery, autonomy, and freedom, in an atmosphere of pleasure, gratification, and play.

Lovaas (1966), unlike Bettelheim, imposes on the autistic child what might be considered a very tight structure. Applying and extending learning theory to the analysis and modification of the behavioral repertoire of autistic children, Lovaas (1966) utilizes "social reinforcement" in his attempts at bringing some control over the responses of his subject, so that he can design and set up the contingencies under which the probability of appearance of the expected or wanted responses will be increased. The assumption here appears to be that the faulty, deviant, unacceptable behaviors of the autistic child are somehow consequent to, and sustained by, a pattern of environmental stimulations, which reinforces such behaviors. By careful analysis of the environmental contingencies which are most likely to favor the appearance of this or that form of autistic response, it would be possible to control such a response by determining which contingency actually sustains, and which actually extinguishes, the response.

At face value, there appears to be a soundness and a clear-cut quality to this type of approach in the modification of autistic behaviors, which is refreshing and inspiring in a field of study so often cluttered with innumerable variables and compounded confusions. Desirable behavior in the autistic child can be established through a variety of sequential primary and secondary reinforcers; undesirable behaviors can be extinguished. Thus, the infinite possibilities of molding the child's behavior to the requirements of the child's environment would seem to be positively correlated with the therapist's ingenuity, imagination, creative capacities, and technological skill in developing more and more refined "reinforcers," for more and more complex behaviors. Furthermore, the controls established over any behavior can be so tight that the powerful therapist can test out their effectiveness by making any contingent behavior appear or disappear at will. Finally, the ultimate determination of what behaviors shall, or shall not, be placed under the therapist's control remains totally in the hands, and within the moral, ethical, and professional responsibility, of the "modifier." This means, of course, that what behaviors will be subjected to modification are chosen on two grounds: One, is the behavior desirable or undesirable (either for the safety of the child or for the satisfaction of his environment); two, is the therapist—in terms of learning theory, child development, and behavioral understanding—professionally and technologically equipped to analyze and modify this or that behavioral response. The fact is that some of the most usual and ordinary behavioral sequences in a child are most complex and, in recognizing this, Lovaas, for instance, looks forward to the day when the success in complex behavioral modification may hinge on the possibility of engineering a total community environment to sustain or extinguish certain forms of behavior (see Lovaas, 1968).

Obviously, the tight, controlling "structure" which the "behavioristic" approach imposes on the autistic child to determine his behavior has little in common with the "human structure," which we have defined earlier as central to our own program. Where we are concerned with siding with the natural developmental energies in the child by keeping them aroused and goal-directed through an active, and impactful, sensory and affective interaction with the human environment, the behavior therapist appears to ignore what is known of human development and "slices off," from the total life of the child, those behaviors which appear to him, for humane or social or professional reasons, to be either in need of modification, or amenable to existing modifying experiments, without any major consideration given to whether the child is developmentally, or psychologically, ready to "fit" the imposed behaviors within the total schema of his response capacities. By ignoring some of the basic laws of child development, the behaviorist may keep his mind uncluttered and his experiments clean, but he also curtails the effectiveness of the very learning principles on which his modifying efforts are based.

We are touching here on the concept of "reinforcement" which is the most important tool in the operant conditioning efforts of the behavior therapist.

It is indeed in the context of this concept of reinforcement that our own approach in "modifying" the infant's behavior can be viewed as having considerable affinity with the behavioristic approach. Like the behaviorists, we also establish conditions for behavior changes to take place; the affective arousal of the child in our presence, evidenced in a behavior which is directed at us and which, in turn, influences our own responses to him—this is the reciprocal communication which is the stable contingency of all of our transactions with the child: He must be aware of himself and of us in these interactions. We do not "slice off," however, which behavioral response in the child will be acceptable to us in this relationship and communication with him; the child's responses are left to his initiative, his spontaneity, his curiosity, and his "autonomy," within the human structure (communication) of our interactions with him. Our acceptance of the child is noncontingent, just as is the child's acceptance of us. The point to be made here concerns the reciprocity inherent in a learning process taking place in the interactions between two human beings. Our behavior is geared to influencing and arousing the child to our presence; the child's response to our stimulating intrusions affects in turn our reactions to him. We do not set ourselves up as the measure and standard of the child's behavior any more than the child does, except that both sets of responses, the child's and ours, have to retain their genuinely spontaneous and autonomous human qualities. If the child happens to smile after we tickle his stomach eight times, we do not decide that his smiling response is contingent on being tickled eight times; we immediately and naturally smile back in the actuality and spontaneity of the felt pleasure we have at seeing him smile. Our response not only creates a new "contingency" for the child (he may smile now as a consequence of our smiling at him), but it constantly keeps aroused a whole sequence of associated behaviors, all colored with a similar affective element. Similarly, if the child is in pain we go to him not necessarily to remove the pain (because it is already a good sign for an autistic child to start being able to feel pain), but to help him tolerate it or progressively feel it go away in the warm and pleasurable feeling of our contact with him. Our going to the child, in such circumstances, is not contingent on his giving us a hug, or a kiss, or on his saying thank you. We unconditionally stay with the child, again providing him with the awareness that his behavior affects us just as much as ours affects him. It is in this awareness and arousal of the child to the stability and aliveness of our presence to him that we see the central reinforcers of all of his behavioral responses. In other words, where the behavior therapist appears to view reinforcement as the appropriate primary or secondary reward (or punishment) given, from the outside, to a behavioral response which the therapist has decided to establish (or extinguish) in the child, we view reinforcement as an *organic* condition within the child which is independent, as such, of any specific reward or punishment, but which is directly related to the degree of affective arousal in the child (see Chapter IV; also Routenberg, 1968). Thus, if we were to define the reinforcing effects of our stimulating contacts and activities with the autistic child, we would have to say that we set the stage for the reinforcer (System II) to operate.

Lovaas himself (1968) has discovered what he considers the extraordinary reinforcing qualities of "play" as a contingency in modifying the behavior of a child; but he admits that he has no way of understanding how play achieves such a high degree of reinforcement. Perhaps it is in this type of confrontation with what is truly natural and human in a child's development and growth that the behaviorists may find a more accurate and adequate understanding of what constitutes reinforcement in learning. It is natural for a parent to rescue his child if he sees him in danger or in pain; such rescue action, with the affective qualities of concern, fear, and love which drive the parents to the side of the child, constitutes what we would view as setting the stage for the child's response of holding and clinging to the rescuing parent. How unnatural, on the other hand, is a situation where, in order to force the child to run to an adult, he is placed in a situation of pain (an electric grid) while the adult (who is in no pain) looks on. That from such a situation the child will never learn the true pleasures of human contacts which he could seek at any time and under any circumstances, is quite understandable (Lovaas 1965). All that can be learned in such a situation is how to avoid pain, not how to enjoy closeness.

Our therapeutic approach is an attempt at exploiting the normal energies of development in the child to the end of insuring that those functions and behaviors which are part of growing up as a human being will emerge in a differentiated and, at the same time, integrated and internalized way, so that the child will become a real person, capable of relating and communicating, realistically and profitably, with his environment.

Chapter IX

"O Mother, I Am Lost"

the participation of the parents and of the schools in the treatment

Releasing bound energies

It has been fashionable, during the past 50 years or more, to consider parents fundamentally responsible for the personality difficulties of their children. The assumption here appears to be that, when a child is born, parents are faced with a small, living mass of helplessness and malleability, which needs to be shaped and formed by the loving ministrations and concerns of the parents. The child, it is implied, is a *"tabula rasa"* on which all the assets and the deficits of the parents are to be inscribed; so that whatever the child turns out to be as a person—normal or deficient, troubled or happy, successful or defeated, rich or poor—should be brought back to the parental acceptance or rejection of the child. Such a view of parent-child relationships, in the early phases of the child's development, places such a burden of responsibility upon the parents, the mother especially, that whenever anything goes awry in the child's development, the first questions that parents always ask themselves is: What have we done wrong?

167

Confronted with an autistic infant, who seems to be such a complete failure in terms of human development, is it surprising, then, that the parents frantically search their hearts and souls to find what mistakes they have made, and where they have gone wrong? The guilt they experience, and the anxiety they live with, become a motivating force in many of the efforts they make to establish some sort of contact and communication with their autistic infant. But they feel rebuffed by the child, their efforts are in vain, and the defeat they meet serves only to increase their sense of failure and guilt. Their frustrated attempts at being parents to a child who seems to turn his back on them may even arouse feelings of angry disappointment, which in turn adds to their guilty reactions, so that whatever they had wanted to do for the child, or had even tried to do for him, they now hesitate or refrain from doing for fear of doing more damage to him. Under the circumstances, they may want to turn the child over to someone else; but seeking "professional help" becomes for them just another instance of being found responsible for their child's plight. Instead of carrying their torment and guilt only in their heart, it is now made public, and the sophisticated professional, whose help was sought, aligns himself with the "unwanted" autistic child and—with or without rescue fantasies coloring his mind—gives the parents a look that says: How could you!!

Blaming the parents for the autistic condition in an infant may be traditionally sound, but contributes little to the life of the child, any more than arresting a lifeguard after an apparent drowning can restore breathing to the drowned swimmer. We have indicated earlier in this book the reasons why, in our work with autistic infants, we took a positive stand toward the parents. Our theoretical viewpoint, as to the etiology of early infantile autism, made plausible this stand with respect to the parents. From a developmental point of view, the reciprocal influence that exists between mother and child had lead us to hypothesize that it is really the child that makes the parent, even more so than the other way around. Part of our project here included testing this hypothesis. If we could arouse the child, shouldn't we expect the parents— the mother especially—to react in a normal parental way?

This was the basic reason why we included from the beginning the parents as co-therapists in our work with the autistic child. First, of course, we had to tell the parents what we thought of them. We thought well of them. They had a good family life. They were doing a good job at raising their other children. The anxiety they had at not being able to cope with their autistic infant was normal; they were baffled and puzzled as everybody is by such a child. It was very important to make this clear to the parents—for their sake and ours. We needed their help in working with their child. The energies bound and tied up in anxious and guilty concern needed to be released for normal and effective responses to the child's demand for stimulation and growth. Their useless preoccupation with the questions of who is to blame for the child's autism had to give way to constructive activities on behalf of the child. On the other hand, we ourselves, by accepting the parents as the proper and normal instruments of growth in the child, could now shed any fantasy of our God-given special call to protect the child from his rejecting family. The parents could be our allies; and regardless of whatever we could give to the child, we could also give to them the freedom of being normal parents.

A second important reason for having the parents join us in our work was the absolute necessity of insuring the continuity of the therapeutic and educational action between the clinic and the home. Whatever impact on the child our approach might have in the therapy room, we had to make sure that its effectiveness would be maintained outside the clinic. It was up to the parents to provide the continuity of the therapeutic action at home, and to insure that the gains made in one situation became generalized and solidified at home and on the outside. This did not mean that we would ask the parents to repeat at home what we did at the clinic, at least not in a literally imitative sense. The essential message to the parents was: Do for your autistic child the same things you do for your other children; only more so. In other words, having accepted the parents as good, ordinary parents, we asked and expected of them, once they had understood what task needed to be done with their autistic child, that they should assume their parental role in a normal, sensitive, and intelligent way toward a child who needed them so much.

The parents wanted to know what needed to be done, and in what way they could do it. Over the years and months of frustration and failure in their parental efforts towards their autistic child, their supply of faith and hope was at a low ebb; and even their love had been more than rebuffed. We had to rekindle these energies in them; help them overcome their discouragement; show them that they need not be afraid to further hurt and alienate their own child, when the child himself was waiting for them. To carry this out we had each parent, at the beginning of the project and at various intervals subsequently, spend 20 to 30 minutes in the therapy room with their child, to do whatever they pleased. We observed their behavior and took movies of the transactions between child and parent. When the parents had an opportunity to see themselves interacting with the autistic child, they could understand very clearly what was effective and what was useless in their responses to the child's behavior. They could, furthermore, discuss with us their fears and their hesitations, or inhibitions, in the approach they took with their child.

These fears and inhibitions were quickly overcome for the most part when the parents observed the therapists working with their child. This was also a requirement of the program. Since all therapy sessions were carried out in public, so to say, where anyone interested could view the entire proceedings through a two-way vision mirror, parents were asked to attend as many sessions as they could. This had a number of advantages. First, it had motivating value in that the observation of their own child, alive and responsive to the therapist, gave the parents a new vision of their child. A typical comment in the early phases of treatment: "I've never seen her run so much or laugh so much! She's not any different than a normal two year old child!" The child, who had been so isolated from the family, and who had appeared so impossible to reach, seemed now, in the eyes of the parents, as a real child, alert and seeking human contacts, a playful child giving the impression that life was rather fun! To observe and discover that a child, who had seemed so far removed from human life, could smile and enjoy the company of other humans, gave the parents renewed strength in the parental task of giving life to their child.

A second advantage of viewing the therapeutic sessions can be described as the removal in the parents of the fears, which had been built up over the years, that whatever they would attempt with their child would be more harmful than good. They had learned the hard way that their autistic child behaved as if he didn't want to have anything to do with them. Intruding upon him had been met with complete indifference or wild irritability. Here was a child who never wanted to be held, or loved, or even attended to. The parents had so often been rebuffed in approaching him that they were now afraid of disturbing the child, except when it was absolutely necessary. This child was not with them; he wanted no part of them, as far as they could see; this child was a frightening enigma to them. Yet when these parents saw us invade this "empty fortress," which was the indifferent and aloof stance of the child; when they saw with what amount of relentless persistence we aroused the attention of the child to our presence through the wide variety of stimulating activities described in the preceding chapter, their fears subsided, and their inhibitions disappeared. These activities were interactions that any parent engages in with any normal child, except that they were done more forcefully, more playfully, and more persistently. Just more of everything. The parents certainly felt capable of doing that; they had always wanted to do it. And now they could see that it brought a positive response in the child, who not only did not reject these sorts of activities, but initiated them himself, and sought more of them.

In this respect, it is important to make clear that we did not want the parents to imitate at home what they saw us do in the clinic with their child. We needed the parents as co-therapists in the task of arousing the child, whose low threshold of affective responsivity had been so damaging to his personality development and human growth. But they should operate in this effort in ways that were natural and congenial to them, not as second-rate substitutes for us. In the same way that we did not see our task as offering the autistic child a poor parental substitute through our interactions with him, similarly we wished to make sure that the child's home would not be just an extension of the clinic, and the parents, mechanical imitators of our behavior. Fortunately, our approach could not be encompassed by a recipe book of specific techniques; rather it emphasized an attitude toward the child, a climate in which the child came alive, a structure that enhanced the conditions of growth in the child. Thus, observing us at work, the parents, even if they had wanted simply to copy what we were doing, would have found it difficult to choose any one thing or activity which seemed to work best with their child.

The fact is, as was mentioned earlier, that most of these parents had actually tried with their child much of what they saw going on in the therapy room, but with little success. They wanted to know what made it work for us, as they could observe it themselves. This was another real advantage of having the parents in the observation room during therapy sessions. They could talk about what they had seen; ask as many questions as they wished concerning what we did at the clinic and what they did at home; and, prompted by their constant queries about the various problems they met with their child, we, in turn, could discuss with them our understanding of the autistic child, and the basic rationale of our

treatment approach. Such discussions made the parents feel truly partners with us in the adventure of awakening their sleeping child, and
provided us with ever-increasing information about early infantile
autism.

Treating the parents as partners in our therapeutic work with their
child reinforced the communication we constantly tried to make to them
that they were normal parents, faced with a difficult child who needed
special attention, but whose difficulties were not to be blamed on them.
Thus, in answering their questions or in discussing any aspects of the
program with them, never did we attempt any analysis of their behavior
toward the child or conduct any form of psychotherapy with them. But
we demanded a great deal of them at home. Theirs was the major responsibility of maintaining in their child the continuity of the therapeutic impact they had observed at the clinic. Whatever energies they
had as parents they should mobilize in the direction of making their
presence to the child felt and experienced; the child could not be allowed to ignore their presence. To help them in this task, we required
that they bring us, as often as they wished (but at least once every
week), a detailed account of the behavior of the child at home; of their
responses to this behavior; and of the feelings they had with regard to
this behavior. We asked, furthermore, that they fill out rating scales
covering the entire spectrum of the child's development at various intervals. We also met with them at the clinic or in their homes, and we had
them join all the other parents for monthly group discussions. In these
ways, we were able not only to maintain a high degree of motivation
and participation in the parents, but also to insure that the reciprocal
interaction between the autistic child and his parents would create, for
the child, healthy conditions of normal personality growth; and, for
the parents, the possibility of discovering how to be normal parents to
their autistic child.

Learning to be a father and a mother

The discovery by the parents that not only could they be real parents
to their autistic child, but that there was a real job ahead for them and
that they weren't, in truth, the helpless and baffled people they had resigned themselves to be, created for them the most challenging situation of their lives. The task ahead of them was, in the most meaningful

and deepest sense of this word, one of education; that is, they had to arouse the dormant child, and help him grow and live as a human being. What they had seen us do at the clinic, they now had to maintain and continue at home. Their ability to do this rested on two reciprocal conditions: One was their own alertness and responsivity to their child's communication and cues or messages; the other was their child's ability to send out such messages, and somehow express his need in reaching out to them.

Our working hypothesis was that the parents could do their job well if their child maintained this communication to them. The child would do this if he were kept in a state of affective arousal and sensory alertness to them. Thus, theirs was a double task, similar to our work at the clinic: In their transactions with the child, they should, first, create a highly impactful affective stimulation; and, secondly, offer a wide variety of sensory experiences, through tactile, kinesthetic, and proprioceptive contacts. Their presence to the child had to be impressive, and their responses to the child had to reinforce his initiative, his curiosity, his discoveries, and his expressions of delight at being with them and receiving from them. In other words, whereas, in ordinary circumstances, a child spontaneously "gives" to the parents in the very process of naturally reaching out to them, so that the parental narcissism is reinforced and motivates further attentive ministrations by the parents, here, in the case of the autistic child, there is only that much giving by the child as can be aroused by the parents; their own narcissistic needs are constantly threatened, and it requires a "brave and bold" new faith in their child, and in themselves, to "educate" the baby.

In the early months of the experiment, Kathy's mother (and this was true of all the mothers in our group) found it very difficult to believe in herself. She had done a good job with her first child, a son, three years older than Kathy, but the two years she had spent with a child who not only gave her nothing, but even more tellingly seemed to want nothing from her, had left her with a deep sense of failure. To expect of this mother that she should now begin anew her life-giving functions toward a child who had never been her little girl, enclosed as Kathy was in a "circle of silence" and aloofness, appeared in many respects to be like asking her heart to open up again for more hurt and pain. Yet, as Leon Bloy writes: "Man has places in his heart which do not yet exist, and into them enters suffering, in order that they may have existence."

Kathy's mother was willing to take a chance on suffering. She was willing to learn how to be a real mother to Kathy, but Kathy had to tell her how.

Kathy had her own ways of communicating her needs, but her mother was not always "tuned-in" to the child's channel of communication. For instance, a few weeks after treatment began at the clinic, Kathy, who at home could always be counted on to be quietly in her room, facing the wall and scratching at it, was now roaming through every room in the house, kicking at objects and people (especially her big brother, who was delighted to see her around) in order to get acquainted with them. This by itself was enough to throw the organizational structure of the household into mild chaos. If the mother happened to be washing the kitchen floor—a chore which had always gone undisturbed—Kathy might run in and kick over the water pail; this was new and delightfully exciting in Kathy's life, but, to say the least, mother's reactions were mixed. Should she tell Kathy to stay in her room? But Kathy had been in there for the past two years! Should she scold her, and make her understand that washing buckets were not to be kicked over? But Kathy had just now discovered that water buckets even existed! Should mother stop cleaning the kitchen floor? Our answer: "Yes, yes, emphatically yes." Stop and pay more attention to the child, and less to the water on the floor! But how can one do this and still maintain the orderly sequence of housekeeping chores! Kathy's mother would have to make drastic adjustments in her life.

It's never easy to make drastic adjustments in one's life. Yet this becomes easier when the motivation is the rebirth of one's own child, especially when the child is right there making it evident that she wants to be with the mother and, even in a clumsy, disorganizing way, have something to do with the mother. In many respects, it is natural that most of the parent-child transactions took place in the kitchen. This is mother's domain, and if the child wants to find her, most of the time she'll be there. Elizabeth's mother caught on to this very quickly. Instead of allowing the child to absorb herself in autistic contemplation of a spinning plate, she recruited Elizabeth as a "helper." She had her dad make a small bench on which Elizabeth could stand, then filled the sink with plates and cups and had Elizabeth "washing the dishes," while the mother, cheering her on, carefully wiped them (all this, when a perfectly good automatic dishwasher was at hand!). Similarly, June's mother learned that she could be present to the child in a natural and pleasant way by recruiting her to set the table for meals, and entertain her little brothers and sisters while they were waiting for their food.

It was also in the kitchen that Tommy's mother rediscovered how much fun it is to gambol and dance with a child. Tommy, in his restless roamings, could create havoc with any plans that the mother might have for preparing a meal or feeding the baby. Tommy wanted her for him, which was a completely new development in the life of this little boy who had always ignored everyone, and would screech and scream at being held or cuddled. The mother had to learn to respond to her child reaching to her, and, at the same time, maintain some sort of schedule in her household chores. She managed this by interrupting her work long enough to take Tommy's hands, whirl and twirl in graceful dance motions, to the delight of the child, move away from him to attend to her work, and return again playfully to her little boy. Tommy had discovered that life was fun; his mother was now discovering that life could be fun with her son. It is so easy to forget that the fertilizing ingredient in any child's human growth is the playful and pleasurable quality of his interactions with those close to him, who care for him and love him. To be confronted daily with the disheartening behavior of the autistic child had been for the parents a tragic experience; how could life be fun with such a child! This, too, the parents in our project had to learn over: the discovery of the joy of playing with their child. Tommy's mother told us in one of her notes that she had forgotten how much fun it was to dance again, and run, and frolic. What Tommy asked of her made her come alive again. And, to her amazement, Kathy's mother, too, had so much pleasure helping her child play in the snow, that she wondered why every mother on her block was not outside with her children enjoying the snow!

But the joy of discovering, not only that one has a *real* child, but also, more poignantly, that one possesses within one's heart the responses which keep that child alive and real, was not reserved solely to the mother. In our project, we counted very much on the father to offer the child a different quality of reality than the mother could. The father we looked to for a double task: First, he had to draw the child away from the mother by offering the youngster stimulating sensory and affective responses, through which the child would be alerted, and for which he would reach out; secondly, the father had to draw the mother away from the child by offering her (the mother) the adult interest she needed as a woman. This, of course, we saw as the usual and normal function of the man of the house, and it was important to keep the family life of the autistic child as normal as possible. But the fathers also were baffled and puzzled by their autistic child. When we placed them in the observation room with their child, at the beginning of treatment, they held their distance and appeared quite reluctant to move in on the child. Rather, their entire behavior reflected how much they needed the child to tell them what to do next; and since their child was quite content to ignore them, they were left with little inspiration and considerable self-consciousness. By the same token, however, when they were able to see their child come alive and reach out for them, their responses were immediately forceful, imaginative, varied, and effective.

Especially did the fathers enjoy throwing the youngsters in the air, somersaulting with them, helping them build trains and towers out of large cardboard boxes, showing them how to solve form and picture puzzles, recognize pictures in books, teaching them how to hold pencils, and how to say words! It has been our experience that, whereas mothers can tolerate considerable amounts of frolicking, negativism, and poor discipline, the fathers very quickly in their relationship to their autistic child introduced structure, achievement, and discipline. In this respect, as soon as they would realize that the child would catch on and respond to their directives and instructions, the fathers' enthusiasm and involvement became dramatically effective. Kathy's dad made her a small stove and sink, as soon as she showed interest in washing dishes and in setting the table. Similarly, when Elizabeth overcame her fears of swings and rocking chairs, her dad put his skills to work in providing her with a safe swing and a rocker. When Tommy began to push furniture around in order to reach the light switches on the wall and marvel at how this clicking machine produced light and dark, his dad taught him how to jump off the chair into his arms, and progressively learn to overcome fear of heights.

The fathers, in other words, whatever amount of time they spent with their child, tended to use the opportunity to teach the child control and mastery. They were not content, for instance, that the child found it amusing to throw a ball any which way; they demanded real "ball playing." They did not accept that the child, holding a colored crayon, just scribble in a senseless way (which the mother would have easily accepted as an exercise in eye-hand motor coordination). They structured the "art work" so that the child produced a circle, or a line, and so forth. They did not rejoice at just seeing the child make sloppy attempts at eating his food (which the mother thought was at least an improvement over having to feed each mouthful to the child), they helped the child hold the spoon and maintain some sort of acceptable behavior at the table! In these efforts, the fathers, obviously, were not always immediately successful. Their patience, with a child negativistic and sometimes completely uninterested, was frequently taxed to the limit. They had to learn to accept the child's "moods" at different times and pace their efforts to the rhythm of these moods. This was not always easy, and quite often fathers became more discouraged than mothers.

In these moments of discouragement, the fathers sought strength in discussions with the therapists. Their questions were more of a theoretical nature than immediately directed at solving a practical current problem. They wanted to know more about child development, about developmental arrest, about our neurophysiological model of autistic behavior, about the differences between autistic infants and schizophrenic children. For the therapists, such discussions were of the greatest value, since it demanded of them that they constantly clarify their own thinking on these matters, and thus be able to communicate to the parents the type of understanding which would make their participation in the bringing up of their child a truly co-therapeutic one.

The schools are involved too

As soon as possible, after instituting the treatment program for the children, we took steps to insure the participation of schools in our total reeducational effort. For Kathy this meant going to nursery school after 17 months of treatment (at age 4); for Elizabeth, after 5 months, at age 3½; for June, after 3 months, to kindergarten at age 5. Connie was already attending nursery school where her mother was a part-time teacher; Tommy was too young, developmentally, to place in school at this time. (Note: Tommy is now, at age 3½, in a special education school on the East Coast, where his parents moved; he appears to be doing very well there, and we wonder whether we did not underestimate his full potentialities by not placing him earlier in a regular nursery school!)

Our decision to send the children to school was met by the parents with mixed feelings. Would the children be able to withstand such an experience? Would the schools accept such children? Were there any existing special schools for autistic children, or were we thinking of "ordinary," "regular," "normal" schools? In the same way that in setting up our program, the approach to the parents had been to deal with them as normal individuals capable of effective parental tasks toward their autistic child, we recommended that the parents enroll their child in a good neighborhood nursery or kindergarten class. To the parents, this proved to be much simpler than they had anticipated. The various schools contacted were quite receptive to our plans, but wanted to know more of whatever we thought they should know in order to give us effective cooperation. Mostly our response here was to emphasize the "normality" of the autistic child's behavior, and the constant challenge to their affective and sensory responsiveness which should be given, and which they needed in large dosage. This, however, was not half as influential in getting the full cooperation of principals and teachers as our frequent visits to the schools; our discussion and conferences with the personnel; our sharing with them our problems and concerns; and our offering them support, advice, suggestions, directions, and deep respect and admiration for their work. Whenever we went to visit the schools, we not only observed the children in their activities and recreations, but we also took movies for comparison purposes from one visit to the other. Thus the school personnel understood very quickly that nothing drastic had to be changed in the usual routines of the school, just because of the presence of an autistic child in their midst!

Except for June, who began attending a kindergarten class within the public school system, the other children were enrolled in private nursery schools for normal children. Kathy's first weeks of school were somewhat hectic. For some time prior to this, she had been in one of her "phases." Every time she met or came close to an unfamiliar child or adult, she either kicked the person or pulled his hair. In school, where so many new faces surrounded her, Kathy had a field day. She kicked everybody in sight, pinched, and pulled hair! Under this wholesale assault, the teachers bore up remarkably well, one half their time protecting the other children, the other half, protecting themselves! They took Kathy's shoes off at all times, to reduce the kicking damage; they kept her nails closely clipped; they sat her apart from others when Kathy's hair-pulling exercises would have disrupted group activities! Fortunately this phase didn't last too long: Kathy, in her anxious timidity in the face of the unfamiliar and new school situation, didn't know how to get acquainted with all these children and grownups, except in this aggressive and rather intolerable way. She wished very much to be part of all the group experiences, as evidenced by the enthusiasm she would show at leading the children as they marched in file from one room to the other, or at holding hands to dance in a circle, or at rocking with another child in a "row, row, row your boat" exercise on the floor. Thus her antisocial phase came to an end when she obviously realized that she was missing out on too much fun when her cruel antics forced the teachers to keep her away from the other children. Also, after a few weeks, she knew everybody there and didn't need to use violent tactics to get acquainted with them.

Perhaps some will object that our choosing to view Kathy's cruel behavior as an expression of her need to experiment with being close to others who appear to her, in their unfamiliar and strange actions, somewhat frightening and unsafe, has too much of a lenient and sentimental quality, inconsistent with our philosophy of structure and limits. Kathy's behavior could have been modified much sooner, some will suggest, if contingencies had been established to extinguish her antisocial and aggressive responses, and to help her learn, through a variety of rewards, the value of socially acceptable behavior. A good deal of damage to others from kicking, pinching, and hair-pulling could have been avoided, and Kathy would have emerged a sweet, nice child to have around in school!

Without questioning the soundness of this argument, it is necessary, nevertheless, to explain why it would have been rather paradoxical for us to adopt the procedures it suggests. In sending Kathy or any of the other children to school, we had one central goal in mind: to widen the autistic child's world of experience. Here was a child who just then was beginning to discover how wonderful it is to be alive, to be a small child in a world of accepting human beings. True, this world was not always easy to understand; it was full of surprises, and sometimes terrifyingly strange and unpredictably varied. But this was the world that our children had demonstrated, to us and to their parents, they wanted and loved. In approaching it, their fears could not be allowed to thwart their initiatives, or their clumsy experimentations and trials. We did not send the children to school to learn how to sit on a chair, if sitting on a chair meant the end of their enthusiastic curiosities and discoveries; or to learn how to "conform," if conforming meant simply imitating others; or to learn not to kick, not to pinch and pull hair, if not doing this made you become "invisible" (a most descriptive term coined by Leland [1966] to explain that the goal intended in modifying certain undesirable behaviors in a retarded child is reached when the child draws no more attention upon himself through his behavior). Kathy's behavior unquestionably had to change, and the simple fact is that her behavior, after the first few weeks, did change, *because she changed it.* The behavior modification was not imposed on her by the arbitrary fiat of the teachers intent on making her a nice, sweet kid. Kathy's behavior changed, not because she wanted to avoid pain or punishment, but because, feeling more comfortable and safe in an environment that had become more familiar and predictable, she could now trust those people around her who had not destroyed her zest for life in the process of extinguishing her unacceptable social behavior. In the actuality of being with others, playing with others, feeling happy and safe with others, Kathy gave up undisciplined and uncontrolled experimentation with an environment that was new and frightening to her. This is what we had hoped to achieve. There is a fundamental difference between punishment which destroys pleasure and leads to avoidant behavior, and discipline which guides and insures a greater or wider experience of pleasure. Similarly, there exists no affinity between structure which supports initiative, creativity, and spontaneity in the child's functioning, because it leads to a channelling of the life energies at work in the child toward the discovery and possession of life; and a programmed design for living, into which the child is trapped, and against which he has no recourse, because no choice is given to him except to behave along lines that have been traced for him by others.

Whether our views here are correct or not, the teachers at the school seemed, intuitively perhaps, to grasp what we were striving for. When Kathy started climbing on tables, they did not put an electrified grill to stop her from jumping from one table to another; they put colorful table cloths on each table. It beautified the room, and Kathy would never climb on a beautiful table! When June, easily distractible and restless in a large classroom, could not resist the temptation of walking around to investigate whatever had drawn her attention, the teacher did not tie her to her chair or threaten her with expulsion; the teacher gave her papers to distribute, or requested she collect school work from the class, or sent her with messages to various parts of the school. What if she got lost on the way? June never got lost! What if she unduly dilly-dallied? Well, there was always some "normal" child itching, like June, to go on an errand to retrieve her. In fact, in our frequent talks with the teachers, the principals, and the directors, we received more help and ideas for our own work with the children than we were actually able to offer them. Frequently, the teachers made simple suggestions with regard to changing certain behaviors in the children, which in their experience with others had worked well, but which we had not thought about. Thus, for instance, Elizabeth, a chubby little girl, seemed unable to run without slipping and falling frequently, so that she preferred to rock on the "horsie" rather than join with the other nursery school children in their walking or running games. Her very fine teacher noticed that her shoes were somewhat too small—Elizabeth, who had remained very small for her age, grew up dramatically once treatment began—and moreover had leather soles which were slippery, and therefore not appropriate for walking and running games. She suggested rubber-soled shoes, of adequate size, and Elizabeth did the rest! Common sense? This is exactly what should dominate the education of the autistic child. We were fortunate that the teachers had a good dose of it.

In this respect, another important aspect of the autisic child's education requires consideration: language and speech. Of our five children, only June possessed some amount of speech when we first started working with her. Kathy was completely silent; her first sounds were of laughter after a few weeks of treatment. Connie grumbled, growled, screeched, and blew bubbles (in a razzing sort of way), but very seldom made sounds that could be construed as words. On the other hand Elizabeth could say "socks" and "pretty," but otherwise had no speech. Tommy made noises like a roaring tiger, and sometimes appeared to say "water" or "light," and that was the extent of his vocabulary. As we indicated earlier, in our work at the clinic we talked and sang constantly with the children, but made no special effort to "teach" them speech, unless they made it obvious, at different times, that they were trying to articulate a word, or modulate a sound. Similarly, throughout the project, we encouraged the parents to speak to their child and stimulate as much verbal communication from the child as the child was interested in mastering. This general rule was also followed at school.

At the time that the children entered, they all understood very well what was said to them and, therefore, could follow most of the instructions given them. This was enough to insure their participation in group games and learning exercises. They now discovered, however, surrounded by all the other children who seemed to get things done faster when they talked to the teacher, that speech had some sort of wonderful value. Fortunately, the teachers were quite willing to allow them to experiment as much as they wanted with words and sounds. Thus Elizabeth found it quite pleasant to entertain herself and others, singing (Old MacDonald had a farm) "ee-i-ee-i-o" and eventually putting the right words to "Three Blind Mice," before she could put a few words together to communicate a wish or a request to the teacher. On the other hand, Kathy, who always appeared to rehearse within her own mind, for long periods of time, any new accomplishment, was able, more quickly than Elizabeth, to put together various isolated words she had learned to say, like "eyes," "nose," "hair," "Carole," "pull," and so forth. Typically, in view of her irrepressible, obnoxious behavior at times, her first word combination was: "Pull hair!" More important, however, than learning in this slow experimental way the verbal instrumentality of language to communicate their needs, their discoveries, or their wishes, the children in school learned to identify themselves verbally. June discovered the pronoun I, and both Kathy and Elizabeth were finally able to refer to themselves by name. "Kathy, don't kick" became a self-imposed injunction in Kathy's vocabulary, and "Lizabeth, horsie" expressed the child's affection for a rocking horse.

The striking feature of this new achievement in the children is that at no time was their speech inappropriate, nonsensical, out of context, or purely echolalic. By giving these children the opportunity to experience themselves making sounds in situations where they were involved doing or enjoying something, the words they acquired became meaningful to them, so that whenever they used them there was a true communicative quality to them. (See Lewis: *How Children Learn to Speak;* 1959.) Again, it should be stated that the teachers, by allowing the children the pleasure of discovery, and by encouraging with genuine and affectionate attention every move the children made toward the mastery of speech, were able to instill, somehow, in these youngsters the personal and social value of the words they were mouthing, so that a much truer communication could be derived from it than if the teachers had systematically rehearsed the children in pronouncing words, or in attaching words to things and actions, and then directing words at others expected to understand them (in this respect, see Lovaas and his problems, 1966). Thus school, for the autistic child, seemed the appropriate milieu to acquire social skills and communicative behavior within a personal developmental process which, for each child, allowed for the emergence of these skills and of speech at the time the child was ready and interested in developing them.

In summary then, the participation of the parents and of the schools in our treatment and educational program for autistic children permitted the impact of our own work with each child to be extended to the home and to the community. This required close contacts with the parents, and frequent communication with the schools. Learning from each other's experiences, as the project went along, and being constantly faced with meeting new problems and difficulties which, seemingly every day, challenged the scientific security of the investigators, the hopes and expectations of the parents, and the patience and understanding of the teachers, made the entire effort of "awakening the sleeping child" an exciting adventure. Would Kathy really wake up? If she did, would she remain awake, happy to be alive, and able to develop (slowly perhaps) as a normal child? The following chapters begin to give an answer to these questions.

Part IV

*. . . And straightaway the
child rose up and
walked . . .*
Mark V : 42

Testing of Autistic Children

Formal testing of autistic children, between the ages of two and five years old, is no simple task. Standardized scales measuring rate of mental development, intellectual functioning, learning potential, or social maturity, have been validated on normal populations of infants and preschool children. Such instruments, if they are to reflect in a comparably valid way the rate of growth in autistic children, must be used judiciously, and with clear awareness of the difficulties involved in testing these autistic children. Areas of difficulties stem from the severe and basic developmental deviations in these youngsters. These difficulties include: (*a*) the attention-interest condition in the child at the time of the testing; (*b*) the preverbal mode of the autistic child's communication; (*c*) the severe negativism of the child; (*d*) the sequential order of test items, and their measuring value as related to the chronological age of the child; (*e*) the tester's own experience and skill in obtaining the most accurate measure of the child's development and functioning.

In the following paragraphs we will discuss in detail these problem areas, with illustrations from our clinical data.

a) *The attention-interest condition in the child.* The usual difficulty in testing normal infants and children, of obtaining their attention or interest on a specific task or item given in a standardized fashion, is increased a hundredfold when testing an autistic child. The "aloof" and "indifferent" attitude of this child, his capacity to be physically "there" and yet completely "out of it," his "private" preoccupations and absorptions in self-stimulating activities, and his tendency never to "look at" anything, but rather "beyond it," or "through it"; all these typical symptoms of the autistic child's behavior make it absolutely important that, in using any test item or task to measure his development or functioning, every means be taken to assure the attention and interest of the child. The examiner cannot take anything for granted here; he should keep in mind the farmer's admonition that when you want to have a donkey do something for you, first you must hit it over the head to get its attention! The intrinsic interest value that any test item may have for a normal child—such as reaching under a cup to retrieve a colorful block (Cattell, 11th month)—cannot be assumed to be sufficient to attract or motivate an autistic child. To measure such a child's capacity to observe an object being put under a cup, to remember that the object remains under the cup even though it has disappeared, and to be able to retrieve it, the examiner may have to use a colorful and "tasty" piece of candy rather than a block. This presupposes, of course, that the child likes candy and would want it; he may just as well like a shiny bracelet and want it. Thus, throughout any examination period, the examiner must remain alert to any show of interest on the part of the child in any object or activity and use these judiciously in alerting the attention of the child to any specific task or item of the test. This type of procedure is nothing new in testing infants or children; most manuals of administration of preschool tests make such procedure mandatory for accurate measurement of young subjects (cf. Cattell, Stanford-Binet, Vineland, Merrill-Palmer).

The rapid and unpredictable fluctuations in attention and interest to which the autistic child is subject demand, at times, that the entire context of the testing situation be modified or altered. Kathy, for instance, had demonstrated adequate skill in putting the pieces of a puzzle in their proper place. However, her interest in, and attention to, such a task was minimal; she was far more interested in being swung and thrown across the room into the arms of the therapist. To have her attend to a puzzle and put it together, it was, therefore, important to "reward" her attention to the task with the delight she experienced at being given a "swing." Provided this reward was forthcoming, Kathy was quite willing to attend to, and exercise her skills on, any test item presented to her. In this fashion, Kathy was able to complete the entire sequence of performance items on the Merrill-Palmer Scale, demonstrating not only her true developmental level, but actually going beyond the normal range of functioning for her age level, and driving herself to superior accomplishments on some test items. But it is clear that here the entire testing situation, as it is usually set up, had to be altered considerably. In the examining room with Kathy, not only was there the examiner, but also the two therapists and whatever else was needed for Kathy's delectable swing. The examiner confined herself to the administration of the test items; after each completed task, Kathy would be "thrown" across the room, following which she would gleefully return to her chair and the test table to resume her examination.

It should be noted here—though this was discussed more thoroughly in the chapter on the psychotherapeutic process—that the interest that the autistic child develops in the people, as opposed to objects, and which comes about through an alerting and intrusive type of therapy relation with him, can also interfere with the testing of the child. As a matter of fact, this type of interest can, at times, make it impossible to test the child at all. For instance, Kathy, who was completely untestable before beginning therapy, could very well be tested after three months, when some of her fears had been overcome, and some of her indifference and aloofness dissipated. But for the next nine months she was, for all practical purposes, completely untestable; not because she had regressed or had made no real progress in personality development (the ratings on her, on the contrary, show steady and amazing development), but rather because she lost all interest in objects, and much preferred what other people did to her, with her, around and about her. As far as Kathy was concerned, people were much more fun than toys or games; jumping, dancing, singing, hiding, noise making, were infinitely more stimulating and pleasurable to her than putting a cover on a small box, when asked to do so during a test session, or fold a piece of paper (S-B age III)! Thus, the examiner who, at times like these, would attempt to test the child, would find herself thwarted and frustrated at every turn in the face of a subject who ignored every test item in favor of the examiner herself, who was being asked by the child to run, jump, or dance with her!

Another challenge which the quality of attention and interest of the autistic child presents to the examiner is evident in those test items that are *timed*. In testing a normal child, the same problem has been noted, but occurs much less floridly or frustratingly. The Wallin Pegboard, which is a test item on both the Cattell and Merrill-Palmer, will serve to illustrate our point here. In the Merrill-Palmer the form A of the Pegboard is used at four different levels: as item number 5 for ages 18 months to 23 months, when all the round pegs must be put into place in 38 seconds or less; as item number 15 for ages 24 months to 29 months, time limit 25 seconds; as item number 28 for ages 30 months to 35 months, time limit 20 seconds; as item number 38 for ages 36 to 41 months, with time limit of 17 seconds. Under normal conditions, a normal child of 2 years of age can usually pass the test at level number 15, and if he is bright, at level number 28; this means that the child will place the round pegs in the round holes in the time prescribed, even without being told to hurry. But what happens with an autistic child? After the examiner has secured his attention and interest to the point of having the child pick up a peg and place it in the hole, any number of behavioral bits on the part of the child may make the task of "clocking" his performance an extremely difficult one. The child may, for instance, proceed as if there was nothing at all to the task and dutifully place all the pegs in the holes, except one! This one, the child notices, has a small white mark on its side; he starts pondering over this mark, scratching at this mark, turning, twisting the peg in every direction to savor fully the magnificent discovery of this small defect. If the child had taken exactly 15 seconds to place the first five pegs when he stopped being interested in the task in order to attend "autistically" to the peg, the examiner, cannot, in fairness to the child, continue to clock the "autistic episode"; the watch must be stopped, and the count should resume when the child attends once again to the pegboard and the task.

Similarly, the child may place three or four pegs in the holes in very short order and then retrieve them all for the simple joy of putting them back in! He may do this two or three times and finally complete the task. Should he be clocked all the while he is retrieving and replacing the pegs? Should the count begin over every time he resumes the task? But suppose, instead of retrieving all the pegs he had placed, he takes only a few of them and resumes at the point where the other pegs are? Should you start reclocking only after he has put back the pegs as far as he had originally gone? It can be seen that the examiner's alertness in timing such a child on such a test can be taxed to the limit. It has been our experience that when two independent "timers" are assigned to this task—the examiner and an observer—there can be a difference of as much as 10 seconds between the two reported times.

Many more examples could be given of the distractibility of the autistic child in performing test items presented to him; and in evaluating his performance one should clearly keep in mind the purpose of the test itself: most developmental tests aim at measuring whether the child can or cannot perform a certain task standardized for a certain age level; these tests do not intend to measure the emotional maturity of the child nor his idiosyncrasies. Normal children are curious; they are attracted by the novel and fun quality of what appear to be games; their attention and interest can be obtained by giving them directions, instruction, encouragements, telling them what you want them to do. Not so with the autistic child, who tends to fear novelty and prefers to persevere in the repetition of limited stereotyped forms of behavior. Such a child cannot be counted on to respond to verbal directions, especially in an unfamiliar test situation. This will be discussed at length in the following paragraph.

b) The preverbal autistic mode of communicaion. To insure that a valid measure is obtained of a child's performance on a test, it is important to communicate somehow to him what he is expected to do. When verbal directions are used, or when relatively complex signs are given, the child must be able to understand the words used or grasp the meaning of the signs. With an autistic child who has no language—four of our five subjects were in this category—the task of insuring his understanding of the response he is expected to give to a test item becomes extremely difficult. The preverbal and presymbolic modes of communication possible with such a child require that the examiner keep clearly in mind the intent of the test measure he is using, and present the item to the child in such a way that this intent is communicated somehow to the subject. Take for instance, the Drawing-up String test, which is item number 17 for ages 24 to 29 months of the Merrill-Palmer Scale. The intent of the test is to measure how well a child can use both hands in drawing up a string to which is attached a colorful small stick. Normally the examiner places the stick on the floor and slowly draws the string saying, "Come on, stick, come on, little stick," thus demonstrating to the child what to do, and adding, "There's the stick. I made it come to me. Now let's see if you can make it come to you." When presented with this task, Elizabeth, who is extremely skillful in using her hands, repeatedly ignored having to pull the string and just walked over to pick up the stick, since this appeared to be what she was expected to do. The verbal directions were useless, and the "demonstration" was confusing to her. It was confusing because what was being demonstrated put the emphasis on the stick, rather than on using both hands to pull up the string. If, however, you sat the child in a chair, and had the examiner sit beside her holding the string, then pulling it, making obvious hand motions on the string, and thus retrieving the stick, Elizabeth had no trouble at all using both hands to pull at the string, which is what the test intends to measure.

The absence of speech as well as of understanding of spoken words, the inability to use words and ordinary signs and symbols meaningfully, can unduly penalize the autistic child in a test situation. All items involving verbal commands or instructions, repetition of words, or "action-agent" types of requests demand of the examiner judicious consideration of the degree to which, for any one child, it is possible to make him understand what is wanted. This is especially true for an item like Obeying Simple Commands, which is number 1 on the Merrill-Palmer Scale for ages 18 to 23 months. Just telling the child, "See the box. Take the box from the table and put it on the chair"; or "See the ball. Pick up the ball and put it in this box," might be enough to attract the attention of the child to the examiner, but not necessarily be understandable as far as what needs to be executed. The autistic child may very well pick up the box or the ball and carry them around the room, but unless the examiner, while the child is holding the box or the ball, demonstrates somehow what he wants the child to do with these objects, the child will fail the task. If the intent of the test is to measure how well a child will obey, then any familiar command would serve this purpose, such as, "Come over here, Kathy"; "Don't touch the water, Tommy"; "Put out your foot, Connie." But of course, these commands are not part of the standardized scale and, therefore, cannot be scored. If, on the other hand, the intent of the test is to measure how well the child grasps the words used in giving the command, then the autistic child cannot be expected—until he acquires some degree of symbolic functions—to carry out the command. Therefore, it would seem more valid, in testing such a child, to omit those tests involving verbal requests or instructions, when it would be impossible to translate in nonverbal ways these requests or instructions, without invalidating the intent of the measuring instrument being used.

In this connection, the examiner may need to distinguish between the failure of the child on such test items because he does not understand what is requested, and a failure due to the child's not wanting to perform what is requested. The negativism of the autistic child has many forms, and will be discussed in the next paragraph.

c) The severe negativism of the autistic child. This is probably the greatest source of frustration in attempting to test an autistic child. The patience and ingenuity of the examiner are taxed to the limit, and many tests are scored *Failed*, when, if the varieties of negativistic behavior of the child were taken into account, they should be scored *Refused*. A major form of negativism, which the autistic child presents in a testing situation, stems from the fear and the anxiety which lead him to turn away from, or aggressively to remove, anything new or unfamiliar. For this reason, it is very useful to "expose" the child to certain objects, materials, or tasks closely resembling those used as items, in the tests to be administered. This is not a matter of training the child in the performance of test items, or of rehearsing a testing session with the child, but rather of relieving the anxiety of the child by making a situation, similar in some ways to the testing situation, more familiar and thus more comfortable to the child. An example may be useful here. Kathy had never strung beads. Stringing beads is an item on the Stanford-Binet, age III. To make her familiar with this task, we played a game of bead stringing, card stringing, and block stringing with her. Thus, when the actual test item was presented, she did not turn away from it or throw it on the floor. She had seen similar things before.

However, the negativism out of fear frequently develops, at some period, into what we might call an arbitrary negativism. Here the child does the opposite of anything that might be expected of him, even though the task to be performed may very well be within his ability to achieve it. In such instances, of course, the child is untestable that day, and the attempt should be abandoned.

But there is another form of negativism which, far from being arbitrary, is used by the child to draw the attention and interest of the examiner upon him. The child refuses to do any specific task as long as he thinks the examiner wants him to do it. Kathy was an expert at this. As soon as she understood that a certain performance was expected of her, she would do the opposite. To the command, "Throw me the ball" (MP number 2, 18–23 months), she would deliberately throw it in a different direction! To the instruction, "See if you can put them back in their holes" (Wallin Peg Boards), she would simply refuse to have anything to do either with the pegs or with the holes! It is obvious that such behavior cannot be considered a *Failure* in scoring the test. As a matter of fact, there is a rather successful way of overcoming this selective and personalized form of negativism. It consists of beating the child at his own game! You make clear to the child that you do not want him to do what you actually want! You act as if you couldn't care less; you even distance yourself sufficiently away from the child that it appears you have no interest in what he might be doing! At this juncture, the child usually does what was intended in the first place, cleverly thinking that he is defeating you or longingly hoping that you will come back to play with him. So much so, that our only speaking subject would go as far as to say, "Tell me *not* to take your cup!"

Finally, there is another form of apparent negativism which, especially in a testing situation, can easily escape the examiner's understanding. This is the negativism motivated by the need in the child to assert his own capacity to make a choice. You want the child to do one thing; he prefers, at that moment, to do something else! You want him to build a tower, and, at that moment, the child would like to do a puzzle; the tower is refused, and the child busies himself with one of the available puzzles. What should the examiner do? Clearly, he should follow the child's initiative, forgo his own misdirected intentions, and allow the child to perform on items of his own choice—which leads to another area of testing problems.

   d) The sequential order of test items, and their measuring value in relation to the chronological age of the child.   Choosing the right test items at the right time, under the proper conditions, constitutes a central problem in the testing sequence of an autistic subject. The examiner's judgment, in this respect, is of the utmost importance. The examiner must be sensitive to what might be called the life experience of autistic children. This life experience, viewed in a panoramic sort of way, amounts to very little. There are test items, for instance, on the Cattell Developmental scale, which an 8-month-old child can easily deal with, because he has been exposed to a similar situation. An autistic child may fail such an item, either because he does not understand what is expected (as when you hold up a loop and a string, and expect the child to reach for the string) or because the task required has no interest value (such as rattling a spoon inside of a cup). The examiner may easily decide then that the child does not possess the skills of an 8-month-old infant! Yet, that same child may perform beyond his age level on a different, but chronologically interesting, item of another developmental test!

It is therefore of the utmost importance that the examiner take into consideration the chronological age of the child with reference to the interest value of any test item. Tommy, for instance, may quite readily fit round pegs in round holes, but will have no understanding of a test requiring him to put a pellet in a small container. Yet he may be quite interested in putting a large ball in a wastepaper basket, just because this seems more interesting to him! Similarly, Elizabeth may find "Making a Block Walk" (MP number 6, age 18–23 months) a completely uninteresting item, whereas she will be fascinated by piling up the blocks of the "Little Pink Tower" (MP item number 40, age 36–41 months). Evidently, the examiner has to take into account what is appropriate to the child's life experience and to the child's actual chronological age, as well as his retarded developmental level.

e) The tester's own experience and skill. Thus we come to the final item of our discussion of the difficulties in testing an autistic child: *the examiner's own experience and skill in obtaining the most accurate measure of the child's development and functioning!*

In the preceding discussion, constant reference was made to the examiner and to the qualities of sensitivity, alertness, patience, and flexibility he must maintain in testing autistic children. Obviously, an examiner with considerable experience with a wide variety of children is needed. But experience here is not enough. The autistic child, through his indifference and aloofness, has a demoralizing influence on even the staunchest of examiners. The demoralization appears first to be experienced as discomfort and uneasiness or anxiety in the presence of such a child. The child is there, and yet not with you, and nothing—most of the time—seems to break through what has been referred to as his "circle of silence" or his "glass ball". There is so little to hang on to that the examiner ends up by feeling very acutely that he is being tested to the limits. Thus, beyond experience, what seems to be needed from the examiner is a sort of "care-less" faith and hope; that is, the capacity to adopt an attitude of complete confidence in the possibility of testing the child, while, at the same time, maintaining a complete indifference with respect to whether this will be accomplished. This means that the examiner cannot allow himself to work under pressure of any kind; his goal is to get the most out of the child being tested. And this can be achieved only if the examiner does not experience this attempt as a matter of life or death!

The following note from Dr. Krall is very much to the point here, in clarifying this actual discussion.

> The first feeling I had was of extreme frustration—there must be something I could do to elicit more appropriate responses. Then when the breakthrough occurred, I was not prepared for it. Thus, the examiner must be prepared for a sudden spurt in performance; he must be prepared to change, on the spur of the moment, to a more advanced instrument, in order to be at the new level of functioning. At the same time, he must be prepared to go through a long period of "nonperformance" without being discouraged, and always being prepared for the new achievement.

Whatever amount of time is needed, whatever number of interruptions must be suffered, whatever degree of frustration must be endured, the examiner, in testing an autistic child, should come out of the experience feeling: Well, this wasn't too bad today! At least I'm still in one piece, and the child is a little less autistic for having spent this time with me.

The difficulties encountered in obtaining valid and reliable results from psychological tests administered to autistic children are not insurmountable. The design of our educational experiment with these children (see Chapter VI) included the administration of a variety of such measuring instruments at frequent intervals during the entire period of our project. For those readers unfamiliar with psychological tests, their purpose, their measuring value, and their limitations, we will describe in the following paragraphs each of the psychological tests we used in evaluating the changes in growth of our subjects during the period of our work with them.

All of the tests (the Cattell, the Stanford-Binet, the Merrill-Palmer, the Vineland), except the Leiter International, contain verbal items— the Cattell as early as 8 months, and from then on with increasing frequency. The majority of these Cattell items are, however, of the nature of receptive speech, and even the mute autistic children develop this capacity relatively quickly once in treatment. However, at this point, and perhaps even initially, there is such a great discrepancy between the chronological age of the autistic child being tested, and the chronological age level for which the test items (verbal and performance) were developed, that they possess no interest for an older child either normal or autistic. This is well illustrated as mentioned above by the three-month testing of Elizabeth, at which time she attains an IQ of 52 on the Cattell, as contrasted with an IQ of 76 on the Merrill-Palmer, which is a more age-appropriate and interesting test for her. A further difficulty with the Cattell is that there is no "approved" method of prorating the score for a mute youngster (this applies equally to the autistic, the deaf, or the aphasic). Since the Cattell is considered the downward extension of the Stanford-Binet (beginning with the Cattell third-year second half, test items are identical with the Stanford-Binet year III), this lack of provision for prorating is carried over to the Binet and becomes an even more serious problem. It is, in fact, insurmountable unless or until the child develops language, since practically all items on the Binet require receptive language and verbal concepts in order for the child to even understand what it is that he is expected to do. Indeed, even after the child has developed very good receptive language, though still without any but minimal (words and simple phrases) expressive language, he automatically ceilings at certain levels of the Binet in which all items require extensive expressive language (e.g., IV–6). In these situations it is appropriate for the examiner to go on to higher levels and establish a second ceiling. Further, it is an often stated observation that, even for the normal verbal preschool child, the items on the Binet at this level are not particularly interesting and lack the "fun and games" quality necessary to obtain from these young children an accurate IQ evaluation. If this is true for the normal child, it is even more true for the child emerging from autistic isolation who, at his best, is still far less cooperative (more negativistic) than the normal child, though he may be of equal intelligence. At this point the reader may well ask, "Why, then, was the Stanford-Binet used at all in the evaluation of these children?" The answer to this question is simple, and yet at the same time extremely (and perhaps naïvely) optimistic. One of the assumptions about autistic children basic to this entire experimental treatment was that they are potentially or essentially capable of normal development—in all areas, including language and verbal concept formation. For this reason, and also because the Stanford-Binet has long been regarded the best predictor of school achievement, we wished to obtain as early as possible a "base" on this test in order to follow the future progress of these children, that is, their progress beyond the year-long period of treatment to be reported here.

Turning next to the Merrill-Palmer Scale, we find a test that is in many ways ideal although it, too, has certain critical limitations. On the positive side, even though it contains both verbal and performance items, the vast majority are performance. Further, what the child is expected to do is often communicated by demonstration rather than by verbal instruction or request. Even in the latter case it is often possible to translate the verbal instructions into gestural ones. One of the strongest points in favor of its usefulness with autistic youngsters is that provision in scoring is made for omitted items (in this case verbal ones such as repetition of words and phrases, answering questions, and so forth), and for refused items. This latter feature, provision for dealing with refused items, enables one to not penalize the child for his occasional displays of negativism. But beyond this, the test materials themselves seem to have a great deal of intrinsic interest even for the autistic child; he likes puzzles, peg boards, blocks, form boards, nests of cubes, and sorting and matching. This test seems to have the quality of enough sameness with variety such that the child becomes neither bored nor confused. There is really only one major limitation in the use of the Merrill-Palmer with autistic children, and that is the factor of timing. Here the frequent inattentiveness of the autistic child, or his sudden intense preoccupation with all the wondrous facets of the surface and shape of a square peg, or of the star on the Sequin form board, in the middle of an otherwise perfect performance, consume additional time and consequently penalize him on those items where time is an important scoring factor. To accurately stop and restart the watch so as not to penalize the child for these brief, though often frequent, periods of inattentiveness or preoccupation, is difficult for the most conscientious examiner and is often best done, if at all, by an observer strictly concerned with the timing aspect of the testing and with nothing else.

Turning, finally, to the Leiter International Performance Test, we have what appears to be the most adequate test for autistic children who are well along in the process of emerging from their primary autistic condition, but who are still mute. All instructions given in this test are by way of nonverbal demonstration. Tests at successively higher levels become increasingly more difficult; i.e., they progressively involve more complex, less concrete, more functional, and, finally, abstract concepts. Yet the procedure to be followed by the child in accomplishing the tasks at all levels is based on the simple paradigm introduced in the first task at age level II: that of placing colored blocks in the stall representing the color of the block. Once the child "has that idea" he knows what is expected of him in every subsequent, more difficult task. This test, even more than the Merrill-Palmer, fits well with the child's own needs for structure, while at the same time providing variety within the structure. It has the further advantage, over the Merrill-Palmer, of being an untimed test. Even though this test is entirely nonverbal in administration and content, it correlates highly with the Stanford-Binet which attempts to measure these same levels of concept formation, but in a predominantly verbal way.

A few words regarding the Vineland Social Maturity Scale are in order. This instrument attempts to measure the level or development of social maturity in the specifically defined categories of locomotion, communication, socialization, occupation, self-help general, self-help eating, self-help dressing, and self-direction. Age levels contain varying numbers of items. Some age levels are more heavily weighted with some categories than with others. This scale was originally developed for use in the evaluation of social maturity of mental defectives of all ages, most of whom possess verbal communication abilities. The mute autistic child often develops, prior to his late acquisition of verbal language, many very effective devices of nonverbal communication; these, of course, are not tapped by the Vineland. Aside from this minor limitation, the scale is very useful in following the development, in the process of treatment, of the child's socialization as a reflection of his increasing affective involvement with people, and with his social environment in general. This, needless to say, is an area of prime interest in any attempt to treat autistic children. The steady increases in Social Quotient (SQ) speak well for the emergence from isolation and indifference, and the growing involvement with people and the environment. This steady increase is in sharp contrast to the measures of intellectual development which often show long periods of untestability and/or sudden jumps in level of achievement. This again is a reflection of the problems related to "testability" discussed above. It is always possible at the three-month test interval to obtain a Vineland score, since this material is supplied by the mother. Further, it should be noted that the problems of untestability generally occur early in the treatment. Hence, they may be a function, to some extent, of the fact that the child has to develop a certain degree of sociability before he becomes truly testable. Whether these periods of untestability occur, and the extent of their duration, is unique to each child, and to his specific pattern of development as it unfolds during the treatment process.

Finally, it is important to keep in mind that increases in Quotient values, intellectual or social, indicate that the child is moving faster in these areas than the rate of his chronological development, i.e., he may gain four or six months intellectually or socially in a three-month growth period. If he simply moves month for month the Quotient remains the same. If he moves at less than a month-per-month rate his Quotient will decrease; yet, even if this is true, he may be moving faster than he ever has in the previous years or months of his life. Thus, it is extremely important to note whether there is an increase in mental age (MA), since it may be increasing even though the Quotient is decreasing (see Connie, Table 3, in this regard).

The information given in the Tables in Chapter X includes chronological age of the child (CA), developmental age of the child (MA: mental age; AE: age equivalent), and Intelligence or Social Quotient after the inception of treatment. The scores on the Leiter International Performance Scale, which has a mean of 95 and a standard deviation of 20, have been subjected to linear transformation to equate them with the Stanford-Binet Scale which has a mean of 100 and a standard deviation of 16. No such comparison transformation is available for equating the Merrill-Palmer to the Stanford-Binet although the Merrill-Palmer is reported to correlate $0.79 \pm .019$ with the Binet (Freeman, 1962, p. 314).

Chapter X

"And Their Brand New Eyes Opened to a Brand New Morning!" (Péguy)

the evaluation of the subjects in treatment

In the preceding chapters, we have attempted, first, to present our understanding of the early infantile autistic behavior: This, we said, appeared to be a developmental arrest consequent to a low responsive capacity, in the child, to affective and sensory stimulations. Second, we outlined a plan of action aimed at breaking through the barrier of affective isolation in the autistic infant, and at reinstating conditions of learning and personality growth. Finally, we described the steps we took to achieve this, through a concerted effort which involved not only a professional therapeutic intervention, but also a concomitant ongoing educational effort by the parents and by school personnel. At this point then, we ask: What has this all accomplished? What have been the results of this intensive therapeutic and educational effort? On what basis can these results be evaluated and their validity assessed?

201

It is important to emphasize here that, in the discussion that follows, each child in the program is used, for purposes of developmental evaluation and measurement, as his own control. That is, we do not lump all the children together and average them out; each child, on the contrary, is compared only to himself in terms of affective, intellectual, social, and personality development. This will not prevent us from pointing out common developmental features in the children, but rather will help us focus on individual differences in the effects of our approach on the developmental process of the children in our program.

Another point which needs to be stressed here concerns the types of evaluations and measures which we used in our efforts at assessing, as objectively as we could, the personality growth of these autistic children throughout the period of treatment. We used developmental scales, behavior rating scales, standardized intelligence tests, therapy observation notes, home observation notes, and notes from the mothers and from the school teachers. It is clear that these data cannot be considered uniformly objective; the conviction they produce, however, increases with their concordance and convergence. That is to say, if several people who have the opportunity of observing the same child at different times and in different situations reach comparable conclusions, and if these conclusions agree with the objective test findings, the probability that the observations made and the conclusions reached are valid, and not grossly distorted by subjectivity, is very high. It may be argued, for instance, that in the evaluation of their child's progress the parents would be the most biased judges. But if one recalls that these parents had lived for many months and years with a child in whom they did not expect any real behavioral change, it will not be surprising that each moment of growth observed in their child will tend to be accepted with a certain degree of disbelief and skepticism. When these parents report observed changes in their child, and when these reported observations concur with observations made and reported by others, can we chalk all this up to subjective bias and parental overexpectation?

What then did we expect would happen to the autistic infant insistently alerted by the intensive therapeutic and educational stimulation which we imposed on its developmental arrest, and which we viewed as a developmental sleep? We expected the following: (a) A breakthrough in his affective isolation, that is, the child's behavior would change from a condition of aloofness, detachment, and indifference to the human environment, to one of interest and involvement in, responsiveness to, and reaching for, human others; and this would also be reflected in differentiated expressions of feelings and emotions. (*b*) Because of the intimate relationship which exists between affective experiences and learning, we expected that as the autistic child began experiencing situations in an affectively felt atmosphere, these situations would acquire meaning for him, so that his initiative and curiosity in seeking such situations would progressively provide him with a sequence of integrated and meaningfully associated experiences. (*c*) We expected, then, that the child's development would take place in all important areas of personality or ego functioning—motoric, adaptive, communicative, and social—basically along lines of normal personality development in children, although lacking at times total synchrony between areas.

SUMMARY

Age at Outset of Treatment: 2 years, 9 months.

Treatment Period: April 1965 to June 1967.

Schedule of Sessions: 3 hourly sessions per week on outpatient basis.

Drugs: None (Amphetamine tried for 10 days without appreciable effect on behavior).

Schedules of Testing and Results: Initial diagnostic evaluation, March 1965 (untestable, Vineland Social Quotient 31); tested at three-month intervals thereafter (see Table 2); final evaluation, April 1967, at age 4 years, 9 months (Vineland SQ 73; Stanford-Binet IQ 69: MA 3 years, 4 months; Leiter IQ 100: MA 4 years, 6 months).

Language: Initially mute and no receptive language; at end of treatment, full receptive language and expressive language developing at rapid rate and normally.

School Placement: Enrolled in private nursery school for normal children September 1966—currently enrolled in kindergarten.

We could have referred to Kathy as the "Cautious Kitten" for this expression would highlight most dramatically the developmental picture which is impressed upon us as we review the behavioral changes in her over the two years of intensive work with her. Of all the children in our group, Kathy represents undoubtedly the most "classic" case of Early Infantile Autism. The central characteristic of her behavior can be described as aloneness. She had established her life in complete isolation from the environment; indifferent and distant, she appeared to have no need for anyone, and whatever energies she had were used to preserve the stability of the limited physical environment in which she thoroughly isolated herself. This child was extremely terrified by change, by the new and the novel. She related neither to people—never looking at them, always looking through them—nor to objects. She refused to use her hands, except occasionally to pick up and then drop, or throw, an object; usually, she approached such objects by cautiously kicking at them. Her history was one of spending hours in her room, scratching at the wall, or flickering her fingers in front of lights, or staring at lights. She often rocked in her bed with such vigor as to move the bed halfway across the room. She never gave any indication of hunger, refused to feed herself, to chew bites, or to eat anything but junior foods. She would eat and drink only out of her own "special" plate and cup. Never did she drink water, just milk and orange juice, and these only at mealtimes. She was completely mute, and only on rare occasions uttered any sound at all. She showed no indications of having receptive language.

Such was Kathy when she came to us at the age of 2 years, 9 months. At that time, though we were able to obtain from the mother a Vineland Social Quotient on Kathy of 31 (age equivalent: 10 months—she could stand, she could walk, avoided simple obstacles and hazards, and didn't drool), it was impossible, completely terrified and overwhelmed as she was by the strangeness and newness of the testing situation, to obtain any scorable estimate of her developmental level (Cattell); furthermore, the Fels Child Behavior Rating Scales were, for the most part at this time, totally N/A (nonapplicable). In fact, we had at this time no objective basis from which to assess any developmental change in Kathy.

First six months of treatment. In the light of our theoretical postulates, our immediate goal became that of making Kathy affectively responsive to our presence by relentlessly and insistently making our presence felt by her. Surprisingly enough, the effects of such an intrusive and highly impactful affective contact on Kathy were immediately evident. It was as if Kathy had waited a long time to have somebody boldly and daringly, and yet sensitively and cautiously, penetrate the isolation that others had respected so much before, but which Kathy herself did not necessarily wish to preserve. From the mother's vantage point of an observer of the early therapy sessions, we have the following comments:

"There was almost immediate, noticeable improvement once Kathy's therapy sessions started. The sessions lasted an hour, and during that hour Kathy was simply not allowed to withdraw. If she started to stand and wave her hands in front of her eyes, Carole (the therapist) would take her hands and clap them. She stayed very close to Kathy all the time, so Kathy just couldn't go off and be by herself. She would have Carole right there with her. Carole had constant activity going, and she was very patient all the time as well. She was very aggressive, yet very affectionate towards Kathy.

"One early activity was learning to throw a ball. Carole wouldn't simply throw the ball, and then give the ball to Kathy and expect her to throw it. She would put the ball in Kathy's hand, clamp her fingers over the ball, and throw the ball with Kathy. After many trys and endless patience, Kathy would pick up the ball and toss it by herself.

"Kathy did a lot of kicking but had no awareness that she was hurting anyone or even which leg was kicking. Carole made her aware of her legs and kicking by exaggerating what Kathy was already doing, and by making a game out of it. She would stack up cardboard blocks, and have Kathy kick them all down while cheering her on.

"After Carole and Kathy were well acquainted, Dr. DesLauriers joined in the play sessions more often, and for a longer part of each session. The room was small, and with two people to play with, Kathy had no opportunity at all to withdraw."

It was only six months later (September, 1965) that it was possible to obtain some general estimate of Kathy's development through the Cattell; she obtained an IQ of 26 corresponding to a mental age of 10 months (chronologically she was 3 years, 2 months). We are using this word "estimate" advisedly, since this testing session consisted mostly, on the part of Kathy, of running about playfully and throwing to the floor nearly every object presented to her. The fact, however, that she could tolerate the presence of a total stranger in the therapy room with her, without any great fear or major panic, attests to the great strides she had made in overcoming her fears and her affective isolation in the preceding months. The emergence of the affective responsiveness in Kathy is well illustrated in the following excerpts from the mother's weekly notes, as well as from the therapy observation notes:

July 19, 1965 (three months after inception of treatment)—mother's notes: "Kathryn came out of her room carrying four things at once to play with. I didn't see how she managed to get it all picked up, but she had a good supply to play with.

"She is getting to be quite brave about climbing. Her stuffed animal was still in her crib, and she climbed up on the side and was trying to reach Fuzzy. She had to step up about two feet, and did so very well, and seemed to have no fear at all. This is very new. She has never tried to climb in or out of her crib before. . . .

"I think she is beginning to be able to show a little affection. When I get her up in the morning and hug her, she puts her cheek on mine and pushes. She smiles at me like she enjoys being loved and wants to return a little also."

On July 29, 1965, we read this note of the mother: "Kathryn fell down and bumped her knee that was already skinned. She cried this time and like always, I offered to hold her and comfort her and, as usual, she rejected my offer and left for her bedroom to cry alone in her pillow. Much to my surprise, she took only a few steps away, and then turned around and ran back to me with her little arms up to be taken. We rocked in the chair until she felt better, and I really don't know which one of us felt best."

During this same period (July 22, 1965), we read in the therapy notes: "For the first time, Carole placed a small doll on the table. As soon as Kathy came into the room, she grabbed the doll and knocked it on the floor. Obviously, she was intrigued by it. She soon got around to touching it with her hand through a series of stages: first with the back of her hand, then with a broad swipe of her hand, and finally touching it with her fingers. Then she picked up the doll by the head and started scooting around with it on the floor as though completely delighted, smiling, laughing, and affectionately bumping her head against the head of the doll. When Carole placed the doll on the floor in a sitting position, Kathy sat in front of it, and very purposely spread her own arms and legs in perfect imitation of the position of the doll."

On August 5, 1965, the therapy notes read: "This is a very active and interesting session, where both Kathy and Carole are together very much through the game of pulling against each other. Kathy makes a great deal of sounds; these are more modulated, mostly high pitched, with some cheek-puffing and some lip-moving." And on August 23: "Kathy's in fine spirits. The session begins with intimate tug-o-war. There is much squealing, giggling, half-laughing, and half-crying on the part of Kathy. She attacks the rag doll suspended on the hinge of the door, and after a short struggle gets it to fall down. She takes off her shoes by pushing the back of each with her foot. Carole steps on the toes of the socks and Kathy fights to pull her foot out. Kathy seems to have found out that she can put on a 'phony' cry in order to be held on Carole's lap."

During this period also, Kathy discovers her father; he seems somehow to have made a hit with her. On August 16, the mother writes: "Kathy's becoming more aware of herself. Her daddy likes to tickle her, and she has always been completely helpless, just squirming and giggling. Last night he was tickling her in the middle of the back and she giggled a lot, but also she put both of her hands over the place that was being tickled. I've never seen her take any defensive measures before.

"A room in disorder doesn't distress her so much any more. I reported a while back how upset she was when we painted our room and had the furniture out of place, and so forth. My husband's current project is the kitchen. Yesterday we took the curtains down, and he was working on the woodwork. I expected Kathryn to take off for her room, but instead she stayed with us and watched her daddy. He was standing on a small table, and she climbed up on a bench to watch better and 'smooch.' She was rubbing her cheek on his leg."

Thus, in six months, Kathy was happily coming out of her shell, and awakening in a delighted and affectionate way to the presence of important persons in her life. She was still rather uncooperative, as we mentioned earlier, when the Cattell Development Scale was administered; but on the Vineland Social Maturity Scale, we noticed a dramatic gain of 10 months, giving her a social quotient of 54 (age equivalent: 20 months).

Sixth through 18th month of treatment. The history of Kathy's response to formal testing in the next 12 months can be readily summed up: Kathy would have nothing to do with any standardized statistical evaluation of her personality growth. Part of this failure can be unhesitatingly credited to the monstrous ascendance of negativistic and oppositional attitudes in Kathy. All forms and varieties of such negativism, as described in the preceding chapter, she had cultivated with the fiendish relish of a gourmet intent on finding something wrong with each bite he savors. It was with Kathy mostly that during that period we learned to discover the step-by-step efforts of a child, in slow motion as it were, attempting to differentiate herself from others and assert her own identity. These were trying and frustrating months for all, and yet, from a developmental point of view, Kathy was far from standing still.

Another part of her failure in accepting any formal testing can be traced to our own blindness in not recognizing early enough, at that time, the complete age-inappropriate quality of most of the items on the Cattell Scale. We have discussed this question earlier (see the preceding section on testing of autistic children) and have come to recognize that the rejection by Kathy of such test items, far from representing an inability on her part to meet the task adequately, was on the contrary an expression of her having, so to say, transcended that level of infant activities. In this connection, it is not unusual, as many child psychologists will attest to, to see a bright baby at 20 months fail many items of 0–12-month range while passing items far beyond this 20-month age level. Thus, in insisting that, at 3 years, 5 months; 3 years, 9 months; 4 years; and 4 years, 3 months, Kathy be subjected to a measuring tool which was inappropriate for her, we were asking for exactly what we got: Kathy's contempt.

That Kathy remained untestable on any standardized measuring instrument for nearly a full year should not be construed, however, to mean that the promising development she had evidenced in the preceding six months had become arrested and blocked. On the contrary, the awakening process in Kathy appeared in all areas of personality functioning—motoric, perceptual, affective, and adaptive. Attesting to this developmental surge are notes from the mother, our own therapy notes, and approximately 10,000 feet of 16 mm. film. Excerpts from the mother's notes follow:

September 28, 1965: "Kathryn was unusually playful yesterday, and for a much longer period of time. She came to the living room and stayed most all afternoon. . . . She is letting her grandmother pick her up and hold her. . . . She has gotten quite interested in magazines. She pages through them and looks at pictures, and then she tears the pages out and wads them up so she can carry them. . . . We have a new problem at the table. When she finishes eating, she lifts herself up and shoves the big block off the chair. Then she stands on her chair and swings her foot over the table. . . . Mark (her brother) thought she was so funny, he just sat there and giggled, and that seemed to encourage Kathryn."

October 1, 1965: "In the afternoon I turned on the FM station for some music, and Kathryn came right up to the radio. When I got up she started to dance a little, and then put her arms up for me to take her and dance."

October 3, 1965: "For the first time, she has started to take notice of our telephone. She picked the receiver up four times and threw it down."

October 10, 1965: "Kathy has started another little game also. Mother and I were both reading in the living room. Several times Kathryn would run out to the door and wait for *both* of us to say 'Hi, Kathryn.' Then she would smile and laugh, and gayly run back to her room to return very soon for another round of greetings."

October 11, 1965: "Three years and three months is a very long time to wait for your little girl to give you a kiss, but it was worth waiting for. This morning I got her up, and she gave me a half-dozen kisses. I didn't think I could ever put her down and get her breakfast. After breakfast she gave me three more!"

October 20, 1965: "Today was just full of surprises! I came to Kathryn's room after breakfast and sat down on the bed beside her. She jumped up on her knees like the whole act had been a ruse. She cleared the bed, pushed me off, and put her legs up to play 'flip.' I played quite a while, then left her to get some housework done. A little before noon she came out to the kitchen, took my finger, and pulled towards the door (she wanted to go for a walk). She has never asked to walk before. The greatest thing happened after dinner—she was in her room, Mark was watching television, and my husband and I were in our room going through some papers. Suddenly we heard a lot of babbling and jabber (ya-ya, ma-ma and many unconsonanted noises). We tiptoed down the hall to listen, and there was Kathryn, jabbering away at a toy."

November 5, 1965: "What an afternoon! After lunch she came out in the living room and went on a regular rampage. She kicked, hit, pinched, made noises, and made herself a little impossible to manage. She started throwing things at me. Then the real shock came. She went to the kitchen, and I could hear her banging around; then silence. I came in to check, and no Kathryn. She had climbed down the basement stairs, and was busily scattering my washing over the floor. I carried her back up, and she turned around and went right back down—she has always been so frightened of the basement and never wanted to go down there —that she would go down by herself and want to stay just amazed me."

November 9, 1965: "Last night Kathryn showed a little interest in responding to discipline. The 'kitty litter' is behind a chair in the living room (great place!). Kathryn was climbing on the chair; she spied the litter box and got down and started around the chair. I said, 'No, Kathryn,' and she stopped for a moment, and then ran back to her room and cried. I was confused as to what to do next, as I was afraid she would stay in her room. She solved my dilemma by running back out to the chair and I again said, 'No, Kathryn,' and she left for her room but didn't cry. She repeated this several more times and finally gave up."

November 22, 1965: "I forgot to note this on Monday. Kathryn is making a little more progress in coming to us to make her wishes known. Sunday, she came out to the kitchen to get her daddy to go into her room to flip and toss her on the bed. She tugged and pulled at his leg, led him to her room, and then pushed him into position at the foot of the bed. She has never come to get him like this. . . .'"

November 29, 1965: "Kathryn and 'Kitty' are good friends now. The string pulling was a success. Kathryn runs with the string and Kitty's right after her, and both have fun. Kathryn has also taken a new interest in her brother. I noted last week that Mark started a 'chase' game with her. She really has gone overboard in her enthusiasm. She is after Mark all the time to chase her."

December 2, 1965: "We had a wonderful time with Kathryn this evening, and she was so happy and having so much fun that she cried when we finally put her in her crib. She *never* has cried when put to bed before."

December 13, 1965: "I put mustard on her thumb, and she now likes mustard. (We had suggested this as a possible device for keeping Kathy from sucking her thumb!) She wiped as much off as she could, studied her thumb very carefully, put it in her mouth, removed it and made a face, put it back in. End of tale."

December 17, 1965: "She is really interested in the Christmas decorations. I pointed out balls on the Christmas tree for her, and she looked at each one as I pointed. Then I took her to the kitchen window and pointed to the lights outside along the eaves. She looked right where I pointed and smiled. . . . Last year she was terribly frightened of the tree, and wouldn't even notice anything outside."

December 20, 1965: "Kathryn has been standing in front of the Christmas tree and making lots of sounds. She just 'talks and talks' to the tree, and it really gets sad. If she just had some words! She wants to say something so much and just can't get the words out."

December 28, 1965: "Kathryn had a wonderful Christmas, and she made it such a happy day for all of us. On Christmas morning Mark was up first and had the packages all separated into piles. He had the living room pretty well filled up, and Kathryn didn't want to go in there, so I took her presents one by one to her room. The first was one of those weighted-bottom, plastic things that you hit and it bounces back up. I started to open it from the top, and she got the idea and opened the rest of it all by herself. She accepted it right away, kicked and pushed it, and laughed when it came back up."

When Kathy had this Christmas, her first truly happy Christmas, she had been in treatment 70 hours. It is obvious that far from standing still, she had acquired in the variety and tempo of her behavior the curiosity and initiative which is typical of personality growth in any child. A brand new world seemed to be opening up to her, and though she still approached any new situation with the cautiousness of a kitten ready to jump back at the slightest indication of danger, her zest for fun and play gave her the driving courage to attempt anything at least once. Her involvement and interest in so many different things at home, through which was expressed the emerging need in her to relate and communicate with others, never diminished, however, her intrenched need for independence. She did only what she wanted to do, and only when she was ready to do it. The various forms of negativistic behavior during this period, which so frequently challenged the patience and steadfastness of both the therapists and the parents, stand out as a solid monument to the child's determination to retain the basic foundation of her separated and differentiated self. She seemed quite willing to give up her isolation and find, in the support and rewarding qualities of warm and affectionate human contacts, sufficient reason to reach for others, and establish with them the type of communication that made her feel alive and happy to be with them. But with each step, it was as if she needed to reassure herself that in giving up her isolation, she was not giving up her independence.

In the months between her "first" Christmas and the following September, when it was finally possible to obtain from her the type of co-operation needed in a successful testing situation, Kathy put everyone through what a harassed mother would call "the wringer." Any time she sensed that the therapists or the parents wanted or expected a special bit of behavior from her, she definitely went about frustrating them. This was the period when she learned what "no-no" meant. In the therapy room, a black wire was strung out from a microphone set on the table to the next room where recordings of her behavior were being made. Kathy had never bothered with this wire, until she discovered that the therapist liked it that way. Then, with the fiendish zeal of an experimental psychologist demonstrating the effects of a maximum stress situation, she used every opportunity to test out how long the therapist could stand the forbidden and relentless exploration on her part of that black wire. The same behavior was true, also, with regard to her snatching up and throwing across the room a bar of soap which she had been told to let be. For a long time, to assert herself and show us how much she felt that this bar of soap was the symbol of her defiance of rules and regulations, her first move upon entering the therapy room would be to dash across to the sink, grab the soap, and gleefully fling it with a vengeance. The therapist's "no-no, Kathy," and Kathy's silent, and yet mischievously expressive, "What are you going to do now?" resounded alternately in the room for many weeks. We were at that time somewhat reluctant to impose on Kathy any form of forceful discipline, which we were as yet unsure she could understand clearly. Fortunately, she did see our point and became more compliant to our requests. Kathy, however, never surrendered unconditionally. She complied with us, but when her parents were asked to join her in the therapy room for an observation period, she once more asserted her triumphant stand by making a beeline for the soap dish, grabbing the bar, and giving it a vigorous fling.

Her negativism was not all defiant, however. Frequently it was her way of slowly assimilating and accommodating herself to a new experience. Kathy, for instance, had very little interest in putting things into her mouth; her first exploration of any new object was always with her feet. She didn't even like candy. It was important, however, that Kathy give more attention to her mouth, that she discover its existence and its function. Ultimately she would have to use it not only for eating, but for all forms of verbal communications. Thus, we set ourselves to the task of helping Kathy discover her mouth. First we had to awaken her interest in a suitable object which could be introduced in her mouth in a playful and nonfrightening way; we chose a lollipop. This, the therapist could hold and offer to Kathy in moments when she could easily associate this experience with some other ongoing pleasurable activity. Soon Kathy became intrigued by this lollipop which the therapist at various times would rapidly introduce into Kathy's mouth and just as quickly withdraw. We had her interest now, but she still wasn't sure of this new object. In the weeks that followed this mild form of "shaping," Kathy made sure that the lollipop was safe. Every time she came to the clinic, she expected the therapist, who by that time had become thoroughly addicted to lollipops in all flavors, to have one available for her. Not that she was ready to have it in her mouth; she just thought it was a great game to see the therapist lick away at it, and time and time again quickly give Kathy a small lick. For all practical purposes, though, she still refused to have and keep the lollipop in her mouth. It was at this point that the therapist invented for her the game of "reverse-negativism." Exploiting Kathy's interest and curiosity "lollipop-wise," the therapist would draw Kathy's attention to the lollipop, then make "as if" she were going to offer it to Kathy, and then "as if" thinking better of it, decide not to give it to Kathy and keep it for herself. The game was on, a game called "The last thing in the world I want you to have is this lollipop." Therapy notes describe one such session (February 10, 1966): "Therapist takes out a lollipop while Kathy expectantly watches. Therapist then goes through act of not letting Kathy have it; that is, hiding it behind her back, while looking to make sure that Kathy is quite aware of what is happening to the lollipop. Kathy follows it around. At different moments, therapist takes a quick lick of the lollipop, while at the same time shielding the candy with her hand or turning around to hide it, and making loud 'yum-yum' noises. Then therapist, as if thinking better of it, pretends to start to offer it to Kathy, but then again pretends to change her mind and withdraws. By this time Kathy is so thoroughly intrigued with the lollipop that she's mildly panicked at the thought that she might never see it again. So she starts wanting it; she will not, even if it takes all her courage, let it escape from her. She backs up to it; leans her face closer and closer to the lollipop, keeping her eyes tightly closed, as if she couldn't bear the thought of seeing herself give in. Finally, Kathy reaches for the therapist's hand, which shields the lollipop, and pulls it away to expose the 'forbidden fruit.' The lollipop is still not hers, however. So she reaches out and pulls the other hand, the hand with the lollipop, toward her, so that she can pull away from it, and yet allow it to touch her mouth several times. This, for Kathy, expresses her basic position in life, to wit: How to win a lollipop without losing face."

There were many such sessions, and Kathy not only discovered her mouth as a receptacle for lollipops, but also as the instrument with which she could blow on the therapist's hair and face, and from which she could make a variety of sounds in constantly attempting to imitate the therapist. The game of reverse-negativism was not successful, however, when we attempted to use it to entice Kathy into playing puzzle games. Obviously, the intrinsic fun value of puzzle pieces was insufficient to retain Kathy's attention or interest. We had to invent some other game. First we had to bring Kathy to the point where she would sit in a chair long enough—and find pleasure in doing so—to have a chance to see for herself how a puzzle could be put together. To achieve this, we transformed a "swinging" game which she loved dearly into a sitting and swinging game. Instead of swinging Kathy from a standing position, we made clear to her that she would have to quietly sit in a chair, and wait for the therapists to swing her from that position. She caught on to this very readily, and we in turn exploited her cooperative attitude by having her sit at a table where the puzzle was laid out in front of her. Still, Kathy had no interest in the puzzle-pieces, and any attempt on our part to have her place a piece usually resulted in her contemptuously and defiantly throwing it to the floor. But at least she was sitting there long enough to see the puzzle, and she understood quite well what we wanted of her. She wanted to swing and, therefore, she sat; we wanted her to do the puzzle and, therefore, we had to combine swinging and puzzle-solving. This, then, turned out to be the new game. Any attempt, in any way, which Kathy condescended to make as far as any positive move in the direction of solving the puzzle, was accompanied, supported, and cheered on by the dramatic display on our part of what might be called a "really swinging scene."

It is important to emphasize again that our main concern in setting up the stage, so to say, for bringing Kathy to the point where she could solve a puzzle, was not directed so much at teaching her puzzle solving, any more than the lollipop game was intended to teach her how to lick a lollipop. Rather, our efforts here were aimed at helping Kathy overcome her fears in the discovery and mastery of new skills and new functions. Thus, throughout this puzzle-solving–swinging sequence, what we tried to maintain and encourage in Kathy was the pleasant feeling that could be part of anything she did, or any discovery she made. That Kathy truly sensed this is illustrated by the fact that, the more often she was successful at solving puzzles (because our game really paid off), the less frequently did she demand that her successes be "rewarded" by a swinging scene. She became intrigued by the puzzles and, smilingly, became enthralled by her own masterful capacity to put together the pieces of a variety of puzzles. Time and time again, after successfully completing one of these, she would turn to us and beam, and then turn back to her accomplishment as if to say, "Isn't that neat?"

It was in the same context, and within the same affective climate, that we helped Kathy get acquainted with words and speech. As she lovingly and delightedly looked upon any picture she had put together in her puzzle-solving efforts, we told her what the picture was about, using those words that are so appropriate for a child's frame of reference: Every lady was "mama," every man was "daddy," and so forth; and each mama and daddy had a face with eyes, a nose, a mouth, ears, hair, and so forth; just like Kathy had eyes, a nose, a mouth, and so forth; and just like Carole had eyes, a nose, a mouth, and so forth. And they had also, all of them, arms, hands, fingers, legs, feet, toes, just like Kathy and Mommy and Daddy and Carole. To learn words, for Kathy, at whatever rate she was ready to learn them, should be a meaningful experience and a playful one, where, in an atmosphere of delightful discovery, each word would make real sense to her. Needless to say, each approximation which Kathy might make of a word was cheered on by us with a great display of affection, and a wild dancing or swinging scene. Kathy, however, at this stage was still not ready to say too many words.

During that summer (July, August, 1966), we attempted to enlarge Kathy's "possession of the world" by offering her an opportunity to master some of the outdoor games of children. As often as we could, when the weather permitted it, we took her to a nearby playground where swings, slides, monkey bars, and tunnels were available. Kathy enjoyed running through the grass on our way there; she would pick and sniff flowers along the way, the smile in her eyes reflecting her complete delight. Therapy notes of July 14th describe a "session" at the playground: "We tried the swings first and it became obvious that Kathy was too frightened, and she would swing only if allowed to sit on Carole's lap; so we dropped this activity very quickly. Next we tried the 'jungle gym.' Kathy would climb up on this a little, holding Carole's hands, but again it was evident that she was not sure enough of herself to find any great fun in this activity. So next we tried the slides. This was a tremendous success in short order. We lifted her up to the top of the small slide and as she slid down one of us caught her at the bottom. She had that wide-eyed, frightened, but mostly delighted, look on her face, and she wanted this game repeated immediately. The following move was to get her to climb to the top of the steps herself. Kathy was quite willing to try her luck on this, provided the therapist either preceded or followed her up the steps. Very shortly, as soon as she reached the bottom of the slide, Kathy, after kicking the gravel to raise a bit of dust, would run to the steps and climb up the slide by herself; this gravel-kicking ritual seemed to work as a tension releasing device, so that she became less and less frightened. Other children were enjoying the playground also; upon seeing them climbing the big slide (about 20 feet in height), Kathy ran over to them, and when the therapist started up the steps she followed. At the top, he sat her on his lap and both went down; she thought that was great! The next time she climbed up first and, encouraged by the therapist, had her first solo performance on the big slide."

The next time we took Kathy to the park (August 1), her mother came along; and that day, as if to show off in front of her mother and possibly also reassure her that fears can be overcome, Kathy willingly sat by herself on a swing and, strapped in, allowed herself to be pushed, smiling to herself while she eyed the big slide which would be the next event for her that day.

Kathy's capacity to generalize such experiences to other similar situations is well illustrated by her mother's notes (August 14): "We found a play park not too far from here and rode over after dinner tonight. We should have taken the movie camera! Kathy took a turn on the chair swing, the belt swing, and a horse swing. Then she went on the merry-go-round and down the slide several times, and climbed up on a train made out of iron rods. Then we climbed through a tunnel, and she did much better than I did. She didn't seem to be at all afraid and was eager to try out everything, but yet she was cautious, and kept close watch to see that I was with her. She enjoyed watching other children a lot more than she usually has. A couple of girls were winding up on the swings and then spinning, and Kathy really got a bang out of watching them. She laughed and laughed.

"When we got home, she headed right for the back yard and the 'tree house.' She needs a little help to climb up there. The stairs are straight up and down instead of at an angle like the slides. When she got down from the tree house, she ran to the fence and started climbing it. That is a new 'first' for her. She is getting to be a regular monkey. She was doing more climbing of the basement stairs today alone. Climbing has sure generalized!!"

This, then, was Kathy by September of that year; affectionate and responsive; independent and negativistic; frightened but wide-awake to the discovery of her widening world; capable of greater attention span and motor control; not really speaking, but obviously understanding much of what was said to her and delightedly trying out articulated sounds. She had made great strides in toilet training and had given up diapers. She had been enrolled in nursery school, and was ready for new adventures and new progress. Mostly, from our research point of view, she was ready to be tested, though Dr. Krall at the time thought we had lost our minds in asking that the Merrill-Palmer be administered to Kathy; she acceded to our request especially since, having met with another complete failure on the Cattell, she felt she had nothing to lose in trying out the Merrill-Palmer Test Scales.

"Kathy was able to attend to test items and responded to them for the most part without negativism [writes Dr. Krall]. The items were administered between swings by the therapists. This kept the testing for the most part full of excitement and surprise for Kathy. As a result of this method of administration, Kathy could be persuaded to do all items judged to be within her mental age range."

The results were only slightly less than astounding. On the Merrill-Palmer Scale of Mental Tests, at the age of 4 years, 3 months, Kathy's scores gave her a mental age of 3 years, 10 months, and an IQ of 90. All items requiring verbalizations (such as Items number 4 and number 19, Questions: What does a doggy say? and so forth; Items number 9 and number 12, Repetition of Words: Kitty, ball, birdie, and so forth) were "omitted" as is provided for in the administration of this scale. Only three items were scored "refused," and these were at level 18 to 23 months (Item number 1, Commands; Item number 2, Throwing a Ball; Item number 11, Folding Paper). She based at Item number 14 (last item before her first failure) and achieved a total count of 59, which represents a mental age of 46 months. Of the 13 Items within her own chronological age (51 months) level (48 to 53 months), she passed 7 and failed 4 (2 were "omitted"); her failures were on Items involving buttoning two and four buttons, and on building a six-cube pyramid. Her successes, however, went beyond her age level; she passed three Items at the 54- to 59-months level (Manikin; Picture Puzzle number 2; Mare and Foal); this latter Item (Mare and Foal) was successfully completed also at the 60- to 65-months level.

Her Vineland Score at that time gave her a Social Quotient of 54 (age equivalent 2 years, 4 months). In this connection Dr. Krall writes: "Kathy's mother and I discussed why Kathy functions below the Merrill-Palmer on social tasks. There are a number of things that Kathy could do that she is either not encouraged to do, or about which she becomes negativistic; for example, washing and drying her hands, undressing, eating with a fork, cutting with scissors. We also discussed verbalizing Kathy's wants and activities, to further encourage verbal comprehension and speech."

Eighteenth through 21st month of treatment. In the next three months, Kathy gained eight months on the Vineland, giving her a Social Quotient of 67. This impressive increase in social competence can be attributed, in great part, to Kathy's participation during that time in nursery school activities. This experience not only brought her in contact with other children but also introduced her to cooperative games and a greater degree of self sufficiency. She also acquired a wider range of receptive language, so that we felt that she was ready to be tested with a greater variety of standardized instruments.

At 4 years, 6 months, Kathy obtained an IQ of 55 (mental age 2 years, 7 months) on the Stanford-Binet. Kathy, without expressive language, was severely handicapped on this test. It was necessary to go down to the 20-months level on the Cattell—which contains no expressive verbal items—to establish a base. Likewise she reached a ceiling at the 4-year, 6-month level which contains only verbal items. Repetition of the Merrill-Palmer indicated the reliability of the test in measuring her developing intellectual functions; she obtained a mental age of 4 years, 1 month, which gave her an IQ of 93. This time, however, the basal was at Item number 41, and the total count was 64. She succeeded in one (Manikin) of the three Items at the 61- to 71-months level (upper limit of Scale), and the higher basal score of 41, compared to her previous basal at Item 14, indicated considerable consolidation of developmental gains.

The introduction of the Leiter International Scale at this point was an attempt on our part to assess on a broader range, and without the handicap of expressive language, the validity of the scores obtained on other intelligence tests, and also to measure Kathy's level of conceptual development. This nonverbal test has also the great advantage, as indicated earlier, of being untimed, which allows for a more complete estimate of the child's true intellectual potential. Kathy, on this test, achieved an IQ (corrected to S-B mean of 100 and S-D of 16) of 94; she based at 3 years and reached her ceiling at 6 years. At year 4 she gained six months in mental age, passing two tests, Form and Color and Eight Forms, while failing Counts Four and Form, Color, Number. At the 5-year age level, she also gained six months by passing Genus and Two Color Circles, but failing Clothing and Block Design.

Obviously, Kathy was holding her own, but her overall development, mainly because of her lack of expressive language, remained uneven.

Twenty-first through 24th month of treatment. In her final evaluation (April, 1967), two years after the beginning of treatment, Kathy, at the age of 4 years, 9 months appears still to be progressing. Notes from the mother give us a glimpse of Kathy's emerging personality at this time.

April 16, 1967: "Kathy is showing a lot of interest in flowers and gets a real thrill out of following us around the yard. She wants to learn the names of everything she sees, and the colors of the flowers. I picked a violet for her, and showed her how to smell it, and that was real sweet! She put it up to both John and me for a smell too, and then carried it around with her to sniff at now and then. I'm really looking forward to this summer with Kathy. We had lots of fun with her last summer, but at the same time there was a constant effort on our part to keep her with us, and keep her interest and enthusiasm alive. I don't quite know how to explain it, but I just feel like she now wants to be an active member of the family and will be with us whatever we are doing.

"This morning we had a hail storm, and Kathy was so interested! She looked out her window and then out our window, and then the living-room window. She just had to check every view, and she wanted me to tell her about it. John went after some nails and screws, and for the first time Kathy waved bye-bye to him from the window. He sure looked surprised!

"The jabber continues and increases, and is more often directed to one of us than just a monologue. I accidentally pulled her hair when I tied her bib on her and she said: 'Ow! Don't pull!' I about fell over!"

April 24, 1967: "We went up to the Aquarium yesterday to look at the fish. Kathy was so interested, pointed and jabbered, and wanted to have a closer look almost all the time! I learned a lot about fish just to keep up a conversation with her! I thought just big fish, like sharks, had teeth, but Kathy noticed teeth quite often. She would point to her teeth and the fishes teeth—ditto for nose, eyes, mouth. Some fish made her laugh and nearly every fish brought on some jabber. She was every bit as interested and 'with it' as any child there, and maybe even more so. I know we spent more time studying and talking about each exhibit than anyone else; we were always passed up. She liked to sit on the railing so she could see better. I'm really anxious for our trip to the zoo this summer. She was saying 'fish' and 'fins' too, along with all the other jabber."

May 5, 1967: "Today was the Hawaiian Luau at Nursery School, and Kathy came home with a sack of 'loot' and in good shape, though a little tired. She had a little Japanese fan which quite intrigued her. She just now came out and fanned the cat, and went back to her room saying, 'fan!' I just heard her blow on her Hawaiian flute all by herself a couple of times. Mark showed her how it worked, and I stuck it in her mouth and told her to blow. She did and now is doing it on her own. I showed her how the fan spreads apart, and we chatted about the pretty flowers on it, and then she wanted Mark and I to leave so she could

further study her new toys. It is really delightful to see her take immediate interest in new toys and play with them in a normal way!"

Kathy obviously is reaching at this time for "normality." An increase
of seven points on her Vineland Social Quotient, age equivalent 3 years,
6 months, reflects again the earnestness with which she seems to be attempting to make up for the time she has lost (she gained an extra three
months during this period).

On her final Leiter test, she showed definite improvement compared
to three months previously. Her IQ increased from 94 to 100, which
over a period of three months was an increase of six months in mental
age. She gained three months at year 4 on Form, Color, Numbers which
she had failed earlier; and three months at year 5 on Clothing which she
had missed before. As in her first performance on the Leiter, she based
at year 3 and ceilinged at year 6, thus demonstrating no drop or fluctuation in what had been established, but rather an increase in the scope
of her conceptual development.

Excerpts from Dr. Krall's test report state: "Kathy varied in her behavior during the tests to some extent during one session. She put her
knees up to her chin and did not want to engage in the testing. But
during most of the sessions, she related in an attentive and interested
fashion. Her early negativism seems to have largely given way to cooperation and interest in activities for themselves. She could be tested this
time without any other person being present [sic]. . . .

"On the Leiter, the Mental Age score increased from 4–0 to 4–6 and
resultant IQ from 87 to 95 (not corrected for comparison with the Binet).
The items added are Form, Color, Number, and Clothing, reflecting both
increased attention and some improvement in concept formation."

Kathy's performance on the Stanford-Binet also reflected a dramatic
increase from a mental age of 2 years, 7 months to a mental age of 3
years, 4 months, giving her at this time on the Binet an IQ of 69. Thus,
on this test, Kathy gains, in mental age, nine months over a chronological growth period of three months. Her basal level was placed at 3 years
since she passed five of the six subtests, missing only the verbal Picture
Vocabulary. At 3 years, 6 months, she passed the only two nonverbal
items, Patience: Pictures and Sorting Buttons, for two months credit.
At year 4 she passed the only nonverbal item, Discrimination of Forms,
for one month credit. She failed all items, which are all verbal, at year
IV–6, but passed one item at year V, Patience: Rectangles. The second
ceiling was established at year VI, which is entirely verbal in content.
It may be argued that with regard to the Stanford-Binet test, a prac-

tice effect may be operating here in the increase we see in Kathy's scores. Control studies have indicated that such a practice effect appears to be present whenever the Stanford-Binet is repeated at intervals of less than six months. There are, however, definite limitations to the magnitude of the increase expected from practice. (See Freeman, 1962.) In Kathy's case, an increase of nine months over a period of three months goes far beyond any expected gain to be accounted for by practice alone (usually on the order of 2 months.) Furthermore, what has to be understood here is that those ego functions which are being measured by the items of the Stanford-Binet test as well as by the other tests used here are products just as much of maturational factors in development as they may be of learning experiences. A child of 4 years, 9 months *cannot* usually, with *any* amount of practice, for example, draw a diamond (S-B-level VII) unless he is unusually precocious in the area of visual motor development. Kathy obviously was progressing at a much faster rate developmentally than could have been predicted on the basis of normal chronological statistical expectations. And with specific reference to the Stanford-Binet, when we compare it to her performance on the Leiter, her struggle with the acquisition of expressive language remains crucial to any increment in her performance on this test.

At the end of her second year of treatment, Kathy appeared well on her way to catching up with a level of functioning normal for her age group. Her greatest handicap remained her lack of expressive verbal and language achievements; in the past 12 months, especially, she had made great strides in this respect, but she had still not developed a truly effective vocabulary of words to communicate her needs or assert her presence. Her receptive language, on the other hand, was broad enough now to permit her to respond appropriately to most demands, to follow accurately most instructions, and, in short, to be, as her mother indicated, a full-fledged member of the family.

Ratings of her behavior in a variety of situations at home, and at the clinic, underscore the steady and, at times, dramatic direction of her personality development. On all of the 15 scales (see Table 1) which we extracted from the 30 Fels Behavior Rating Scales (because of their specific relevance to assessing changes from idiosyncratically autistic behavior to patterns of behavior more in line with normal functioning in a child) Kathy showed significant improvement. (This was true in the ratings of all four raters and the Friedman Two-way Analysis of Variance applied to the ratings was significant, in this respect, at the .001 level;

Table 1

Fels Behavior Scales	Characteristics Measured
1.1 Affectionateness:	Affective contact and responsivity
1.2 Aggressiveness:	Assertion of self; effort to get others to do his bidding
1.5 Cheerful-depressed:	Affective responsivity
1.7 Conformity:	Indication of learning; imitation; interest in and awareness of others
2.11 Curiosity:	Breaking away from sameness
3.11 Emotional excitability:	In either direction affective responsivity
3.14 Friendliness:	Indication of awareness of and interest in others
3.15 Gregariousness:	Indication of awareness of and interest in others
3.22 Obedience:	Awareness of standards; awareness of loved person; desire to please
4.1 Patience:	Self-control; ego development; frustration tolerance
5.1 Planfulness:	Intelligence; learning
6.1 Negativism:	Normal development; assertion of self; establishment of boundaries and limits; implies also awareness of others
7.1 Sense of humor:	Affective responsivity
8.2 Suggestibility:	Conformity; learning, obedience
8.3 Tenacity:	Ego control; frustration tolerance

see Appendix.)* Because Kathy was our first case—our "pilot"—these scales, as well as the home observations, were not introduced until the beginning of the second year of treatment. Qualitative inspection of the actual ratings before ranking them for statistical analysis, reflected clearly that Kathy showed the greatest amount of improvement on the following scales, which we have grouped here according to the common aspects of development they are believed to reflect:

* This is especially significant since all four raters observed the children under different conditions and for different and varying periods of time. Nevertheless, for Kathy as well as for all the other children (with the exception of Connie who was withdrawn from the program before the end of one year), statistical analysis (Friedman Test) of the ratings on the Fels scales indicated a pattern of significant change in all children by all four raters beyond the .001 level of confidence. In view of this established statistical (quantitative) significance of the direction of the changes on the Fels scales, our discussion of the scales will focus on the more qualitative aspects of these changes.

1. Affectionateness (1.1) and Sense of Humor (7.1): affective contact, sensitivity and responsiveness to people.
2. Friendliness (3.14) and Gregariousness (3.15): awareness of others (also sensitivity and responsiveness to others).
3. Obedience (3.22) and Suggestibility (8.2): conformity, awareness of standards (and of others), learning.
4. Curiosity (2.11) and Planfulness (5.1): intelligence, breaking away from repetition of sameness and autistic preoccupation.
5. Patience (4.1) and Tenacity (8.3): self-control, frustration tolerance, ego development.

Regarding the remaining scales, Aggressiveness (1.2) and Cheerful-Depressed (1.5) were rated relatively high to begin with, since the most dramatic changes in these areas were made during the first year. Conformity (1.7) increased, but not too dramatically! Kathy liked her independence. Negativism (6.1) showed some variations, but can possibly best be described at this point as a function of expediency or mood; that is, negativism now is rarely defensive or fearful; rather, it is attention-seeking opposition or self-assertive type of opposition. Finally, Emotional Excitability (3.11) clearly increased, but here we can still see definite residues of the high threshold of sensitivity so characteristic of the autistic syndrome.

Thus, as we look back at the mass of data which we accumulated of Kathy's behavior during the two years of efforts made at overcoming her autistically arrested development, the various sources of empirical observations and measurements converge in one direction: Kathy is truly awakening to a meaningful experience of life. In this awakening, we have the refreshing sight of what seems to be in some respects a time-lapse moving picture of a step-by-step emergence of the child's personality. What seems so easy for a normal child, and what we so freely take for granted, in the growth, the organization, and the integration of ego functions as products of motivation and learning, takes on, in Kathy, the appearance of a slowly deliberate and, at times, painful process. Her awakening takes time, as if each part of her self needs to be discovered and fitted into its proper place. Each new experience demands of her new courage to assimilate; driving initiative to pursue and accommodate to; and long pauses during which she appears to rehearse her responses before performing them. She still retains the cautious kitten quality of her original approach to the world around her, though she may lead some observers at times to call her Dennis the Menace! But she is now very much part of this world.

Table 2
KATHY

	Initial Evaluation	Months in Treatment						
		6 Months	9 Months	1 Year	1 Year 3 Months	1 Year 6 Months	1 Year 9 Months	2 Years
Chronological age	2 years 9 months	3 years 2 months	3 years 5 months	3 years 9 months	4 years	4 years 3 months	4 years 6 months	4 years 9 months
Vineland	SQ 31 AE 10m.	SQ 54 AE 20m.	SQ 53 AE 22m.	SQ 50 AE 22m.	SQ 48 AE 2 yr	SQ 54 AE 2–4	SQ 67 AE 3 yr	SQ 73 AE 3–6
Cattell	Untestable	IQ 26 MA 10m.	Untestable-negativism—tests age-inappropriate					
Stanford-Binet							IQ 55 MA 2–7	IQ 69 MA 3–4
Merrill-Palmer						IQ 90 MA 3–10	IQ 93 MA 4–1	
Leiter							IQ 94 MA 4–1	IQ 100 MA 4–6

Connie

SUMMARY

Age at Outset of Treatment: 5 years, 1 month.

Treatment Period: December 1965 to November 1967.

Schedule of Sessions: 3 hourly sessions per week on outpatient basis.

Drugs: Mellaril and Atarax advised by pediatrician to relieve pain and irritability caused by spastic bowel condition.

Schedule of Testing and Results: Initial diagnostic evaluation, December 1965 (Vineland SQ 22; Cattell IQ 8: MA 5.2 months); tested at three-month intervals thereafter (see Table 3); final evaluation, October 1966, at age 6 years (Vineland SQ 30; Cattell IQ 12: MA 8.4 months).

Language: None and little improvement in expressive but definite improvement in receptive language.

School Placement: Prior to treatment had been enrolled in private nursery school for normal children (because mother was teaching there) and continued during period of treatment.

We were all sad and disappointed when Connie was taken out of the project. She had been with us just 11 months, and we were not at all prepared for such an abrupt termination. Just one week before, Connie's mother, in her note to us—the last one, as it turned out—had sounded so encouraged and so encouraging to us: "Connie has been much more cheerful—less crying and irritability—since she's been on Atarax. It still makes her sleepy and I have been adjusting the dosage downward 'til she gets over it. When she does have irritable spells, I think they're tantrums more than anything else. . . . Facility on the stairs slowly improves. Interest in toys has remained about the same since last note. She does seem to try to get our attention more with grunts and facial expressions. There is more looking at you than thru you. . . . She has been very verbal the last two weeks, and she sings quite a bit. The other day at the clinic she saw a girl filling a pitcher at a waterfont; she went there and made a sound which I knew indicated she wanted water. I lifted her up and she drank quite a bit. This is a first. Her father has noticed a difference in her crying. It seems to be changing from an open-mouthed infantile

226

cry that can indicate most anything, to a more meaningful thing to indicate she is tired, mad, and so forth. . . . I think I told you in my last note that she was no longer getting out of bed since we moved her furniture around. This kept her from getting out on the right side which was the only side she ever got out. This past week she has started getting out again, on the left side! The only way she can! I observed her one morning, and noticed she actually had difficulty maneuvering her body to get out on this side (the left side). Her feet kept going over the footboard, which is slightly higher than the mattress. She would crawl forward, and maneuver to the left with difficulty, and try again with the same results. Her feet would hit the footboard. After about four tries, she finally got the feet over the left side and got out. She gets out of bed by sliding backward on her tummy, feet first. . . . Her appetite has somewhat diminished the past few weeks. It doesn't concern me, because I think she's well padded; but I wonder if the Atarax may be the reason for this, or maybe it's just a phase. . . . She demolishes her Cheerios in the morning almost like a pro, and with a spoon! She expects us to use the spoon! She seldom digs in with her fingers any more, even if I'm not looking. I put the spoon in the bowl to begin with, and she takes it from there!"

In this note, Connie appeared to be holding her own at home, showing some independence, some initiative and ingenuity, and progressively mastering some simple social skills. There were no indications she would be withdrawn from the program shortly afterwards. Even our own last therapy note had sounded optimistic: "This note (November 14) summarizes a full week's therapy. In this period we were gratified that a number of important changes were apparently taking place in the parents' attitude toward Connie's treatment, and with respect to their own family relationship. First, both parents read a current monograph on Early Infantile Autism, and they had questions about the book. . . . Second, the mother brought us extensive notes for the first time since the beginning of Connie's therapy. Third, both parents appear to have started enjoying life a little more, by planning a weekend at South Bend to see Notre Dame football; they are also planning a vacation to Louisville in the near future. Our impression is that life may begin to be good for them! . . . Concomitantly, Connie's progress has been most impressive in these past sessions. Pursuing our efforts at increasing her attention span, her retention, and her muscular control, we placed her beloved banana candies inside a small cage, so that she could see the candies. The cover on this cage can be lifted like a small top door tied down by an elastic hinge. Connie's task was to learn how to lift the cover, make sure it stayed open, reach into the cage, and retrieve the candy. Connie had some difficulty meeting all these requirements but was very persistent in her attempts until she was successful. We noticed, however, Connie's uneasy reaction to our swinging her seemed to have led to a much clearer, purposive, and aggressive attempt at solving the riddle of the 'cage.' It was as if Connie, in her effort at protesting against our swinging her, would become angry enough to express herself in very directed, intentional, and meaningful, controlled action. Thus, she was able, in those moments following her "swing," to march over and retrieve her candies without fumbling over the lid, or fumbling over the candy inside the cage. . . . In the past 10 days, then, Connie has shown increased attention, self-control, appropriate affect, and effective motor coordination. We took some movies of this which should help illustrate our procedure."

That Connie, at this point in her treatment, should be removed from the program caught us completely by surprise. It is true that, from the beginning, Connie had presented a number of special problems. First of all, she was the oldest one of our subjects, coming into this project at the age of 5 years, 1 month, after having been through a variety of diagnostic evaluations (see Chapter VII), and when her parents were finding it extremely painful to maintain any hope for her. Secondly, after we had satisfied ourselves, as well as we could, that her behavior could best be understood as that of an early infantile autistic child, we were confronted with the fact that this behavior in Connie had acquired, over the years, an inveterate quality, a sort of chronic habituation, which was constantly reinforced by the inconsistent and erratic pattern of communication and handling with which her parents dealt with her. When we first saw Connie, her behavior could be characterized as including restless hypermotility; ritualistic clasping and unclasping of the hands; no eye contact with anyone in her environment and no meaningful affective involvement with others; an incapacity for any independent activity such as feeding herself, walking up or down the stairs, controlling her bowel movements, and so forth. She was flaccid and limp whenever we tried to lift her up; she didn't resist and stiffen, she just withered and collapsed. She had no verbal communication except raucous sounds accompanied by constant grinding of her teeth, and she blew saliva bubbles in a razzing sort of way as if to say: Not another series of treatments!

Withal, there was an engaging quality about her which made us confident that we would enjoy working with her. Yet we knew also that the task of awakening this child would be no simple problem. Her age, the extent of her developmental arrest, the habits she had acquired over the years, the conflictual and somewhat desperate attitude of her parents, these were all factors we would have to contend with. Our efforts over a period of 11 months, yielding slow and nonglamorous gains, taught us how important these factors can turn out to be in selecting a subject for a program such as ours, and in prognosticating the success or failure of our methods in a situation such as Connie's.

What gains in overall development and growth Connie made during the period she spent with us are difficult to assess. For all practical purposes, she remained throughout the experiment completely untestable on any of the standardized developmental or intellectual scales we had chosen in this project. The Cattell obviously offered limited interest to Connie who, in her initial evaluation (at age 5 years, 2 months), attained a mental age level of five months, and an IQ of 8. Clearly these numbers, the only ones we had to use as a point of reference, did not come close to giving a representative picture of Connie's total development at the time. Her Vineland Social Maturity score came somewhat closer to her actual level of functioning: 14 months (SQ: 0.22). Such a low starting point made it difficult to find any of the Fels Rating Scales applicable to Connie's behavior at this point. As we indicated earlier, our work with Connie was cut out for us; she presented a real challenge.

First three months of treatment. Our immediate effort with Connie was to make her clearly aware of our presence in her life. Because of her peculiar and selective capacity to respond to certain songs, we used this as an entry into Connie's isolation and indifference. Two songs especially turned out to be her favorites and most alerting to her, "The Incie-Wincie Spider" and "Go Tell Aunt Rhody." These songs enabled us to bring a great deal of sensory stimulation and pleasure to Connie, and, in a very short time, they served for her as indicators that she was now back in secure company with us, and for us as a sort of leitmotiv for our work with her. Her pleasure, as we sang to her, was always expressed in sparkling eyes and a bright smile, and in deliberate efforts at clapping her hands to the rhythm of the music. However, on those days—which were many—when for some reason she was either uncomfortable, irritable, or mildly agitated, our singing would have a strongly soothing and quieting effect on her. Many sessions in the early weeks of treatment were spent with Connie, her head resting quietly on the therapist's lap, with the clear intent of providing her, in our presence, with a few moments of quietness and peace where there would be no restless clasping and unclasping of the hands, no raucous sounds or grinding of the teeth, and no saliva bubble-blowing. We were demanding nothing of her at that time other than that she should feel good with us.

Very quickly Connie appeared to look forward to the sessions with us, even as she entered the therapy room. Our note of the fifth session reads: "Child in very good shape today; her mother brought her alone. She enjoys Carole's singing, and for the first time with us laughs out loud (previously she had only smiled when happy). Looks intently at therapist and learns from her to pucker and smack her lips. Makes many happy sounds and also tries to say 'ma-ma.' No teeth grinding. Mother observed part of the time." From the nursery school which Connie had been attending because her mother did some part-time teaching there, we have also an optimistic note at that time: "More pleasant sounds; generally happier. Placed her hands in plaster of paris and pushed teacher out of the way to get to the water in the sink." From the mother the following note: "Connie seems to pay more attention (looking at my face) when I talk to her. A slight bit more interest in things lying around the house. Picks up papers off table or desk and brings them to her mouth, or crumples and throws them down. Went down to floor on her own to pick up a dropped cookie. She has done this only once before in spite of much prodding and encouragement to do so."

Connie's awakening was coming slowly. At Christmas time, one month after the beginning of treatment, the mother writes: "Connie's picking up more objects. She either looks at them, carries them around, or throws them away; not toys, but papers, books, and so forth. She would not let Grandmother's Christmas tree alone; hitting the branches, pulling at the tinsel, grabbing a string of lights and shaking it up and down repeatedly. She kept this up for over an hour. She had not bothered our own Christmas tree up to this point, but is doing so now. She's also doing a lot of 'singing.' She is getting into things a little more. She found a pack of graham crackers in the pantry; she couldn't open it, so she threw them on the floor. I gave her one. She returned later to get more and helped herself. Both the pantry and the crackers are in a comparatively out-of-the-way spot, but she had remembered where they were. Lately, both at home and at school, she has hidden her hand behind her back when anyone has wanted to hold it and lead her somewhere, making it clear she didn't want her hand held."

At the end of three months Connie's gains in awareness of others, in attention to others, in motor control, and in affective responsiveness are reflected in a three-month increase on her Vineland Score (SQ 0.26; age equivalent 17 months). She now reaches for familiar persons; she demands personal attention; she can follow simple instructions; and she plays with other children. On the Cattell this time she bases at 7 months (compared to her initial basal of 4 months), and reaches a ceiling at 12 months; her attention span is greater, her motor coordination better controlled, and her interest is better maintained and directed.

Third through sixth month of treatment. In the following months, we continued relentlessly our efforts at improving Connie's general awareness of, and mastery over, her own body movements, in an atmosphere of warm and affectionate acceptance of her severe limitations and deficits. We took advantage of her insatiable but highly selective taste for candy—none of our other subjects had any special interest in candy—to help her further develop coordination and control over her movements. Of all the kinds of candies which we offered her, her favorite was banana candies (circus peanuts) which were attractive to her, not only because they smelled good and tasted fine, but also because she could see them and grasp them fairly easily. These candies were never offered to her as a reward for a specific task which we had set for her to accomplish; rather the appealing candy was always part of a situation in which the reward was her own feeling of mastery, as well as the playful and affectionate quality of our own interaction with her. If for instance, Carole and Connie were playing "row-row-row your boat," the therapist kneeling in front of the child and Connie (her arms extended on the shoulders of the therapist) delightfully enjoying being pushed back and forth, a banana candy might be placed on a cardboard block close to the therapist so that if Connie chose to reach for it between stanzas, she would have to bend down to pick it up. This maneuver not only would force her to develop good balance but would demand of her also adequate coordination of her fingers grasping for the candy, and precise control of her hand and arm in bringing the candy to her mouth. An example of generalization of such behavior is reflected in the mother's note at this time: "Connie is handling her spoon better. This morning she actually filled it a couple of times. This weekend I made cookies and gave her the spoon with some batter on it which was sticky enough not to fall off. She had to do a good deal of manipulating to get the batter off the spoon and into her mouth. Also I noticed she's walking down stairs with a little more facility. Her attention to me continues to increase. She seems to understand and comply a good deal of the time when I tell her to 'hold still' if I'm dressing her, or to 'stay there' when I have her seated and have to run off to get something for her."

Similarly, games of tickling Connie on the tummy in front of the mirror in the therapy room, as well as pushing her legs and feet back and forth to the tune of the "Anvil Chorus," seemed to find some generalization in Connie's increased interest at home in her body and her movements. The mother reports: "Connie is feeling many things; parts of her own body; clothes; things spilled on the table such as jelly, milk, and so forth; and she also likes to play in these things. She has been playing with her image in the mirror. Her dresser mirror is at the side of her bed and she's been sitting on her bed amusing herself in the mirror when she's supposed to be asleep. She thinks she's funny. She will also watch us in the mirror as we play with her. Formerly, she would only be attracted to the mirror when she could bring her face and mouth up to it. The mirror she looks into now is about four feet from her bed."

As Connie discovers herself, she appears also to be developing a certain degree of independence and self-assertion; she is more aggressive in resisting being pushed around and in demanding to be paid attention to. She is also becoming more capable of expressing affection. A few notes from the mother illustrate these points: "Yesterday morning Connie was crying uncontrollably. I held her on my lap trying to sooth her by stroking her back and talking to her. She pulled away and threw her arms around my neck. After a short time, I pulled her arms down so I could talk to her, but again she pulled me to her and threw her arms around my neck. She did this once again. She has never embraced anyone this way before even with coaxing. She is going up and down stairs much more easily now. She will often go down the last two steps unassisted.

"Connie has been doing, as a regular routine the past three or four days, something which she only did on occasion in the past; that is, pushing your hand away when she doesn't like what you are doing to her, such as dressing, combing her hair, and so forth. She does the same with other children who want to lead her, push her, or pull her around; she gives them a big shove when she's sick and tired of it all. The other day I was watering flowers with a glass, and Connie indicated with a sound that she wanted and needed the water more than the flowers did. I told her I would give her some, and she followed me into the kitchen to get it."

More alert, more individuated, more differentiated in her behavior, and more capable of expressing genuine feelings, Connie is slowly becoming a person in her own right. We again have to rely on her mother's descriptions of her behavior to measure those small gains in personality development which at the time our treatment began seemed so far out of reach for Connie. "For the past two years at nursery school (Mother's note, April, 1966) Connie has roamed around the room during story time, while the other children sat on a blanket in front of the teacher. In the last month she has been sitting down with the others, not rocking, not playing with her fingers or doing lip noises. She sits perfectly still watching the teacher read. If I didn't know better, I would think to watch her that she understands the story. I had to observe this myself to believe it!"*

"She is doing more sitting down on chairs and sofas at home, either to watch TV or just to sit quietly doing nothing. She is also going up and down the stairs now with much greater facility, bearing her own

* Note from nursery school, June 1966, after six months of treatment:

"Connie has just finished her second year at Nursery School and is now capable of performing several physical actions she was unable to do previously. These include running; going down steps unassisted; coming up one step into the school room, unassisted; and running up as well as down a small embankment outside. Most of these accomplishments have come in the last several months and running is as recent as the past 10 days.

"Connie has been more noticeably alert and observant this past semester, although not always consistently so. She is very capable of recognizing anything edible and shows great determination in obtaining these edibles by either direct or devious means. She usually chooses the latter method, twirling away from it, and then quickly approaching and grabbing what she is after. One occasion when the other children were popping corn, she snatched some from the dish, but upon finding it was somewhat hot she did not take any the second time, showing she was aware of perhaps being hurt from the heat.

"Recently, while the teachers were having coffee, she took a piece of sweet roll from one teacher, and after a second teacher offered her some of her roll, she then returned to the second teacher for more, showing she was able to distinguish between the two.

"At story time, we have found that placing Connie on the spread in the middle of the group of children often keeps her quiet for the duration of this period. She has even appeared to watch the teacher at times, although not usually. She is also quite responsive to music time.

"Her physical actions of twirling, clapping or wringing her hands, and so forth, remain about the same.

"In general, most of the children have enjoyed Connie, and although she is larger than some of them, they consider her a baby and for the most have treated her gently. Connie seems to enjoy their attentions but has at times become very frustrated if the others are overly attentive."

weight and using the banister to help pull herself up instead of leaning on me. She has been very verbal all week with numerous sounds and also singing. There is less hyperactivity. She is more playful and communicative. She has been coming into the kitchen quite often when I call her. A couple of times she came straight in on being called (for cookies or cake) without so much as a twirl on the way. This morning her dad was walking from room to room, and says that Connie was playfully chasing him. In fact, she has been following us around more. I must put this incident in writing. I keep a box of animal cookies hanging on the radio knob of the car dashboard (the cookie box has a string handle). I left Connie in the car while I went into the cleaners. When I got back the box of cookies was on the floor, and there were two cookies next to Connie on the seat. I'm intrigued about the way she might have gone about getting these cookies, because the lid on the box was only partially up and the wax paper lining was crushed over the cookies. She really had to make the supreme effort to get them out. Even the fact that she went after them surprises me, because they're not in reach from where she sits. I don't know if you are interested in this aspect of Connie, but before the first of this year, she would not and had not touched a vegetable since she was a year old. I could not even get away with smashing a pea and hiding it under her meat. She will now eat a variety of them and seems to love them, including spinach and broccoli. She eats other things she would never have touched before, like hamburgers in any form, hot dogs, ham, potatoes, and pudding. There are few things she won't eat. Also, when she's seated at the table and anyone is walking around the kitchen, she does contortions in her chair to watch their every move."

There were no striking changes in the Cattell scores at the end of six months of treatment (7.8 months to 8 months) and we felt very much handicapped in measuring Connie's development on a scale, the items of which had no appeal or interest value to Connie. The gain of five months in Social Maturity during this period continued to reflect Connie's steady progress, and kept us from giving up totally our efforts at evaluating her behavior through standardized instruments. In most areas of behavior even the Fels Scales remained nonapplicable, though on selected scales such as affectionateness, aggressiveness, curiosity, and obedience, some ratings were possible. The Home Observer describes her impressions of Connie after six months of treatment: "Connie shows some genuine changes in behavior since the last observation. She smiles, and looks more attentively and closely at adults in the environment. She is making sounds and was heard to whisper 'Daddy.' She shows interest in sounds and music. She lifted and threw her toys many times. She imitates mother clapping her hands and plays 'pat-a-cake' with father."

Sixth through 11th month in treatment. What progress Connie made in the next three months, prior to her last evaluation, is best recorded through the mother's notes. Meanwhile, our sessions with her at the clinic continued to emphasize her affective involvement with us, as well as her mastery and control of her movements and of her environment. Connie's physical condition created problems for us at various times— she suffered from what had been diagnosed as spasms of the intestines— and in consultation with her pediatrician several medications were tried which were moderately effective in alleviating her pains. The dosage of such medications had to be titrated very carefully, since for one good effect that one medication might have, there were many side effects which interfered with the child's alertness, attentiveness, and energy level. For instance, on July 14, the therapy notes indicate: "Connie is on 10 mg. of Mellaril for the first time today. Her eyelids appear a little droopy but, in general, for the first half hour she is alert and cooperative, less hyperactive, more attentive, and quite 'gabby,' with none of her ritualistic hand clasping, and no saliva 'bubble blowing.' However, in the second half-hour of the session she all of a sudden 'checked out'!" Four days later, July 18, the notes state that the mother took Connie off Mellaril because she was too drowsy. That day Connie seemed much less able to concentrate on any activity, and though appearing generally happy and good natured, she seemed more agitated and restless.

Another problem which confronted us during this three-month period was the breakdown in the family routine occasioned by the birth of a second child, another girl. Connie missed many therapy sessions and, at home, had to be left to the care of an aging grandmother, who could not cope effectively with a nearly six-year-old autistic child. Nevertheless, the following notes of the mother give some picture of the efforts which Connie continued to make in awakening to as much of life as she could enjoy. "Connie has been very talkative this last week with many new sounds; a lot of consonants with few vowels in between. Very interesting. She is eating her cereal now with only a bit of assistance. This is the only 'spoon' food she has mastered so far. She eats with a fork if I spear the food for her; she then brings it to her mouth, and attempts to get more. She hasn't got the idea of how, but she tries. When she's very hungry, she seems to be aware there is food on the stove cooking, or toast in the toaster. She gets 'pesty and antsy'; she has no patience to wait for it to come, even though I keep telling her it is coming soon. She keeps coming to the stove and looking and reaching. She burned her nose on the frying pan this afternoon trying to get to her egg. . . . I caught her rifling through my purse in the car and pulling things out. I think she was trying to find the candy or gum that usually comes from there. I pulled a few old toys from the attic that she hasn't seen for a while—a large green tractor, a train of four quacking ducks, and so forth—she pushed the tractor back and forth a couple of times; and she picked up the quacking ducks, put them on her lap, and slapped them. Wednesday, after leaving Carole, and apparently ignoring Carole's usual 'bye-bye,' Connie took two steps down the stairs and said 'ba-ba-bye-bye'. . . . Connie seems to be listening to herself talking. Also, she's paying attention to a wider range of toys, and she pushes a truck or a car now and then. She picks up her doll and throws it, and slaps or pats a plush dog. Yesterday I picked a large flower in the yard and handed it to her telling her to smell it. She carried it around the yard smelling it from time to time for about five minutes. She didn't taste it once. I noticed that she grinds her teeth less and less all the time, and that her improvement in climbing up and down stairs continues. She seems to be upset to hear the baby cry. She will stare at the baby and get a glum, puzzled look on her face. A couple of times she started to cry too. Such empathy. . . . A week ago Sunday, I put the pool in the back yard leaving the back door open, and Connie attempted to come down the stairs by herself. I stood at the bottom of the stairs and held my breath. She grabbed the hand rail and walked down all the steps unassisted. Since then she has come down about half the steps by herself, but she won't attempt the first couple of steps without the incentive of the pool awaiting her."

Connie's nine-month evaluation, which was to be her final, could not record with quantitative adequacy the real progress which these notes of the mother and our own observations at the clinic obviously describe. Some estimate of her progress can be derived using the Gesell Developmental Schedules. Thus for instance, Connie is observed at this time to walk securely by herself (18 months) and go up and down stairs, either holding onto the railing or to the therapist's hand (21 months). In terms of adaptive behavior, not only can she uncover a receptacle to retrieve a piece of candy (11 months), but she can successfully remove a series of covers in order to obtain the candy; this increase in attention enables her also to become interested in pictures in a book and pat them (15 months), in toys and pull them (18 months), and in even partly feeding herself and handling well a drinking cup (21 months). Thus from an initial mental age of 5.2 months at the beginning of treatment, Connie over nine months shows a developmental gain of at least nine months which is well beyond what she had been able to achieve in the preceding 5 years of her life. This estimate of her development during the period of treatment is corroborated by the data of the Vineland Social Maturity scale, which reflects a slow but steady growth process.

Perhaps a clearer picture of Connie's condition at this time in her treatment is captured in one of our last therapy notes: "Today Connie, who had started the session in a somewhat cranky mood, showed us that perseverance pays off with her, too. After taking off her shoes, Carole began by having Connie play 'ring-around-a-rosy.' Connie really had genuine fun with this. She would laugh and tease Carole, pretending not to know when to fall at the 'all fall down.' Then we introduced the candy on the table, and again Connie had fun pretending she could take it or leave it, all the time laughing and strutting around like a pheasant who has many more eggs where that first one came from. Eventually we built the bench out of blocks and put the board down for the swing. This time we asked the secretary to take movies of the operation. Connie showed much less distress on the 'swing' and when put down did not put on a 'big scene.' She felt that she deserved the candies hidden on the table, and went to retrieve them very energetically and very happily. But there was no display of anger or dismay. Connie thought that she might as well humor us if we were that intent on having her swing. At one point in the process of congratulating her on her good mood and excellent cooperation, Dr. D. started whispering to her while she attentively and intently looked at him with obvious pleasure. It was during this time that she whispered 'daddy' (the home observer had reported the same thing on her visit a few weeks before). Is it possible that Connie may be able to speak in a whisper before she can speak out loud? In any event, we plan on following through on this swinging bit, and we will take Connie to the playground on a forthcoming visit, in order to try her on a real swing. . . . Connie's capacity to attend and show interest has increased a hundredfold in the past few weeks. She seems to have learned how to play and have fun. Her motoric controls are much better. Her anxiety and frustration tolerance is higher. Her emotional expressions are much more genuine and differentiated. Connie seems to be moving!"

How far would she have reached had we been able to continue the awakening to life of this lovable Connie? We have reported all that happened to her in 11 months; however limited, that was all we could report. Connie is still at home now and there has been no opportunity to measure whatever developmental gains she may have made. But we know from her mother that Connie has not lost any ground. Our experience with her, and her abrupt separation from the program, raise many questions directly pertinent to the applicability of our approach to a child such as Connie, who came into the program at age 5, and to the potential success of our methods under circumstances such as we had to contend with.

With regard to the question of Connie's age at the onset of treatment with us, we have no information at this point which could help clarify whether our therapeutic educational approach, at least in the context in which we used it—that is, on an outpatient basis—can realistically be applied to a child such as Connie, whose deviant patterns of behavior had acquired over many years such an inveterate and chronic rigidity. The issue here cannot be whether the approach can be affectively arousing and lead to behavioral modifications; we were able to achieve this with Connie. Rather, the issue appears to be one of rate at which new developmental gains are possible or made.

Of all the children in the program, regardless of chronological age, Connie was developmentally the lowest (IQ 8; MA 5 months). After nine months of treatment with us, her measured development showed a gain of three full months. Viewed in the light of the intensive effort made, this gain may appear negligible; compared, however, to the developmental growth that had taken place in the five years prior to treatment, the modest gain of three months in nine months looms as strikingly significant. So that, perhaps, the issue of the rate at which development can be accelerated through our approach in an autistic child of Connie's age may not be as central as would appear at first glance.

It is possible that the real issue here concerns the continuity of the intensive treatment approach utilized. We saw Connie for three hours each week on an outpatient basis, and we counted very much on her parents to maintain with her at home the intensity of the high impact sensory and affective stimulation which we provided to Connie at the clinic. Would Connie have gained more and at a faster rate had she been exposed, as an inpatient, to a continuous intensive program such as ours? This is not easy to answer since we have evidence that, with Kathy for instance, the rate of growth was not accelerated by increasing her visits from two to three weekly. Furthermore, the total context of our program included, as an absolute essential, the active and involved participation of the parents as the most natural therapists for their child.

Thus we come to the second question which our experience with Connie raises for us: the total and unconditional involvement of the parents in her treatment. In Connie's case, this quality of involvement by her parents was not in fact lacking, but it did not appear to be stirred or supported by any degree of sustaining hope. This was understandable, since Connie was their first child, and, for nearly six years, their only child. With Connie they had experienced, in so many ways, the heartaches of failure and defeat in bringing up a child whom they loved very dearly, and yet who could not let them know that she loved them too. Thus their feeling of hopelessness over the years had acquired the same inveterate and chronic quality as had Connie's behavior. This may explain why Connie was removed from the program; we don't really know. But it can explain some of the limits and obstacles that remained in Connie's way as she reached, as best she could, toward a vision of a brand new day.

What we have learned in working with Connie, as far as a program such as ours is concerned, might be summarized as follows: There are at least three factors of major importance that we should take into account in attempting to treat an autistic child with our approach. First,

Table 3

CONNIE

	Months in Treatment			
	Initial Evaluation	3 Months	6 Months	9 Months
Chronological age	5 years 1 month	5 years 4 months	5 years 8 months	6 years
Vineland	SQ 22 AE 14 mo.	SQ 26 AE 17 mo.	SQ 32 AE 22 mo.	SQ 30 AE 22 mo.
Cattell	IQ 8 MA 5.2 mo.	IQ 12 MA 7.8 mo.	IQ 12 MA 8 mo.	IQ 12 MA 8.4 mo.

the intervention should be as early as possible to avoid being confronted with inveterate and chronic qualities in the autistic behavior of the child. Second, careful attention should be given to the developmental baseline of the child when treatment is considered, from the standpoint of whether the magnitude and duration of the developmental arrest of the child might have had devastating effects on the parents. And third, the quality of the parents' potential involvement in the treatment should be carefully weighed in the light of the traumatizing and defeating effects which their child's behavior over the years might have had on their attitude towards the child. Obviously these three factors are closely interrelated but they suggest, nevertheless, potential avenues of further experimentation and improvement within our treatment program.

Elizabeth

SUMMARY

Age at Outset of Treatment: 3 years, 3 months.

Treatment Period: April 1966 to June 1967.

Schedule of Sessions: 2 hourly sessions per week on outpatient basis.

Drugs: None.

Schedule of Testing and Results: Initial diagnostic evaluation, March 1966 (Vineland SQ 43; Cattell IQ 54: MA 19.8 months); tested at three-month intervals thereafter (see Table 4); final evaluation, April 1967, at age 4 years, 3 months (Vineland SQ 80; Stanford-Binet IQ 71: MA 3 years; Leiter IQ 96: MA 3 years, 9 months).

Language: Initially no language, receptive or expressive; at end of treatment, full receptive language and expressive language developing at rapid rate and normally.

School Placement: Enrolled in private nursery school for normal children September 1966—currently enrolled in junior kindergarten.

In describing Elizabeth, her mother had written: "Now that I look back, I realize she (Elizabeth) always liked things better than people." It would be somewhat of a simplification to say that the most characteristic change which took place in this child during the year of treatment reported here was a shift in her from a central interest in objects to a major concern and interest in people. Such characterization would not truly give a full picture, because the quality of interest in and approach to objects was essentially retained in her approach to and interest in people. We called her a "bunny rabbit" not only because she was quiet, round, and fluffy, but because her discovery of the world about her always seemed to include a detailed exploration and a careful determination of all aspects of whatever object she encountered; she touched everything with her fingers and with her nose; she looked at them and sniffed at them. She never seemed to be in a hurry in such painstaking investigations; the placid way in which she went about them could be

241

said to have been the only protection she had from being frightened or terrified of them. Thus, when the major focus of treatment became an effort at arousing her interest in people, we had to allow for this same pattern of careful, painstaking, and detailed exploration of the human being which she constantly demonstrated in her discovery of objects.

Elizabeth began treatment at 3 years, 4 months of age. She came to the Evaluation Center with the presenting symptoms of failure to develop in all areas of functioning, with special emphasis on gross motor retardation (she functioned motorically like a 12-month-old infant) and speech delay. Except for the possession of perhaps two or three words, Elizabeth was mute.

She displayed evidence of only such minimal receptive language that, at one point, her parents suspected that she might be deaf since she responded neither to her name nor to the loud clapping of hands. She did not walk until 20 months of age. "It was about at this time," writes the mother, "that Elizabeth started to be frightened if we took her anywhere, other than someone's home. She would cry when we took her to a store or to the doctor's office, and when we tried to take her to church she screamed. In the doctor's office or a small store, she would stand by the door and try to get out each time it was opened. It always amazed me that even in large department stores she would know in which direction the door was." Feeding was also a problem. Elizabeth would eat only mashed foods; she did not chew, and would not feed herself unless her mother (and only her mother) held her hand with the spoon in it. She would drink from a cup but would not hold it herself. Her favorite pastime was rocking. Sometimes she would place an object in front of her, and sit and rock, staring at it; or she would rock over it on hands and knees for long periods of time if not interrupted. Her interest in objects was limited either to this rocking and staring, or to an endless repetitive tactile exploration of this object. She never sought affection and did not like to be cuddled or hugged. She never looked at anyone and typically avoided the eyes of others who attempted to alert her visual attention to them.

In her initial evaluation Elizabeth attained a mental age of 19.8 months which is equivalent to an IQ of 54 on the Cattell. This represented a base at 18 months and a ceiling at 24 months. The psychological test report at that time read as follows: "She was credited for all items at the 16- and 18-month levels. At the 20-month level, however, she passed only two items: the insertion of a square block in the formboard and a pegboard item. [She could not construct a tower of three blocks, nor attain an object with a stick, nor carry out two simple commands with reference to a doll.] At the 22-month level she passed only one item, solving a small formboard. She was also able to perform on the rotated formboard once, although she would not repeat this performance. Consequently, she was also credited for this item at the 20-month level. She failed all other items presented to her at the 22- and 24-months levels.

"Thus, on the basis of the score obtained, Elizabeth would appear to be functioning within the range of moderate mental retardation. However, the pattern which she presents is rather unusual, not only because of her lack of performance on the language items, but also because of her clearly more advanced visuo-motor and visual-perceptual skills. The manner in which she related to the testing situation in general, and to the examiner in particular, especially during the second session, suggests that this child has some severe disturbance in her interpersonal relationships."

This same pattern of retardation and lack of interpersonal awareness is reflected in Elizabeth's initial Vineland Social Maturity Scale. The Social Quotient of 43 (age equivalent 17 months) which she obtains emphasizes again the limited areas of her involvement with the environment and underscores her prevailing emotional isolation. Ratings (Fels Scales) of her behavior with respect to interpersonal contacts and to the quality and intensity of both her emotional responsiveness, as well as of her affective involvements with others, correlate closely with the behavioral picture obtained from the Vineland.

The limitations in her affective contacts and responsivity, as well as in her interest in and awareness of other people, are clearly reflected in the very low ratings she receives on such scales as Affectionateness (1.1), Friendliness (3.14), Gregariousness (3.15), and Sense of Humor (7.1). Such behaviors as are encompassed under the scales of Conformity (1.7), Obedience (3.22), Suggestibility (8.2), Negativism (6.1), and Aggressiveness (1.2) were for the most part impossible to rate at this point. On the other hand, because of Elizabeth's intense involvement in objects and the systematic way she had of exploring them, she could be more adequately rated on such scales as Curiosity (2.11), Planfulness (5.1), Patience (4.1), and Tenacity (8.3). These ratings, however, need to be viewed in the context of her absorption in objects and in object-oriented activities. Similarly, on the two scales Cheerful-Depressed (1.5) and Emotional Excitability (3.11), what ratings (low) Elizabeth obtains are a function of the relatively placid attitude she maintains in the exploration of her physical environment; she can be said to appear to have the cool, objective distance of a scientist methodically examining a specimen under a microscope; there is a quiet cheerfulness in the process, and only mild emotional excitability when interrupted. But the world of human beings is for the most part ignored.

First three months of treatment. Our immediate effort in treatment was focused on arousing Elizabeth's affective interest in, and responsivity to, her human environment. We had first become acquainted with Elizabeth at the Evaluation Center, at which time she had seemed so absorbed in her intensive preoccupation with inanimate objects—manipulating them, spinning them, intensely staring at them—that it was evident that a major alerting intrusive activity would be necessary with her if we were to break through her isolation and make her aware of our presence. She appeared to ignore our intrusions and at times seemed to rebuff them. Somehow we must have made enough of an impression on her so that the first time she came to the clinic for a therapy session, she accepted us quite readily and responded with mild cheerfulness to our presence. There seemed to be little fear in her, and in her quiet and placid way she seemed quite interested in us. We first took off her shoes and socks so that she could feel the floor better with her feet. But since it was early spring, we put her socks back on, all the while making sure that the entire process was playful, sensorily stimulating, and fully experienced by her.

As was our custom, we had emptied the room of any unnecessary or distracting objects or toys so that Elizabeth's attention could be maintained on us. To help Elizabeth fix her gaze on the therapist's face, Carole used a plastic ring large enough to look through, and colorful enough to draw the child's attention. Elizabeth found great delight and amazement at looking into Carole's eyes through the plastic ring and typically sought to repeat this experience. When Carole switched from the plastic ring to her own silver bracelet (which she very carefully took off, making sure that Elizabeth noticed the operation), Elizabeth reacted again with pleasurable surprise and interest at the discovery that she again could see Carole's eyes through a different window. By this time, she seemed reconciled to the fact that human beings could be interesting and fun to be with, and she began to giggle and squeal and laugh whenever the therapist would put the bracelet on her (Elizabeth's) arm, retract it, place it in front of Elizabeth's eyes for her to look through, and then replace it on her (Elizabeth's) arm. At this point, Elizabeth was so much in the spirit of the game that she pulled her socks off her feet and put them on her hands. This pattern of high affective impact in our contacts with Elizabeth was maintained in subsequent sessions when we successively introduced Elizabeth to her own reflection in the mirror; to the feeling of hot and cold water on her face, arms, and legs; to the smooth sensation of baby powder on various parts of her body; and, in general, to the pleasant and pleasurable discovery of all parts of herself and of us with her.

Elizabeth seemed so delighted with each new experience with us that it was easy, within these very first weeks of treatment, to elaborate on these experiences and couple them with new ones. Thus, if she wanted to play with water, we gave her blocks to climb on to reach the sink; if she wanted to see herself in the mirror, the therapist would sit her on her lap, bounce her up and down a few times, and then let her fall towards the mirror so that Elizabeth not only saw herself coming, but had to stop herself with her hands from hitting the mirror. Elizabeth was definitely "with us" by that time, and her mother indicated to us that on her way to her "session" (5th) she became more and more excited and happy as she got closer to the clinic.

Elizabeth's discovery of human beings was also felt very quickly at home. Her mother's notes for this period (April and May 1966) reflected the observed changes in her child. "Elizabeth seems to be increasingly aware of her surroundings. We have noticed that when we are in the car she knows when we reach the cutoff for our block, and if for some reason we pass it by, she starts to whimper. . . . She is beginning to make her needs known a little. For instance, she goes to a kitchen drawer to get a cup when she wants a drink. . . . She is showing an interest in other children. She has approached a couple of them during the past few days, as if she would like to play. She is also playing with her brother Mark more. . . . On Saturday, we had a group of children over for David's birthday, and Elizabeth played a couple of circle games with them; she also went into the middle of the crowd to catch balloons. Usually on these occasions she finds a quiet corner for herself and ignores everyone else. Elizabeth definitely seems to be much more friendly toward them, and I notice that when she hurts herself now she wants to be hugged and comforted. . . . She seems much more responsive toward us.

She will usually come to me now when I call her and will let me sit and cuddle her. I think she is beginning to enjoy it a little. She still goes off by herself to play, although we feel she is doing this less. Lately she seems to be taking more interest in what we and her brothers are doing. This weekend she started walking down the stairs by herself rather than crawling, and she practiced doing so several times. . . . Elizabeth loves to play with her father, particularly when he swings her back and forth by her hands or feet."

At the clinic we also did a lot of swinging of Elizabeth, in a variety of ways, from every possible position, and always in such a way that Elizabeth could not ignore our forceful presence to her. Elizabeth enjoyed this thoroughly, so we swung her by the arms alone, by the arms and feet, in a box, on a board, jumping from a table into our arms, from a sitting position on a chair, or by catching her on the run. We capitalized on her happiness at being with us in these activities by constantly reinforcing her own initiative; we would never allow her to be purely passive in these enhancing and enthralling activities. She, herself, had to actively seek them and somehow let us know which variety or flavor of swinging she had decided on. If, for instance, she wanted to be swung by her hands and feet, we waited until she would come to each one of us and "position us" in the right place so that she could savor the full joy of the ride. If, on the other hand, she wanted a ride on the "board," she would have to fetch the board herself; and if the therapist happened to be sitting on the board at the time, she had to remove it from under him, then bring us the board, make sure that each one of us had a good grasp on each end of the board, then sit herself on it properly, reach for our arms to hold on to—"and away we go."

Placid and quiet, little Elizabeth, in this atmosphere of exciting changes and surprise and of constantly encouraged initiative in goal-directed activities, became a very active and alive little girl indeed. She discovered herself, and us, as real people whom she could touch and feel, whom she could hold and push, whom she could listen to when they sang, and whose faces she could explore. She, too, learned to "sing" with us and she, too, learned to discover the various features of her own face. She especially seemed to enjoy it when Carole would hold her head with her hands and bump heads with her, all the while keeping very affectionate and attentive eye contact with her. On such occasions Elizabeth, as soon as the therapist would pretend to end the game, would reach for Carole's hands, place them carefully over her ears so that her head would be held and then playfully repeat the game. Even during the swinging, Elizabeth sought to look at herself in the mirror, obviously delighted that it was she who was there, floating through the air.

The mother's notes during this period, June 1966, also underscore Elizabeth's newly found aliveness. "Elizabeth is responding to her brothers more and more. When they play with her she giggles and joins in the game. Lately, she seems to be very happy and contented. She smiles and laughs easily. It seems to me she is looking directly at people more; she is also making a lot more noise in the form of sounds. . . . Elizabeth has enjoyed doing a couple of things this past week that she used to be afraid of. One is, she has been playing and splashing around in the wading pool in the back yard, and the other is being pushed in a swing. She used to be terrified of this in particular, but now she really enjoys it. She has started taking her shoes and socks off all the time. I let her go barefoot as much as possible, but if we are going shopping or something like this, of course, she has to wear shoes. We took her shopping the other day for a short time and whenever she had the opportunity, she sat down and took them off. . . . Elizabeth has started to follow her father around, particularly when he is working in the yard. She follows him up and down the yard when he is mowing the lawn or sprinkling. I don't know if she is interested in him, the hose, the lawnmower, or what. It's very difficult to keep her in the house now. She wants to be outside most of the time. She seems to be falling and hurting herself quite a bit, but, of course, she is exploring more and is much more active. She seems to be using her words less but is making more sounds. We have tried to encourage this by repeating them back to her. . . . She is spending a great deal of her time outdoors now. She has learned how to let herself out of the screen door, but has not yet managed the regular door. She particularly enjoys being outside and keeps herself very busy investigating everything in the yard such as bushes, flowers, the grass, and poking around in the dirt. She seems able to take care of herself fairly well in the yard, but I do check on her frequently, because she did wander away on one occasion last week. I found her three houses away, sitting with two little boys, very unconcerned about it all. I think Elizabeth is becoming a little more affectionate, she is letting me hold her more and more. . . . For awhile before dinner, we played together with a doll. I was surprised to find that she was able to point out the eyes, feet, hands, and so forth. She also seemed to be trying to say feet, eyes, hand, and mouth. . . . Today we took Elizabeth to a picnic. When her grandmother arrived, she got quite excited and ran to her, laughing. She seemed to pick out certain people she liked. These she would hang around with and play with. The others she ignored. At one time during the day, she was playing with a toy, and another child came along and grabbed it from her. For the first time, Elizabeth tried to take it back; she didn't get it, in fact he pushed her over, but at least she tried. Usually she just sits and cries if another child takes something from her. . . . She is beginning to balk at doing some things, like walking up stairs, or even just walking; if she decides she doesn't want to do it, she just sits down. . . . Elizabeth didn't want to hold her spoon this morning at breakfast. When I tried to put it in her hand, she stiffened up and started to cry, so I took her dish away for a moment, but that just made her cry more, so I tried giving her the first spoonful. After that she was quite willing to hold the spoon herself, although she still insists on having my hand over hers. . . . We took Elizabeth to church today. She was pretty good; she climbed around a little but didn't make a lot of noise. She is no longer afraid of going to church. At one time she used to scream if we tried to take her in. After lunch we took the children fishing. Elizabeth had a good time; she sat in the mud which she seemed to like, and played with the leaves on the bushes and trees. She loves to touch the leaves on low hanging branches. She feels them and laughs out loud. She picked up a magazine today, with some large photographs of people. She pointed to the eyes and mouths and tried to say the words. She can say 'eye' quite clearly."

This last statement was written July 24, 1966. The next day Elizabeth underwent her first three-month evaluation. And that day, ironically enough, she refused to accommodate the child psychologist examining her, when she was asked to point out the features of a cardboard doll. In the presence of this relative stranger, Elizabeth insisted on pointing out the eyes, the nose, the mouth, the feet, and so forth of the examiner rather than those of the dead-pan, lifeless, cardboard doll. In this examination, the Cattell was repeated, and the Merrill-Palmer introduced; the Vineland was also given. Quantitatively, the Cattell showed a gain of slightly over two months in mental age (MA 22 mos.) but qualitative changes point to developmental gains in some areas. For instance, Elizabeth now bases at 18 months; she passes, at 20 months, Doll, Two Commands, and Doll, Points to Three Parts, both of which she had failed earlier; at the 22-months level, she adds Covers Square Box to Solves Small Formboard; this latter test she solves also in rotated position twice (giving her credits at 30 months and at 36 months). Obviously, Elizabeth's attention span is increasing, her visuomotor abilities continue to be her strong point, and her receptive language is expanding.

The introduction of the Merrill-Palmer allowed for an impressive display of Elizabeth's skills in visuomotor and perceptual tasks. On this test, however, her performance was extremely scattered. Her base was established at Item 2 of the 18- to 23-months level, and her highest success was achieved on Item 60, at the 48- to 53-months level (the Seguin Form Board, which Elizabeth completed in less than 60 seconds!). Thus her performance was distributed unevenly over a little more than a three-year span of developmental tests. She failed all items involving expressive language, and her successful performances were limited, somewhat erratically, to items such as Sixteen Cubes, Wallin Pegboard A, Nest of Cubes, Seguin Formboard, Mare and Foal, and Picture Puzzle No. 1. Elizabeth, on this test, achieved a mental age of 2 years, 8 months, which at a CA of 3 years, 6 months, gave her an IQ of 76. In this connection, the psychological test report reads as follows: "Even this single score is misleading, for while she (Elizabeth) can do no language items down to the 18-month level, formboards are succeeded on as high as the 48- to 53-month level, above her chronological age level. The two formboards succeeded above chronological age level are the Seguin and the Mare and Foal. Yet when she is given a Picture Puzzle, she cannot achieve this. She is apparently capable of manipulating materials where the gestalt is already formed; when she has to organize the concept, she cannot do the puzzle. It would seem that she is manipulating the forms at a perceptual-concrete level." (An interesting point here: Two months earlier, in May, the home-observer had indicated her surprise at seeing Elizabeth complete a 16-piece picture puzzle! The three-piece Merrill-Palmer puzzle may not have caught the child's fancy!)

Both the therapy notes, and those notes of the mother which we have quoted already, give some idea of the gains which Elizabeth made in social development in this three-month period. These gains are clearly reflected in the Vineland Social Quotient of 51 (age equivalent 1 year, 11 months), which represents a six-month increase over her initial evaluation (SQ 43; age equivalent: 1 year, 5 months). What seems to be emerging in Elizabeth's personality functioning is a greater attention to, and mastery of, her environment, as well as increased independence and motor control; that is, as she becomes more aware of herself and of others, her behavior assumes more goal-directedness with reference to the human environment which she is now discovering.

Third through sixth month of treatment.   This same pattern of development was maintained throughout the next three months. During this period, plans were made to have Elizabeth enter a nursery school for normal children (see Chapter IX), and the spurt which we had witnessed in Elizabeth's social adjustment was given further impetus and support through this experience. Her Vineland Social Maturity test, administered after Elizabeth had been in school five weeks, highlights her dramatic progress in social skills. What she had begun to learn at home becomes strongly reinforced in the school setting, where the presence of other children, as well as the attentive and firm interest of her teachers, keep Elizabeth alert and awake to a variety of learning situations. She quickly acquires the habit of removing her coat and hanging it up in her locker; she sits with the other children and does as they do with cookies and juice; she bites and chews the cookies and picks up her own glass to drink; she begins to play cooperatively with others, and frequent notes from her teacher tell us how effectively influential this school environment could be on Elizabeth's total personality development.

September 26, 1966: "Doesn't take her shoes off at all now. When we finally get through to her, she will respond and join the story group. Tim and Susan played 'ring-around-the-rosy' with her and she loved it, but did not want to 'fall down' when it came time to 'all fall down.' They kept trying to teach her—they are all so good with her and not 'smothering' her so much now!" And two weeks later, October 12, 1966: "Elizabeth painted today! And Mother observed Elizabeth put the paint brushes back in the proper jar without being told. She must have observed this or remembered from the only other time we attempted to get her to paint. We explained about the brushes then and their correct place. She enjoyed painting." Elizabeth's Social Quotient of 61 (age equivalent: 2 years, 4 months) represents at this time a total net gain of 11 months in a 6-month period. At 3 years, 9 months of age, she still had a long way to go, obviously; but she was moving much faster than we had dared hope.

Similar progress could not be said to be evident from her results on the Cattell. The increase from 22 to 25.4 months in mental age represents some consolidation in attention span and some broadening in her receptive verbal abilities but still remains at least three months behind her Social Quotient. The psychological test report nevertheless, takes on an optimistic note: "There is a consistent improvement on all scales administered. The nonverbal scale improvement is chiefly in performance material (Tower, Cubes in a Box, Tower Bridge, Formboard Rotated, Stringing Beads, Block Bridge) but there is also some increase in response to language (Doll, Commands). Some of the items passed are at the third year, second half, suggesting potential that may not be tapped by the tests." It is quite probable that, as we suggested earlier, most of the Cattell items were becoming age-inappropriate for Elizabeth. Her impressive performance on the Merrill-Palmer appears to support this view.

On this latter test, Elizabeth based at Item 21 (Repetition of Word Groups) which is at the upper limit of the 24- to 29-months level; she obtained a total count of 53 to give her a mental age of 42 months (3 years, 6 months). The upper limits of her functioning included passing Picture Puzzle number 2 and the Mare and Foal at the 54- to 59-months level; on this latter item she was also successful at the 60- to 65-months level. What is highlighted significantly in Elizabeth's performance here, besides her precocious development in the visuomotor area, is the maturation (she now bases within the 24- to 29-months range compared to her previous base within the 18- to 23-months range) of her capacity to understand and follow directions, and the increased attention span which permits her to stay with the examination and complete it without too much resistance.

From the point of view of our therapeutic educational effort, however, our concern in this period was less with Elizabeth's intellectual development, as such, than with her total personality growth. Whatever else she could or would learn, our main emphasis was that she could develop that quality of affective responsivity toward her human environment which would make her experience herself as a real, live, little girl, delighted to be part of the human race and the member of a family. Her progress in this respect is much more impressive to us within the period reported thus far, than the dramatic demonstration of her skills in the visuomotor areas. The following notes from the mother underscore the degree to which Elizabeth's initiative and spontaneity acquire a warm, affectionate, people-oriented coloring. August, 1966: "Elizabeth was in a very good mood today after we left the hospital. In the car on the way home, she kept putting her face close to mine and was smiling and laughing. She fell and hurt herself during the day, and she came to me to be picked up and cuddled. She put her arms around my neck and clung to me. After dinner we played outside with her doll and on the swing; then we all played baseball. Elizabeth ran after the ball and brought it back to the pitcher; then I helped her take her turn at bat. We used a plastic one so she could handle it. She seemed delighted with the whole thing. . . . At breakfast today, I touched Elizabeth's feet and said 'feet.' She immediately touched her hands, mouth, and nose, and named them. . . . She was playing with her brother, Mark, this morning, giggling and having a good time. She enjoys rolling on the floor with the kids, making faces or joining circle games much more than playing with toys with them. We took the children to a family picnic for the rest of the day. We were very pleased with Elizabeth. She was so sociable. There was a large group there, and I think she went to just about everyone. I was really surprised at her friendliness. She did isolate herself from the group a couple of times, but only for short periods. She said 'I see' again a couple of times today. . . . This morning the kids dressed Elizabeth up in one of my robes with a crown and everything. Then they came down the stairs in a procession with one of the boys holding her train, singing 'Here comes the bride.' The expression on Elizabeth's face was priceless. I don't think I have ever seen her so delighted with a game. She paraded around with a big smile on her face. . . . Elizabeth played in the house most of the day since it was a little cool outside. She played with the other children most of the time. We read to her, and she sat very still and quiet, listening very intently. She occasionally pointed to a picture and said 'eye.' She certainly seemed to enjoy the story, but I don't know whether she understood any of it."

The next notes (September and October) give some impressions of Elizabeth's experience in her first five weeks of nursery school. "On the way to school this morning (first day), we dropped David and Mark off at their respective schools. Elizabeth was so excited when she saw all the children; she started to laugh and make sounds. When we arrived at the nursery school, Elizabeth left me without a backward glance; she wasn't the slightest bit upset. When I picked her up at noon, she seemed a little subdued to me. It might have been because she was tired. She laid down on the bed and took a nap after lunch. . . . This morning when I took Elizabeth to school (second day), she seemed very happy to be there. She took one of the teachers by the hand and started pulling her toward her classroom. She seemed anxious to get going. Later, when

I picked her up, she smiled and seemed pleased to see me. She was hungry and thirsty, and wanted her lunch right away. I managed to get her to eat a sandwich for the first time; she wouldn't hold it herself, but took bites while I held it for her. . . . Elizabeth saw me through the window today (fifth day) when I picked her up from school, but she didn't move from her seat until the teacher told her she could. . . . Elizabeth was so excited when I picked her up from school today (9th day). She ran over to me laughing, and she kept saying 'Hi' over and over. . . . I watched Elizabeth in school this morning for a few minutes. Her teacher helped her take one arm out of her sweater and Elizabeth did the rest. She tried to hang it up and then went over to the table with the other children, and sat down and started to play. . . . I watched Elizabeth in school for about half the morning. The first thing she did after hanging up her coat was to climb into a rocking boat with another little girl; they seemed to be having a great time. Then she started to paint. I was surprised at how well she did. She put the brushes back in the pots as she finished with them. When she was tired of painting, she went over to another table, where several children were playing with colored discs. She tried to take some but when they wouldn't let her have them, she went off and played with a toy by herself. The teacher brought her back to the table and gave her some of the discs to play with, so she stayed. She sat still with the rest of the children while the teacher sang little songs. This surprised me. I didn't think she would be interested. I watched her have her juice and cookies, and she was very careful to push her chair under the table when she was through. Then she noticed that another child hadn't pushed her chair under all the way, so she fixed that."

Elizabeth's progress in her school behavior did not come as easily as her mother's notes may seem to suggest. The teachers had to work hard with her, and the notes we have from one of the teachers in those first weeks attest to their painstaking patience and understanding. Excerpts from these notes follow: First day: "Showed no comprehension of her name. Constantly took off her shoes and socks. Elizabeth often runs up to each teacher and puts her head on our laps; also grabs around our knees when we are standing. She smiles very easily, cries very often, and is quite disturbing to the group. Refuses to move if she doesn't want to at the time she is asked to move. Shows no interest in books, no attention span to stories, songs, or rhythms. Sits passively during story time. Will start loud screaming for no apparent reason; very annoying to the children, and they cannot understand why she does this, and we are unable to get her cooperation. We explain to them that she is small and just learning to listen, talk, and so forth. They are amazingly patient with her." Third day: "She responded when we called to her to get ready to go outside. In story corner, she rocked in a steady rhythm while sitting on the floor. When we read 'What Daddies Do All Day,' she looked at the pictures for a long time. When a child disturbs the story, she does not like it; it's all right, of course, when she disturbs. Dislikes the noise when the group gathers to go outside; placed fingers on ears. Hugs teacher's knees often." Fourth day: "Likes to be held by the teachers, loves the swing. Dislikes, still, the assembling in the story corner but stopped crying and listened to the singing of 'Muffin Man.' Understands that when she puts on her sweater we go home. Delighted to see her mother today." Fifth day: "Watched with interest today the story 'Rain.' Seems to notice the other children more. Drank her juice without help; ate her graham cracker right away without disturbing the other children. She follows the group outside without special help, also to go to the bus." Sixth day: "She sat quietly in group at story time and enjoyed the 'Animal Jump-Up Book,' Got her sweater at bus-time and sat with the group. Makes horizontal marks on the paper with crayons. No words, but many happy sounds while she plays." A week later: "She is listening to stories, songs, and rhythms now. Takes off her coat, and places it in her locker and on her hook. She tried to put her coat on to go home today. She is more aware of the children now and watches their activities. Freddie dearly loves her, but he wants to 'punish' her too. Timmy protects her; he is always patting her or kissing her on the cheek. She comes to the story corner now without having to be led; she responds to our 'come and sit' song. She has a long attention span, but will often annoy the children around her with her constant babble or touching them. She does most of the things the other children are doing, except talking and singing. She must always be coaxed to make the transition from one activity to another. She would escape into herself if we would let her, but this we rarely let her do. Once when she was reprimanded for something today, she cried for 'mommy' quite clearly and for the first time."

Thus, after six months of treatment, Elizabeth appears to have come a long way from the position of detachment and isolation she had maintained, to one in which she can now be heard in a moment of fear and loneliness to scream out: "Mommy, I am lost, you are far away." The

Fels Rating Scales concur in describing Elizabeth at this time as more affectionate (1.1), more friendly (3.14), and more gregarious (3.15); she is seen as infinitely more cheerful (1.5) and emotionally excitable (3.11). On those scales where it had been difficult to rate her, such as Obedience (3.22), Conformity (1.7), Suggestibility (8.2), Negativism (6.1), and Aggressiveness (1.2), raters can now estimate the degree to which her awareness of others, as well as her own sense of identity, becomes demonstrated in her behavior; there is an emergence of the true experience of being with others and sharing with others. There is no lessening in her curiosity (2.11), nor is she less purposeful (5.11) and determined (8.3) in her compulsive exploration of her environment. But these activities in her are directed now more frequently toward people than toward objects. Her patience (4.1) and her frustration tolerance have increased so that her attention span has more breadth; and her capacity to "wait her turn" with respect to others reflects a true beginning of her need to be with others, and to assert her presence to others.

Sixth through ninth month of treatment.   The striking growth pattern which Elizabeth had demonstrated in the first six months of the treatment program was hampered in many ways by her lack of expressive verbal abilities and the limited range of her symbolic functions. In the following six months, we see these functions blossoming out, while those patterns of behavior which had been acquired and established continue to be maintained and consolidated. Our work at the clinic continued to be focused on keeping highly charged what we had come to refer to as Elizabeth's "affective battery." It was easy with Elizabeth to become so interested and amazed by her precocious show of intelligence in dealing with complex activities, such as puzzle solving or mastering the operation of a tricycle, that one's effort with her could quickly become side-tracked away from her constant need for affective stimulation and human contact. Time and time again, if we were not alert or attentive, her absorption in an activity fascinating for her would lead us insidiously into a fascinating (for us) but parallel absorption with her. So much so that at one point our therapy notes read: "In reviewing Elizabeth's therapy hours up to the present (November 7, 1966), it was decided that the therapist was allowing her to spend entirely too much time in 'task-oriented' activities (as opposed to constant high impact stimulation, both affective and physical), even though the therapist was constantly at her side and participating with her in these activities.

Therefore it was decided that, during her sessions, Elizabeth would be allowed very little, if any, time for such tasks (although we were quite aware that all such activities on her part display intelligent and appropriate use of materials, and a real sense of mastery and accomplishment in dealing with them; yet it is precisely in this sense that she readily and easily becomes 'object-oriented and object-absorbed')."

Following this agonizing reappraisal of our interactions and transactions with Elizabeth, a typical therapy note describes the pattern of our sessions with her henceforth: "Again this hour was spent primarily in gross motor and close personal interactional activities; with swinging, climbing on the table and jumping off, standing on the table and throwing the large ball into the waste basket with a great deal of laughter, and intermittent hugs. The rub-a-dub-dub game is played with two men in a tub (the waste paper basket serving as the tub). There is no end to Elizabeth's enjoyment of this game for which, in her usual precise and compulsive way, she establishes definite rules. First she moves the therapist's legs close to the basket, and then picks up one foot at a time and places it carefully inside. Following this, she stands in front of the therapist with her arms extended so that she can be picked up and placed on top of therapist's feet in the tub. Then both Elizabeth and the therapist rock and roll in the basket around the room to the tune of 'Rub-a-Dub-Dub-Two Men in a Tub.' When Elizabeth decides to bring the game to an end, she gets out of the basket and then retrieves the therapist's feet, one after the other, with a great show of kind consideration for the therapist's toes, which have been bent under in order to fit in the basket. The therapist allows Elizabeth to straighten out each one of her toes, making a variety of noises expressing a variety of emotions."

In this atmosphere of fun and close personal contact, we did not neglect any opportunity to reinforce emerging verbal capacity to communicate to us, nor did we allow her any undisciplined expression of her whims and feelings. "Elizabeth is in very good humor today (November 14, 1966). She runs to take Carole's and Dr. D's hands immediately, and makes little singing noises as she trots down the hall to the therapy room. She is generally very affectionate today during the session—sometimes almost aggressively so; she runs and dives into Carole's lap a couple of times. She's also more verbal today than she has even been at the clinic. When asked what is this (Carole pointing to various parts of body and objects), she says correctly, and with very good articulation, 'socks,' 'foot,' 'eyes,' 'nose,' 'mouth,' 'hair,' 'hand.' She becomes interested in Carole's watch, and she repeats 'tick-tock,' she also enjoys wearing the wristwatch throughout most of the session. At one point, while stacking up blocks, she volunteers the word 'block'; and, when she goes to the sink for a drink of water, Elizabeth, after hearing Carole repeat 'drink' several times, smilingly repeats 'drink.' She is also teasing and playful while involved in several games. For instance, while stringing large bead-blocks (which she had become accustomed to inserting into a basket and which she didn't think were fit to be strung), she would stop after a few and then carefully pick up the next one, look teasingly at the therapist, and then throw it away as if to say, 'If you want me to string beads, get beads!' Similarly, at the end of the session, after putting on her shoes and carefully opening the door, she squats down and, with a broad smile on her face, refuses to leave. After making her point, she gets up and willingly goes out the door, carefully closing it behind her." This self-assertive expression of her personality takes on at times more aggressive and negativistic coloring. "She fully enjoys the swinging and the 'rub-a-dub-dub' games, and cooperates well in a game of catch with the big ball. She is amazingly well coordinated at catching and throwing the ball; she throws it with real force, determination, and aim. At the end of the session, she had a small tantrum with real tears. This was provoked by having to part with Carole's wristwatch which she (Elizabeth) had been wearing throughout the session. She stomped her feet a couple of times. She picked up a Kleenex from the floor and threw it vigorously on the floor; then apparently deciding she oughtn't to do that, she picked it up, stomped to the waste paper basket, and threw it vigorously and emphatically in it. End of scene."

There are times when a more direct disciplining attitude was required; this we did most frequently by cutting the ground from under her big "scenes" rather than by any forceful show of authority. An excerpt from a therapy note may illustrate this: "Elizabeth still prefers swinging to any other activity, and Carole has to remove the red box from the room to reduce the degree of temptation for Elizabeth (her preferred mode of swinging at the moment was in the red box). Elizabeth is disappointed and angry. She asserts her disappointment by lying on the floor and crying. At which moment, both the therapists start counting rhythmically, making noise with their hands or their foot as they lie on the floor beside her; they act like a referee in a wrestling match. Elizabeth stops her 'scene' quickly and gets intrigued with the counting, and ends up happy and ready to go again."

Of course, the problems of discipline were attended to both at home and at school, where a great emphasis also was given to the development in Elizabeth of verbal communicative skills. At school, the teachers were patient but also quietly insistent that Elizabeth conform to socially acceptable forms of behavior. "Elizabeth threw a puzzle piece on the floor, and when Mrs. G. insisted that she pick it up, she screamed and threw another piece. Mrs. G. stuck with her and kept repeating gently to pick up the pieces. Suddenly Elizabeth responded, and returned the pieces to the table in their proper spot on the puzzle." Another note from the teacher two days later describes a similar scene. "She threw the entire puzzle on the floor and screamed when asked to pick it up. I waited for a few minutes, went back, and gently asked her to pick it all up. She picked it all up as though I had made only one request. Later in the morning she repeated the whole process, almost like a routine to her. She appears to want only to do things when *she* wants to do them." The development of self-assertive, aggressive behavior in Elizabeth is also noted by the teachers and by the children around her at school. "When Susan took something away from Elizabeth today, she fought back; a very much surprised Susan! . . . Elizabeth now places her coat and hat in my lap before getting dressed to go home. She tries to keep the other children away. If they want my attention, she throws her head in my lap to keep them away. She often appears to want affection. She has become quite aggressive and negative which are encouraging signs to us. The aggression towards the children is the first real indication of her social awareness of them."

At home, the parents also worked hard in helping Elizabeth acquire controls and good social habits. "She wouldn't eat her dinner tonight," writes her mother. "She was just fooling around, so I took her away from the table for awhile. When I brought her back, she ate a little and then started putting her fingers in her food, so I just took it away from her. . . . When we arrived home from the hospital, Elizabeth wanted to go outside so I let her out in the back yard. She played there for awhile, and then she went out front and sat in the street again. I spanked her and brought her in the house, but I wonder if she knows why she is being punished! However, after lunch, Elizabeth and I played outside on the swing, and she had a good time. I left her outside by herself for a short time. She stayed in the back and didn't go near the street."

It is obvious that everyone tends to be rather lenient and gentle in their disciplining efforts with Elizabeth. Somehow everyone knows that

Elizabeth will do things when she is ready to, and that her negativism or slight aggressive outbursts do not require extreme measures of self-defense by adults or children around her. This capacity of Elizabeth's to do things when she is ready finds illustration also in her progressive acquisition of language. During this period, she learned many new words at home and at school which she could use in a discrete fashion without combining them in sentence form. This achievement appeared to be emerging, as is noted by the mother: "Elizabeth walked out of her room just as I came out of mine this morning, and she greeted me with 'Hi,' 'tick-tock,' 'up' ('Hi, it's time to get up'). She was talking quite a bit today. Just after lunch she was trying to repeat almost every word we said to her." We noted also at the clinic this emerging mastery of language in Elizabeth, especially as she would join us in singing accompaniment to various activities. Thus, if we started "Old MacDonald Had a Farm," Elizabeth would chime "ee-ii-ee-ii-o," or if we sang "See-Saw, Marjorie Daw" as we played teeter-totter, she would put her own words: "I see you!" to that tune.

The increasing structure in Elizabeth's life as well as her continued and progressive acquisition of new skills encouraged us to introduce two new testing instruments when she was scheduled for another evaluation at the end of nine months of upbringing. Elizabeth was 4 years old at this point, and the repetition of the Merrill-Palmer scales, on which she obtained an IQ of 100, reassured us that she had not lost any of the skills which are specifically tapped by this test. Furthermore, her continued and dramatic increase in those social skills measured by the Vineland—this time she obtains an SQ of 74 (age equivalent 2 years, 11 months) which represents a seven-months gain over a period of three months, and which illustrates clearly the impact of the nursery school on the development of her social competence—gave us reasons to believe that the time had come to assess how ready Elizabeth might be for anticipated kindergarten experiences and further development of her symbolic and verbal skills.

The introduction of the Stanford-Binet was directly aimed at measuring her verbal achievements; and the use for the first time of the Leiter International Performance Scale, which is an entirely nonverbal instrument, would give us, we hoped, a good measure of her developing conceptual abilities.

On the Stanford-Binet, Elizabeth based at year II, her expressive language having developed sufficiently to enable her to pass the picture vocabulary and the word combination items. She reached a ceiling at year IV, having passed two items Identifying Parts of the Body and Three-Hole Board Rotated at II–6; four items at year III, Stringing Beads, Block Building, Copying a Circle, and Drawing a Vertical Line; and one item at year III–6, Patience: Pictures. Thus with one exception (Sorting Buttons, at year III–6) all failures were on verbal items. Nevertheless, Elizabeth's functioning on the Stanford-Binet gives her a Mental Age of 2 years, 7 months and an IQ of 64.

The Leiter International Performance Scale compared very well with the scores that Elizabeth had obtained on the Merrill-Palmer. She attained a mental age of 4 years and an IQ of 104 (corrected S-B mean of 100 and S–D of 15). She based at year II and ceilinged at VI. Items passed at year III include Four Forms, Picture Completion, and Number Discrimination; for some reason she failed Block Design which we would have expected to be a "cinch" for her. At year IV she passed Form and Color, Eight Forms, and Form, Color, Number; but she could not do Count Four. Items Genus, and Two Color Circles were successfully completed at year V, but Clothing and Block Design were failed. It is evident from Elizabeth's performance that not only is she capable of attention and concentration, but demonstrates in a variety of ways the beginning of functions involving knowledge of spatial relationships and some degree of conceptual thinking.

Ninth through 12th month of treatment. Such functions are products of both maturation and learning, and we have been able to witness throughout Elizabeth's development that new skills and competencies appear only when Elizabeth is ready to express them. Thus it is not surprising that we should see some fluctuations in her test performance three months after the previous examination. This was to be her final evaluation after one year of treatment, and again this time both the Leiter and the Stanford-Binet were readministered. Elizabeth's performance on the Leiter was somewhat more erratic this time, but her functioning on the Stanford-Binet, on the other hand, reflected considerable improvement.

On the Leiter, Elizabeth based at year III and reached a ceiling at year VII. Evidence of her increasing conceptual development appears in her passing one test at year VI, Analogies Progression. But it is clear that concept formation still remains for her in a somewhat fluctuating condition as if it were not fully developed or completely consolidated.

Thus, for instance, items which she had previously passed at years IV and V (Form, Color, Number; Genus; Two Color Circles) are failed, whereas one item previously failed (Block Design) is now successfully performed. Her IQ dropped from 104 to 96, which represented a six-month decrease in mental age and served to remind us that Elizabeth's progress could very well retain the unevenness displayed in any normal child's development.

If we look at the Stanford-Binet, on the other hand, Elizabeth shows an appreciable gain. Her IQ increases to 71 from the previous 64; this represents an advance of five months over a three-month testing interval. This gain is primarily a reflection of her increasing verbal activities, rather than a function of test repetition. She achieves a basal at year II–6: She is able to "identify objects by use, name objects, pass the picture vocabulary, repeat two digits, and obey simple commands," all items which are verbal in nature. At year III she passes Block Building, Copying a Circle, Drawing a Vertical Line and Repeating Three Digits. As she had done previously, one item at year III–6, Patience: Pictures, is passed; also passed was one item, Discrimination of Forms, at year IV. The ceiling was reached at IV–6, a level of entirely verbal subtests requiring much more complex verbal concept expression than Elizabeth was yet capable of displaying. The steady movement forward in verbal and conceptual skills, which Elizabeth was able to display here, gave real hope that plans could be realistically made for her continued participation in school activities the following year.

Additional increments in social maturity made these expectations even more valid. Compared with her Social Quotient of six months ago (61) Elizabeth's Vineland at this time reflects a gain of a full 12 months in social competence (SQ 80, age equivalent 3 years, 4 months). This progress appears even more impressive when we look back at her original Vineland score one year before at the outset of treatment which showed Elizabeth with an SQ of 43, age equivalent 1 year, 5 months.

As a social being, Elizabeth had had many profitable experiences in this year; and in those areas of behavior on which she was rated at this time, and which compare her with normal children of her age, we also see that she has become very much a human individual in her own rights. On all scales picturing the degree of her involvement with people, and her affective responsiveness to them (Affectionateness (1.1), Sense of Humor (7.1), Friendliness (3.14), Gregariousness (3.15)), all raters indicate dramatic improvement; there is somewhat less Negativism (6.1) and more Obedience (3.22) and Conformity (1.7), but there is also an increase in self-assertion and Aggressiveness (1.2). Raters also agree that Elizabeth's Curiosity (2.11) remains high but that it has acquired more Planfulness (5.1), more Patience (4.1) and Tenacity (8.3). Elizabeth continues to be a Cheerful (1.5) child, and the world about her appears exciting (2.11) and worth discovering.

Elizabeth is very much part of this world now. The "bunny rabbit" so fluffy and lovable in her isolation, which we had seen a year ago, has now grown into a real child (even physically, Elizabeth, who in the years prior to treatment, had seemed to remain retarded in her physical growth, showed a sudden spurt during this year, gaining a full five inches in height, as compared to the previous year's gain of half an inch). Of her autistic behavior there still remain some signs, but it is interesting that when we showed movies of her taken at the nursery school, and demanded of a group of professionals to point out the "autistic" child in the school room, not a single one pointed to her. Elizabeth has still a great deal of growing to do, but the hope we had that she could truly be made part of the human family has found support and realization in Elizabeth's own driving effort at expressing the infi-

Table 4

ELIZABETH

		Months in Treatment			
	Initial Evaluation	*3 Months*	*6 Months*	*9 Months*	*1 Year*
Chronological age	3 years 3 months	3 years 6 months	3 years 9 months	4 years	4 years 3 months
Vineland	SQ 43 AE 1 yr. 5 mo.	SQ 51 AE 1–11	SQ 61 AE 2–4	SQ 74 AE 2–11	SQ 80 AE 3–4
Cattell	IQ 54 MA 19.8 mo.	IQ 52 MA 22 mo.	IQ 58 MA 25.4 mo.		
Stanford-Binet				IQ 64 MA 2–7	IQ 71 MA 3–0
Merrill-Palmer		IQ 76 MA 2–8	IQ 95 MA 3–6	IQ 100 MA 4–0	
Leiter				IQ 104 MA 4–0	IQ 96 MA 3–9

nite expectation in her that, given a chance, she could be a normal child.

A note from the mother, written toward this end of the year, gives us the refreshing and delightful picture of Elizabeth, "member of the family": "I let Elizabeth set the table for dinner tonight. She was so excited she kept jumping up and down. I thought she did very well. She knew where to put the plates. She did put two knives in one place, but when I pointed this out to her, she corrected it. The only other thing she did incorrectly was that she put the knives upside down." Elizabeth still has a mind of her own, but in asserting her independence, she still very much wants to sit at the table with all those who are now so much in her heart.

Tommy

SUMMARY

Age at Outset of Treatment: 2 years, 3 months.

Treatment Period: April 1966 to June 1967.

Schedule of Sessions: 2 hourly sessions per week on outpatient basis (due to numerous illnesses and family vacations, Tommy was able to attend only approximately half of the scheduled sessions).

Drugs: None.

Schedule of Testing and Results: Initial diagnostic evaluation, March 1966 (Vineland SQ 54; Cattell IQ 57: MA 14.8 months); tested at three-month intervals thereafter (see Table 5); final evaluation, April 1967, at age 3 years, 3 months (Vineland SQ 73; Cattell IQ 70: MA 2 years, 3 months).

Language: No receptive or expressive language initially; at end of treatment, good receptive language but little expressive language.

School Placement: None prior to or during treatment. Currently attending a day-care treatment center for disturbed children.

We first met Tommy and his parents at the Evaluation Center where he had just completed a series of diagnostic tests. The youngest subject, as it turned out, in this project (2 years, 3 months), he was also, at the onset of treatment, the most difficult to reach. His behavior was characterized by aimless and useless roaming about, complete avoidance of any human contact, loud and frequent whining, or irritability whenever he was approached by anyone. He appeared incapable of showing or tolerating affectionate gestures; he was unresponsive to any demands made on him and was unhappy and isolated most of the time. Fear ruled a great deal of his behavior, especially with regard to spatial situations involving certain parts of the house, or certain parts of certain rooms in the house. He had no way of communicating his needs either verbally or nonverbally; and he had no interest in anything except his fingers, which he twisted and twirled endlessly before his eyes. He presented many feeding problems and initially had a diet which consisted mainly of crackers and vitamins. In the observation room where we first saw him, and in which he appeared completely miserable, forlorn, and lost, he toddled restlessly from one end of the room to the other, whining and crying, without any show of interest in anything. Irritably, he wanted nothing to do with us when we first tried to approach him, deliberately avoiding us, and yet obviously unhappy and lost in his loneliness. Our first move was directed at both restricting the area of his restless roaming, and at somehow forcing some physical contact with us. We both got on our hands and knees on the floor and used our bodies to limit, without eliminating, his immediate life space. If he were to try to avoid us, he would have somehow to bump into us first. In spite of his anxiety and discomfort, Tommy, little by little, became somewhat calmer, which emboldened us to reach for him and touch some part of his body as he passed close by us. First, he paid little attention as if not feeling such stimulations; eventually he became aware that something was happening to him, and though he wasn't sure whether he should like it or not, he was quite willing to tolerate it without too much fuss.

First three months of treatment. It was this same approach which we used a few days later when Tommy was brought to the clinic for his first treatment session. This time, however, the quality of stimulation which he finally experienced, especially when as he passed by us we tickled his ears, appeared to have a truly pleasurable effect on him. At one point, he touched his own ear as if to make sure that the pleasure he was experiencing belonged there, and then he reached out for the therapist's hand and brought it up to his ear to be stimulated again. In this first session, we learned from Tommy that he could be responsive to, and actively involved with, human sensory contacts; we also saw in him a beginning of communication in his efforts at expressing his need for pleasurable sensations. Fortunately, his parents, who had observed our approach to him from the beginning, caught on very quickly to this simple truth: Tommy could be reached by them, and all the irritation and resistance he showed at their overtures toward him should not be taken as a refusal on his part to be with them. The mother's first note, April, 1966, reflected this very clearly. "Tommy seems a little more interested in feeling and touching things. He seems more willing and even eager to hold my hand (but maybe I just never offered it to him as often). He's come to me a couple of times when I asked him to just keep me company (no food or drink involved). He seems to want me to stay very close to him while he eats, and throws his spoon on the floor much less often if I am nearby, but he is eating almost nothing, and that little in the tiniest bites I ever saw. He drinks a lot."

The initial evaluation prior to treatment showed Tommy with a Social Quotient of 54 (age equivalent: 1 year, 2 months, at a chronological age of 2 years, 3 months). He could walk by himself, pull off his socks, and reach for some familiar objects which he would transfer from one place to the other. The psychological test report gives us a somewhat overoptimistic idea of Tommy's performance on the Cattell Infant Intelligence Scale: "On the Cattell, Thomas was credited for all items at the 11-month level. At the 12-month level, he was able to insert cubes in a cup; mark up a paper with a pencil spontaneously, but was quite distracted by the details of the pencil; and he was also able to rattle a spoon against a cup, though he did so very awkwardly. He failed the beating of the spoon and refused to hit the doll in imitation of the examiner. At the 14-month level, the only item which he failed was the pellet-bottle problem, where he became interested in the bottle very briefly and could not be induced to perform any further. At the 16-month level, he was successful on the formboard item and on the pegboard item, but his interest could not be engaged to perform on the other items at that level. Similarly, he was credited for two items at the 18-month level, the cubes in the cup and the pegboard. When asked to play with a doll, he seemed quite frightened of it. He ceased to perform on the formboard item at this level and was not interested in scribbling with a pencil. The examination was discontinued shortly thereafter. On this basis, he obtained a mental age of 14.8 months which corresponds to an IQ of 57."

For all practical purposes, during the entire period of treatment, this was the last we saw of any cooperation on the part of Tommy in any formal standardized testing. His discovery of his human environment absorbed his entire energies. Two weeks after the beginning of treatment, a note from the mother illustrates dramatically Tommy's awakening to a keen awareness of important human beings in his life: "Tommy came running out of the kitchen looking around wildly. As soon as he saw me, he ran right over and burrowed in my lap. After a while he'd had enough and left. Another time he didn't look panic-stricken, but came and went about a dozen times, apparently just making sure I was there. He's been standing up in his crib the last few mornings waiting for me. I don't have to coax him out anymore. He even tries to climb out by climbing on me, if I go in before he's gone to sleep for his nap. His appetite has picked up enormously (maybe because he's not sitting around so much?). Two nights ago I tried scrambled eggs on him for the thousandth time. After a minute or two, he dove right in and gobbled them up as though he hadn't acted as if they were poison for months and months. The first eggs or meat he's eaten in a long, long time! He's eating with such gusto! Most of the time, lately, he seems so much happier. My husband thinks so too. And he very often *wants* to play (that is wants to be fondled, hugged, tickled, and so forth). He acts as though he would actually rather play with us than alone (not always, of course), which is almost unbelievable after all this time. He just seems more friendly and affectionate. I realize it's not that simple, but it certainly does make *us* more friendly."

What Tommy learned with us was to play. At first, even the pleasure he experienced in his contacts with his parents or with us appeared to remain a serious business with him. And it was. To want people; to reach out for people and to find, in interacting with them, some kind of new life flowing through every part of his little self was, for Tommy, something he wanted seriously and relentlessly to explore. ("While I was resting on the bed in Tommy's room, he came over—away from his crib—to see me, and be tickled and hugged voluntarily and eagerly four or five times, maybe more!" Mother's note, one month after treatment began.) Each new experience brought on a mixture of fear and pleasure, but the pleasure was worth seeking, so that the fear progressively disappeared. Even physically, Tommy was thawing out after years of a winter of isolation. His mother pictures this colorfully in one of her notes: "The thing that's really fascinating me right now is that his face is sort of unfreezing. (I hadn't realized that it was frozen.) His eyes seem bigger, as though he's really seeing things, and he has positively smiled and grinned at me, not that faraway smirk. Several times *he* has sought *my* eyes and smiled (not the reverse as is usual)."

As Tommy "loosens up," tentatively initiating moments of tenderness and pleasure, he allows himself, also more buoyantly, to get into the "game" of living like a child. Our therapy notes, in these past months of treatment, capture, in Tommy, the movement from pleasure to play. "Tommy was in very good humor today. His eye contact is improving more and more, and so is his frustration tolerance. The sink and the water remain his great attraction. Carole spent a great deal of time throwing the wet washcloth on his head. He feels the cold water but doesn't seem to react with pain or fear. He pulls off the washcloth and lets it fall to the floor but Carole catches it quickly and throws it on his head again. Occasionally, Tommy walks to the other end of the room with the cloth on his head and throws it on the floor by the door. Though he is obviously not unhappy but rather intrigued by this washcloth business, he seems to be unable to decide whether he likes it or not." Ten days later: "Tommy in very good shape generally, quite friendly. More eye contact than at any previous session. He enjoys being swung in the air, especially being lifted high over the therapist's head; eye contact also good during this. Repeatedly enjoys having wet, cold washcloth thrown on his head. He pulls it off, and either throws it down or tries to put it back over his head himself. Finally may be getting the idea that this is a game and is fun." One week later: "Tommy appears to be discovering that most activities with the therapists are fun. He's learning how to play by actually responding in a less serious way to the various interactions. For instance, when Carole puts the wet washcloth over his face and head, he runs to the end of the room and throws it in the corner. The large grin on his face makes it clear that he is not too serious about the whole deal, especially when he stands expecting the cloth to be put on his head again."

In this atmosphere of play and fun, it was obvious that Tommy was losing a great many of his fears and showing more and more spontaneity and initiative in his behavior. This was not all pleasant but was certainly lively. "He is not throwing his spoon on the floor much now," writes the mother. "He's dreamed up a fiendish variation: He shakes spoonfuls of food on the floor and then looks me straight in the eye as if daring me to do something about it. He obviously knows it is wrong. No luck breaking him of that so far. Sometimes (usually when he's eating, and oh, what a mess) he reaches over and grabs my hair and pulls my face close to his; sort of fun. He's very amused by my touching his tongue; try it, it's really wild! We had two guests recently who hadn't seen Tommy before. Both, when I told them Tommy was autistic, were rather surprised, and said he seemed quite ordinary to them (they had no children of their own, so it is not *that* surprising). What I'm trying to say is that there are times these days when Tommy seems quite ordinary to *me* too. More eye contact and more friendliness, I guess. My husband said yesterday that Tommy darted out of the door (he will do that like greased lightning—my husband forgets) and half walked and half fell down a short flight of steps all by himself. I was going to try letting Tommy go by himself this morning, but he reached up and seized my hand, so I let him have it. He has a grip of iron. Another new thing with him happens occasionally at lunch. If he finishes his lunch first, and I let him down, he tugs at me to be picked up while I sit feeding Susie. He usually stands in my lap; looks like an acrobatic act when we are in full swing. One great thing happened this week. We had gone for a fairly long walk, and he was getting irritable. We stopped outside a building at the university, and he found one of those sand ashtrays and was having a great time heaving the sand around. All of a sudden, with no prompting at all, he came marching over with an old cigarette for me. He ultimately brought me five of them. The first and only gift he's ever given me. Needless to say I was very pleased with him, and he was very pleased with himself. It was heart warming, to say the least. I sure would like to see *that* happen again."

The three-month testing period came and went, and we had no formal results to show. Tommy was very disappointed to have his play session with us preempted by a child psychologist wanting him to rattle a spoon in a cup. He was more interested in the psychologist than in the various items of the Cattell; a cup is to drink with, and a spoon to eat with; he tried this but received no score for his performance. The Vineland, on the other hand, gave some measure of his increased initiative and socialization. Tommy had matured six months during this period, demonstrating mostly his increased interest in his surroundings, his decreasing fears in attempting new tasks and in being in new situations, and overall, his newly acquired capacity to move about freely in his home.

Third through sixth month of treatment. In the following six months, many sessions were missed because of illness or family vacations. Though these circumstances were in some respects unfortunate, they had nevertheless some positive value in enlarging Tommy's world of people, and in helping him overcome his natural fear of strange places. Our work with him at the clinic, in many respects, focused also on helping him overcome a somewhat similar type of fear directly related to physical space. We knew that part of his idiosyncratic response to his home environment included restricting himself to certain rooms of the house and even, within each room, to certain areas. It was as if for him there existed an imaginary line across a room which he dared not transgress. At the clinic, when we first attempted some swinging games with him, we noticed very early that he became very uncomfortable at losing contact with the floor, and that somehow, in order to reassure him, we had to have his feet touch the floor very often during any swinging games. He had to feel the world solidly under him to be completely at peace. And it became very important to help him progressively find, by *seeing* the floor—that is, touching it with his eyes—the reassurance he experienced when he touched the floor with his feet. We exploited his great need to be close to us in bringing him to climb up on chairs by having the therapist climb up first; Tommy would soon follow after. From this height, and in the reassuring closeness of the therapist, Tommy could allow himself to relax and survey the floor below, so that it was progressively possible to have him jump from the chair into the therapist's arms, which of course involved a short moment of swinging. Tommy caught on to the fun of all this, climbed the chair himself, which also allowed him to explore the light switch on the wall, and then jumped off into the therapist's arms, and the swinging would go on. From the chair, we had Tommy climbing up to the little table; this meant that he had to push the chair over to the table, climb on it, stand on it, and from there climb up onto the table. ("One thing to report, Tommy actually climbed all the way up on a small loveseat in the house, twice. First time he's really crawled all the way onto something. I don't think that it's that he's so cautious—just seems unwilling to put forth full effort on anything very frustrating. He now seems to have lost all fear of our bedroom. That leaves only the porch which he is still checking out.")

The mother's incidental comment to the effect that Tommy, in her words, "just seems unwilling to put forth full effort on anything very frustrating," may serve to emphasize that these various activities in the therapy room, which Tommy was able to carry out with us, required of him the mobilization of an unusual amount of energy. He appeared so lazy sometimes, and any effort he would show, for instance, at climbing a chair, had to be accompanied by vociferous, encouraging, and prompting cheers. We considered it a major victory over his "laziness" when he actually pushed a chair over to the wall or table.

But it wasn't complete laziness on the part of Tommy. It was, at this time, when he liked so much to be around the important people in his life, a sort of infinite expectation that if the chips were down somebody would help him do what he felt required too much effort from him. It is in this light that we saw also, in part, his reluctance to fully complete any task that he had set himself upon. For instance, he could very well put round pegs through the round hole in the cover of a small cage; all we had to do was hand him a block and he would shove it through the hole. However, for some reason, he would always stop after three as if to let us know: "Well folks, you've seen it, now let's get down to our regular games." Such performances were very frustrating, and we had to find ways of taking advantage of his interest in games with us to help him extend the scope of his efforts. One of our swinging games involved an old wooden milk bottle box which had been painted red. Tommy discovered that he could climb into the box, sit in it, and, while holding on to the sides, be swung back and forth in front of the mirror. This was such a wonderful experience for him that it became his favorite game. Obviously we capitalized on that. Before any swing, and after any swing, in the red box, when Tommy was comfortably seated in it, we would place the "cage" inside the box with him, hand him the blocks to shove through the cover, and cheer him on. Tommy somehow knew that "he'd been had," and whenever he had put forth the energy required in shoving three blocks through the holes, he would stop and roar if we had the nerve to hand him a fourth and fifth block. This non-violent protest did not dissuade us from our appointed task; we kept handing him blocks and cheering him on. By and by, to the accompaniment of intermittent roars, he not only consented to complete that simple task, but he also agreed to string beads, place puzzle pieces on a board, and stick pegs in a board. His eagerness at completing such tasks —he obviously felt so pleased with himself—even led him to use both hands, reaching for one item while putting the other in place. In the face of such unqualified success we kept praying that the child psychologist, at her next testing of Tommy, would find enough energy to overcome Tommy's laziness. No such luck. The next testing (October 1966) was just as frustrating to the psychologist as it was disappointing to us. Tommy did, however, almost manage to get the examiner into the red box with him!

It is clear from our description of Tommy's response to swinging in the red box that he had by this time managed to overcome in great part his "spatial" fears. This new security in him made possible his enjoyment of many new situations at home, as well as of new environments when his parents took him on various trips and vacations.

A number of notes from the mother give some idea of Tommy's new adaptive competence. September, 1966: "Initially, Tommy was very nervous when we had arrived in Boston; afraid for a little while to move

out of one room, and had his hands going in those funny hand movements like mad. After a while he seemed to settle right in. He even ate
in a high chair *at a table.* As we got closer to my sister's wedding, hordes
of people started to come. Tommy started to become really upset. One
night, I just whisked him away and put him to bed; that seems to have
been a turning point. From then on he was fine—laughed, played with
everyone, and generally had a good time. Adjusted to the crowds very
well, I thought. In general, I think he's come through the vacation all
right and possibly also improved in his relations with people because
of it. We'll see. . . . Wants to go out every day. Very good when I did
the grocery shopping Saturday; very patient and not frightened in the
store. . . . At my husband's parents, he spent hours going up and down
stairs in a sort of crawling, sliding way. His youngest aunt (age 17, a
very bright girl) was just fascinated by Tommy and played with him a
very great deal. They were great friends by the time we left. His other
aunt came to see us yesterday (she lives in Chicago), and he held out his
hands to be picked up. She was pleased to death; he'd never done that
before (she would remember). He found an old coffee pot's insides while
we were at his grandparents and kept putting the stem into the top.
They all cheered and yelled, and he thought it was just great; did it for
ages. I had thought the vacation didn't do him any particular good,
but he's been so happy since he's been home that maybe it did. Coming
back, both kids were in the back seat (filled with pillows) and loose.
They were just great. They played with toys, me, and each other. Quite
a bit of interaction. He was fascinated by her when she was asleep,
touched her eyes, ears, and hair. Still seems more interested in her than
he used to be. . . . Susie is still giving her all. Yesterday she got a box of
wheaties and was giving them to him one by one, and he was taking
them. Was lots of fun to watch; didn't end up in a fight either! She's
trying to catch his eye these days, I think, and sometimes succeeds. She
talks to him off and on, too. This morning it sounded as if she were
speaking his language to him. She's such a friendly soul, and since she
seems to be taking the lead a bit now, I have hopes she may get through
to him. He is playing with toys much more. Very little rocking on the
floor lately."

Finally a note from Tommy's father at that time highlights in a con-
cise fashion some of the main features of Tommy's behavior at the end
of six months of treatment.

"Since, as was noted Monday, fathers are not very good about writing these notes, I am not precisely sure what I should include. But I will make an attempt.

"It seems to me that in the last two weeks or so, Tommy has left a plateau, or perhaps a period of slight regression, and has begun to improve again. In the evenings after I return from work, he joins the rest of the family in the living room or dining room rather than playing alone in his room. He seems eager to crawl all over me, and tonight ventured into areas of the living room that he usually avoids. He also seems to be responding better to commands, requests, and so forth. Last night, when I caught him removing all the books from the bookcase in the living room and told him to stop, he rather hurriedly replaced as many as he could. He did not return them to the shelves from which they had been removed, but he did make the attempt; and he quite obviously knew that what he had done did not meet with my approval. In the past, he would have completely ignored me until such time as I took the books away from him.

"He also seems to be much more conscious of Susie. He used to consider her part of the furniture; now he apparently realizes that she is here to stay. Each of them frequently makes an attempt to upstage the other, and they continually bicker over cookies, a treasured toy, and so forth—all of which is normal and desirable, I suppose.

"It seems to me that Tommy stopped growing following his return from the East Coast in late August. Our vacation in October also probably helped to upset him. But now that our home life has settled into a routine, and his visits to the clinic are regular, he has begun to move forward again, at least in my opinion. It is difficult to document this opinion with specific events; perhaps it will suffice to say that he seems much more aware of people, events, and objects.

"Several of the more obvious antisocial traits have disappeared—spitting on everything, removing his clothes when his pants are dirty, and such. I also feel that he is trying to communicate, although the few words he says are very indistinct. He tells us he wants something by tugging at clothes, climbing on us, screaming, bringing us objects, and so on.

"I'm afraid this has been too general and not very helpful. The one point I do want to make, however, is that Tommy seems somehow more involved in what is going on, more affectionate, more demanding, happier (or sadder, as the case may be)—life seems to be more fun for him."

At the end of six months, Tommy was not any more ready to accept any formal testing than he had ever been, but his Vineland Social Maturity Scale shows a slight decrease in the momentum of his social growth (SQ 63, age equivalent 1 year, 9 months). In his note above, Tommy's father explains in part this decrease by referring to it as a plateau.

Sixth through 12th month of treatment.   There were many more such plateaus in Tommy's adventure with us during the next six months, and it is only at the end of this period that we can record on the Vineland a substantial increment in social maturity (SQ 73, age equivalent 2 years, 4 months). Somehow, though we were truly disappointed in Tommy's slow measurable progress, we were never discouraged with him. There was so much life and exuberance in his behavior, as well as a sort of primitive disregard for anything that would seem to be arbitrarily imposed on him from the outside. Obviously, he needed structure, a type of structure that, in the enjoyment of having found a real, roaring, rambunctious boy, the mother was somewhat reluctant to give him. (Mother's note: "Tommy has continued looking me in the eye as he throws food on the floor. Now he's even starting to laugh after I scold him. I try not to be too stern; so now he knows I'll probably smile after I scold him. When he grins like that I can't help grinning back.")

In the therapy room, Tommy had come to expect consistency and structure, as well as affection and fun, in all of his activities with us. Whenever he roared in protest, we duly recorded his vociferous complaint, but relentlessly pursued whatever task we were engaged in. If he liked the pleasurable sensation of falling from a tower of blocks into the arms of his therapist, he had to build the tower himself, stacking and lining up the blocks properly, even when he tried to let us know that he didn't like to do that much work. If he wanted a drink of water, he had to push blocks or a chair to the sink; and if he wanted to swing on a board or in the red box, he had to bring us the board or drag out the red box. There was no end to his dissent, and yet he was always happy to be with us, so that for him, in the truest way, we can say that his roar was louder than his bite was fierce. This was his form of independence. He maintained it to the end. The struggles his mother had in teaching him how to eat properly are recorded in her notes, and read like the story of David and Goliath. Sometimes the giant had the upper hand, and sometimes little boy David; in the end it was always Goliath who was on the floor picking up the mess that Tommy had been allowed to make. Similarly, attempts at toilet training offered Tommy his greatest moments of fiendish triumph over any conventional rules and regulations. It is not surprising then that even a trained child psychologist could not get him to do her bidding, even in those tasks in which he had proven himself completely masterful and competent. After one year of treatment, his performance on the Cattell is far from reflecting his true abilities. He would not be pressured into a standardized mold, and though the assertion of his independence was in no way tyrannical, his staunch refusal to do anything when he didn't want to do it (because there was no fun in it for him) could be very unnerving to whomever had great expectations.

In order, nevertheless, to obtain some valid estimate of his intellectual development at the end of one year of treatment, some items, both of the Merrill-Palmer Scale and of the Stanford-Binet Intelligence Scale, were administered by the therapist. Tommy was able successfully to pass the Wallin Pegboard tests A and B at the 24- to 29-month level; he could identify himself in the mirror (25-month level), place accurately the forms in the three-hole formboard of the Stanford-Binet (age 2 years) and string beads (S-B age 3). He could also build a tower of eight large cubes (30 months), and could communicate by gestures his wishes for drink or play (24 months). Thus at the age of 3 years, 2 months, Tommy's mental age could more validly be estimated at 2 years, 4 months, giving him an IQ of approximately 70.

In spite of his many absences from the treatment program due to illness or to trips away from home, Tommy's steady personality growth over the year is attested to most markedly by his scores on the 15 Fels Behavior Rating Scales. On all these scales, all raters agreed (agreement significant beyond the 0.001 level of confidence) that, in those areas of behavior described by the scales, impressive improvements had taken place. Most dramatic for Tommy were gains in those patterns of behavior involving contact with people (Affectionateness 1.1; Friendliness 3.14), responsiveness to human interaction (Conformity 1.7; Obedience 3.22), and playfulness (Cheerful-Depressed 1.5). With regard to the variety of fear responses which were so characteristic of Tommy's behavior at the beginning of treatment, the rating scales indicate also a striking change for the better: Tommy acts now with much more social competence, he is attentive and curious, and he can tolerate with a greater degree of patience the small or big frustrations he encounters in his activities.

Thus at the end of one year, the home observer's notes, as well as the ratings, describe Tommy as having moved from complete isolation to a high degree of human involvement; he loves people now and seeks to be with people; he does not avoid eye contact and is not irritated at being intruded upon; he goes easily from one place to the other and his fears of certain rooms or of car rides have generally disappeared; he has learned a certain degree of meaningful independence in asserting himself with his younger sister, in carrying out certain play activities by himself, and in taking care of himself in small ways. Perhaps the last note we received from Tommy's father summarizes best how well Tommy has progressively become a true participant in the family life.

"It has been a long time between notes, but I feel confident that my wife has kept you fully informed. Still, I feel as though I should offer my own observations, such as they are.

"After a rather low period during the holidays, we both think, I feel, that Tommy has made perceptible improvement. He rarely goes off by himself to play these days, preferring to remain on the periphery of the action, if not participating himself. He may dart out of a room for brief periods, but usually does not stay away long. And, rather than just submitting passively to my attempts to play with him, I now find him eager to be tossed around. If he is in an especially good mood, he will grab me by the arm rather forcefully, and insist that I play with him. If, after a long period of play, I try to stop, he becomes very obviously annoyed.

"Tommy seems to interact—if that is the correct sociological jargon—much more with Susie these days. They play together with various toys and with my wife and me, and do not seem to fight over objects as much, except where food is involved. It is no holds barred when one or the other has a graham cracker, for example.

"One new thing we have tried is to let Tommy stay up an hour or so later at night after Susie has gone to bed (approximately 8:30–9:30). His mood is generally good at this time, and he tends to be much more outgoing without the competition for our attention provided by Susie. When she is around, she tends to upstage him. This new arrangement seems to be a satisfactory one in view of the fact that Susie apparently needs many hours more sleep than he does. His naps are shorter; he gets up earlier; and he goes to bed later.

"Tommy still does not react well to new physical surroundings (outside for example), but I feel that this will improve when spring comes (if it ever does), and we can get him outside more. The weather has been so bad that he hasn't been out at all, except to go to the Clinic. New people, however, do not seem to bother him as much as new surroundings.

"I may be wrong—it could be wishful thinking—but it seems to me that on several occasions after prompting, Tommy has said something resembling 'Hi, Daddy.' The inflection is odd, but it sounds like he is attempting to make words. We are, incidentally, more certain that he understands us. When food is mentioned, he scurries to the table, and when he is told not to touch something, he pulls back.

"Toilet training remains a serious problem. He is very irregular, so it is difficult to find the right time to put him on the toilet (we have never hit the right one, in fact). His appetite is good, although the foods he will eat are very limited. So much for specifics.

"In general, I find him to be much more alert and responsive. He is more likely to smile when happy, pout when annoyed, come when called, return affection when it is given, demand something he wants, and so forth."

With Tommy, at the end of one year, our work with him obviously represented just a good beginning. The strides he had made in becoming a real boy, alive and responsive, held the promise that for him also there existed a world to discover and master, and real happiness to possess. In this year, to use the mother's expression, Tommy's face "unfroze," his eyes opened, and he truly began to see himself and others around him; and this vision before his eyes was filled with wondrous delight and infinite expectation. He still had a long way to go, but his parents knew now that their task of being present to him, though a relentless and demanding one, need never be a hopeless one. Tommy was roaring for them.

Table 5

TOMMY

		Months in Treatment			
	Initial Evaluation	*3 Months*	*6 Months*	*9 Months*	*12 Months*
Chronological age	2 years 3 months	2 years 6 months	2 years 9 months	3 years	3 years 3 months
Vineland	SQ 54 AE 1–2	SQ 67 AE 1–8	SQ 63 AE 1–9	SQ 63 AE 1–11	SQ 73 AE 2–4
Cattell	IQ 57 MA 14.8 mo.	Untestable—materials age-inappropriate			Estimated IQ 70

June

SUMMARY

Age at Outset of Treatment: 4 years, 10 months.

Treatment Period: June 1966 to June 1967.

Schedule of Sessions: 2 hourly sessions per week on outpatient basis.

Drugs: None during treatment; recently placed on Dexedrine with resulting marked improvement in attention span.

Schedule of Testing and Results: Initial diagnostic evaluation, June 1966 (Vineland SQ 118; Merrill Palmer IQ 84: MA 4 years, 1 month; Stanford-Binet IQ 87: MA 4 years, 3 months); tested at three-month intervals thereafter (see Table 6); final evaluation, May 1967, at age 5 years, 9 months (Vineland SQ 139; Stanford-Binet IQ 102: MA 5 years, 10 months).

Language: Initially selective receptive language and immature expressive language with some autistic-like peculiarities; at end of treatment, full receptive language and wide expressive language with no autistic characteristics.

School Placement: Prior to treatment, participation in Headstart Program; September 1966, enrolled in public school kindergarten; September 1967, 1st grade placement in public school.

June began treatment at a time (CA 4 years, 10 months) when in her behavior she was showing signs of emerging from a severely autistic level of functioning. Unlike the rest of the subjects included in this project, she had acquired a certain amount of verbal ability, but her language was difficult to understand as she used it less for meaningful communication than for her own idiosyncratic needs. Her involvement with people was minimal, and she carried out her activities as if she were totally unaware of the existence of anybody else. When she was approached or intruded upon, she would fly into a rage, so much so that her parents did not dare come close to her for fear of precipitating a major tantrum. She had a great many negativistic tendencies, arbitrarily refusing to do anything as soon as any request was made of her. She was enuretic; her sleeping habits were unpredictable in that she

278

would get up at all hours of the night to roam the house and disturb the family. She could never be trusted on her own, as she would wander off completely absorbed in autistic aloofness, and often had to be returned home by the police or neighbors who would find her.

Four months prior to coming into the treatment program, attempts at measuring June's level of intellectual functioning were met with her characteristic negativism and lack of interest, so that minimal IQ's of 77 and of 70 were obtained on the Merrill-Palmer and the Stanford-Binet respectively. This represented a mental age of 3 years, 4 months, a borderline defective range of intelligence. These tests were repeated just before treatment began, at a time when June had completed some months in nursery school, and also had participated in the local Headstart Program. These experiences had obviously helped her development; she was more cooperative and testable. On the Stanford-Binet she obtained an IQ of 87, much closer to normal range and on the Merrill-Palmer an IQ of 84. It was, however, on the Vineland Social Maturity Scale that she most clearly demonstrated her true potentialities. Her Social Quotient of 118 (age equivalent, 5 years, 10 months), reflected how far ahead she was in social skills, a competence she had obviously developed out of her constant exposure to the various demands of three younger siblings. In her notes on her first visit to the home, the observer writes: "June is very independent and capable. She can bathe herself and dress herself; she sets the table, and pours drinks for herself and for her friends. It is my impression that she's had to gain these skills because of maternal unavailability rather than because of training. Mother is just too busy caring for the younger children."

Ratings on the Fels Scales at the onset of treatment describe a child who appears mostly unhappy (Cheerful-Depressed 1.5), and whose pattern of independent behavior reflects partly the isolation and indifference resulting from her emotional distance (Affectionateness 1.1) and human insensitivity (Sense of Humor 7.1). Partly, also, her independence or apparent self-sufficiency stems from the fear that the people around her will disturb her routines and whatever arbitrary order she imposes on her life; thus Negativism (6.1) dominates her relationship to others, and there is little tolerance for any intrusion by others into the fixed and set pattern of behavior that she is involved in at any one time (Obedience 3.22; Suggestibility 8.2). Even in those activities she chooses to engage in, there is for her little satisfaction; she never stays with any task for any length of time (Patience 4.1; Tenacity 8.3). And her wanderlust seems to emphasize how lost she experiences herself and how empty are her rewards in life.

First three months of treatment.   From the beginning, we refused to accept June's negativism as genuine. That is, for the most part, when she said "no" we believed that she really meant to say "yes." Thus it was that in our first sessions with her, we made a concerted effort at insuring that she would know that we weren't at all dismayed or inhibited by her loud and tantrum-type expressions of refusal to be close to us. If we had to carry her bodily into the therapy room, we did it, because this offered her some amount of physical contact with us. If once in the room she would begin a tantrum of colossal proportions, in which cries of "go away" alternated with stentorious screams of "I want my mommy," we would join in with her pretending to be delighted that she was finally going to have one of her major explosions with us. "How much of a tantrum is June going to have?" we would exclaim, "a five-minute one, a three-minute one, or just a short one? How about it, June? Is this going to be a really big show?" Confronted with this apparent enthusiastic acceptance of her explosive behavior, June's habitual negativistic inclinations would throw her into a conflict: Should she, or should she not, have a tantrum when the people around her were apparently satisfied with her having one? "Scream a little louder, June!" Her answer, "No, I'm not going to scream!" "Come on June, have a big scene." Her answer, "No! I don't want to!" This one-act melodrama with a confused star soon became a comedy, and June, living up to our expectations, would terminate the play with a dry chuckle and warmly sheepish smile.

We pursued, in these early phases of our acquaintance with June, the same basic pattern of reverse negativism in our determined attempt at stimulating in her more affectionate and pleasurable responses. Whenever, for instance, she would by accident, so to say, come close enough to the therapist (Dr. D.) so that she would actually touch him, he would immediately exclaim loudly: "Don't do that—don't touch me!" This was enough to evoke on June's part an immediate determination to multiply such physical contacts in whatever way she could. She would never allow herself, of course, to do this in any straightforward way; she was supposed to hate physical contacts. Thus she would use what appeared to be mildly sadistic and cruel ways to express her needs for closeness, and at the same time gain reassurance that such closeness was not dangerous. In this respect, she would use whatever opportunities existed to throw a ball as hard as she could, and especially when he wasn't looking, at the therapist (Dr. D.), and delight in a gleefully fiendish way whenever he would pretend to be in great pain. Similarly, she would invent a game in which one of the therapists would be the Monster (Dr. D.) from whom she had to be protected, and under the guise of rallying the other therapist (Carole) to her side, she would frantically cling to her while encouraging her (Carole) to push the Monster into apparent submission.

In truth, June made it clear that she wanted very much this closeness with us. As "Batman," a game which she fell into as soon as we were able to find her a cape (an old smock used by finger painters), and a tall building (a table) from which to exercise her prowess, she would jump into the arms of her therapist, delighted at the idea of having a chance to cuddle and "smooch" in the process. As a detached onlooker to a ball game between two therapists, if, per chance, the ball should happen to be thrown her way, it was difficult for her to remain indifferent: She had to duck or catch it or run away. All of which she couldn't do without somehow getting involved in the game. She preferred to get involved in the game. It was clear that she just wanted to learn ways of being with us and of enjoying being with us. When, for instance, she had managed to knock a bench out from under Dr. D., and he reacted to the fall to the floor with a great show of pain and apparent damage to his leg, June was enchanted with the idea of putting a band-aid on it, and remained concerned over the possible suffering which her therapist was enduring. This, of course, did not deter her from knocking the bench from under him again, because, after all, this was a game.

It may be argued that this approach with June was somehow doing violence to her human right to be isolated and indifferent to us if she chose to be. Why should we take it upon ourselves to assume that she would rather be bothered by us than remain in the emptiness and loneliness of her autistic aloof and detached independence? We could say in answer that our theoretical position dictated the therapeutic stance and goal we had to adopt with June. But even more to the point, we could use our empirical observations of the impact on June that such an approach had, to feel reassured that this child wanted very much *not* to be left alone. It may be also that some will be satisfied with such an answer but, nevertheless, take issue with the specific tactics we used with June in our approach to her. Weren't we making fun of her?

And under the guise of overcoming her negativism through what we called reverse negativistic tactics, weren't we possibly running the risk of confusing her? Without denying this possibility, we should like to emphasize once again the climate of nonserious seriousness which constantly pervaded all of our interactions with June. This might be illustrated by contrasting June's response to her mother's attempts at reverse negativism with June (which she had observed us use), and June's response to similar tactics on our part. "June has been regressing as far as using the bathroom. She doesn't bother to take the time, except in the morning before she goes out to play. If I can catch her long enough to remind her, it is usually too late. I've tried the negative approach as you do: 'June, don't use the potty, it's only for John and Leslie.' This, however, does not work, since usually she reacts with indifference. I'm also concerned that using this approach too often may confuse her and also the other children. I must confess that my patience ran out yesterday (probably because I have two others in diapers, and also because I thought she was over this after age 4½). Anyway, after June telling me that she could not go all morning, she wet her pants and I spanked her. I still have remorse of conscience, since her reaction to this spanking was to weep and say, 'But I love you.' I explained why I was spanking her, and that I didn't want her to do it again. But I'm confused as to whether she really understands or not. Two hours later she did the same thing again. When I asked her why, she replied: 'Last 'member you told me not to use the potty.' That's why I feel I've confused her by using the negative approach." (In her next note, five days later, the mother writes: "June has not wet her pants since her spanking September 7.")

A more touching and forceful indictment of our tactics with June could scarcely be found! Yet our own therapy notes, a week before, on the occasion of a small birthday party we had planned for June at the Clinic, illustrate not only the difference in quality of our messages to June, but also June's clear perception of the meaning of our message, even when couched in reverse negativistic terms. "Today we solemnly marched from the waiting room to the therapy room to celebrate June's birthday. Carole had set a table with cokes and ice cream and cake, each cake adorned with a candle; and small chairs placed for the three of us. June was obviously delighted at this very special surprise ceremony for her, and she understood immediately that she was the guest of honor. Broadly smiling and chuckling, she sat at her place wanting Carole beside her and Dr. D. opposite her. June assumed her role with great delight, and also unquestionable conscientiousness, and for awhile we expected her to start pushing us around and taking over the entire situation. It was her birthday after all. We played it cool and kept our fingers crossed. We allowed June to pour the cokes and dispense the ice cream; we permitted her to arrange and rearrange everything on the table; we even let her start dipping some ice cream into her coke to make a float (but this was getting close to fooling around too much). She must have sensed that we were getting a little nervous so she decided to try her hand at pouring ice cream in everybody's coke with the clear intention of drinking it herself. When she reached for Dr. D.'s cup, he let out a loud protest. 'Don't touch it, it's mine!' The game was on. June, obviously enjoying herself tremendously, knew that she could have as much coke as she wanted but that it was more fun to fight for it. Repeatedly she pretended to reach for Dr. D.'s coke, and everytime she heard 'Don't touch it,' she went into a gale of laughter. When, however, at some point she reached for his ice cream and he didn't shout at her, she stopped, somewhat surprised, and then chuckling and giggling she said: 'Tell me not to touch your ice cream!' She blew out the candles. She accepted graciously our gift of a lunch pail for school and carried the rest of the cupcakes with her to give to John and Leslie."

Undoubtedly it would have been better for June's mother not to try such reverse negativistic moves, since her own lack of understanding and humor in doing so provoked in June what appeared to be either a response of indifference or a response of confusion. On the other hand, the home observer's notes at the time indicate that the father is much more effective in cutting through June's negativism with a statement like "You can't dance to my music" than is June's mother. On June's part, there is no confusion here because the humorous quality of the message comes through, and let's not take ourselves too seriously anyway. To achieve such a quality in the communication made to the child, one has to believe that most of children's fears can usually be overcome if they are allowed to experiment, imaginatively, with what would otherwise appear to them as threatening situations.

June has a good dose of imagination. It was easier for her to pretend she was Batman, in order to allow herself to jump into our arms, than to simply give in to her need for direct physical, affectionate contacts. Similarly, if her mother wanted to take her out to the Purple Cow ice cream parlor, it was easier for her to anticipate the enjoyment of the ice cream if she could imagine that there would be a real purple cow there.

(Mother's note July 30, 1966). With us in the therapy room, there was no end to June's imaginative ways of creating situations which would enable her to practice relating to us on a warm, affectionate level. She invented jails for the therapist to be physically pushed into; she created the monster game so that she could hide in the arms of one therapist as a protection against her fantasied dangers from the monster; she even devised a variation on this theme in which she would be the monster and, therefore, be forced, in her monstrous role, to destroy us and eat us up. Imagination and fantasy, these are the catalytic agents to any child's exploration of the sometimes fearsome unknown world.

June, who had been so reluctant to accept or to give affection, found herself much more expressive and communicative in this respect. Excerpts from the mother's notes in this period (August, September) emphasize this change quite strongly: "June went up to her brother John today and said, 'I love my Johnny.' This was done without any apparent motivation which is a rare thing with June, since she usually turns away from any show of affection. . . . There seems to be a general improvement in June's behavior over the past few months. She is less negative, more reasonable; there is more communication with us, her parents, and with other children; she is a much happier child and, at times, is quite affectionate (more with the younger than with the adults). To any outsider June appears to be normal. Even to me she seems like all the other children at times. However, I realize there is much to be desired. . . . As I mentioned before, June is much more affectionate than she used to be. But in the past week, I noticed that not only is she more affectionate than she used to be, but she is more affectionate with me and her father than any of our other children. This, of course, is when she is well rested, which is in the early part of the day."

We had started working with June at the end of the month of June, and when September came, she was enrolled in a regular public school kindergarten. This was in line with our general policy of allowing our children to be in normal types of environments, but we had, understandably, some qualms over the fact that in the public school situation, the teacher-pupil ratio would be rather large and, therefore, that June could easily be lost. We weren't surprised, therefore, that June experienced her first few weeks of schooling as a somewhat unpleasant event. "June began kindergarten last Wednesday without any fuss," writes the mother. "Her enthusiasm was a little less than average (but maybe average for June). There were several children crying outside, but June

was not one of them. When I met her after school, she had nothing to
tell me and her expression was similar to that of the old autistic June.
This was the same the second day also. On the third day she asked to
walk alone, so I let her go with two other children (second and first
graders). I followed a half block behind on the opposite side of the
street, so she would not see me. After June turned the corner where
the entrance is she came back, alone, crying. I had to go back with her,
and she continued to cry 'I do not like school—I do not like my teacher!'
(According to the other children and other mothers, June's teacher is
very well liked.) This continued for one week. June is brought to the
door of school and delivered to her teacher, crying and protesting. After
school, however, June comes skipping home smiling, but never tells us
anything about school. . . . June's teacher came out to speak to me (this
is the first time). She suggested that someone else bring her, since June
stops crying as soon as she's in school and I'm gone. The teacher also
mentioned that June seldom answers when spoken to; and the few
times she had heard her speak she felt she 'talked baby-talk.' I began to
explain a little of what her problem really was, but I think I did a poor
job of it. She acted all too well as though she understood exactly what I
meant, but I'm quite sure she didn't. We didn't have much time since
the bell was going to ring. But her parting words were: 'Don't worry,
she'll be ready for first grade as long as her problem is only physical!'
I had never said it was physical or mental. Maybe when you have more
time, you could explain to me just how I could explain to others what
is wrong—especially if I have to do it quickly."

We talked to the teacher at that time and chose to ignore whatever
ideas she might have had of June's "condition"; we just wanted to reassure ourselves that she would not allow June to be lost in the shuffle,
and we were satisfied that the teacher understood this quite well. June's
first evaluation following three months of treatment occurred at this
time. The examiner reports: "June was pleasant, friendly, and playful.
She was relatively attentive and even verbal responses were given with
less effort. She was interested in the materials in my box, but could easily
be drawn back to the tests. Sometimes her playfulness expressed itself
in giving a response opposite to the one that was requested; for example, she would give a likeness when a difference was requested. The previously observed negativism, obstinacy, and temper-tantrum behavior
was completely absent. Present test results reveal June to have reached
an average level of intelligence as measured by the Stanford-Binet, form

L-M, Intelligence Test. Gains are made in Comprehension (year IV), Aesthetic Comparison (IV-6), Copying a Square (V); Patience: Rectangles (V); Maze Tracing (VI). These gains reflect some maturation in verbal comprehension, in motor coordination, in visuomotor coordination, and in following instructions. The score on the Merrill-Palmer stays essentially at the same level, suggesting not regression, but an asymptote, in the sense that she performs most of the tasks now, but speed is not increasing and in some instances is decreasing. There are some gains on verbal tests—e.g., in her comprehension on Action Agent—and in motor coordination—e.g., drawing a cross and producing the Six-Cube Pyramid." The mental age of 4 years, 9 months, which her performance reflects, points to a six-month gain over this period (IQ 93), and the Peabody Picture Vocabulary, which we gave June as part of our evaluation, correlates closely (IQ 96) with her Stanford-Binet achievement.

In terms of social maturity, we note at this time an increase of seven points in her Social Quotient, from 118 to 125. Mostly this underlines again June's relative self-sufficiency in terms of self-care (goes to bed unaided, goes to school unattended, bathes self unaided, cares for self at table) and her greater awareness of her human environment ("Performs" for others and Plays competitive exercise games).

Third through sixth month of treatment.   In the succeeding months, we had the opportunity of seeing June in action at school where she seemed, in her independent way, to fit quite well. Well accepted by the other children, she carried out her assignments within the structure and discipline imposed on the group but typically appeared to avoid too much interpersonal interaction. We noticed, especially, her tendency in this situation to be easily distracted by her interest in other children's work; obviously she was happier as a free-lance operator than as a dedicated scholar. We decided to use part of our time with June at the Clinic to help her develop a greater attention span and more consistent concentration on whatever task she set herself to do. Tenacity and perseverance at a task did not come easy for June whose curiosity, unlike that of Elizabeth for instance, never had the quality of obsessive persistence which would have enabled her to carry to the end whatever she had begun. On her part, this weakness was to a certain extent an expression of her independence, but it always amazed us that, even in those situations where the activity or the task in which she was engaged was obviously pleasurable to her, she could nevertheless abandon it suddenly as if prompted by some secret and unpredictable inner mechanism. On the other hand we saw her, for instance, on the occasion of the administration of the Leiter International Test, attend to this grueling task for over an hour at a time. June, more than any of the other children in our program, needed a clear and well-defined external structure in which to operate, but she depended less on external rewards from others (social reinforcement) than on her own sense of gratification in mastering a situation. Thus in her case, though she enjoyed very much the games and the affective stimulation that we provided, she responded even more to the security that the consistency of the discipline and structure which we imposed on her provided. Therefore, we chose to interpret what appeared to be at home (where chaotic conditions so often prevailed) her domineering and bossy behavior, as her own attempt at imposing some degree of structure on those activities in which she wanted to engage. Frequent notes from the mother express this characteristic in June of being an "organizer," and of taking over a situation even though her initiative at times may be viewed as inappropriate and her bossiness as very annoying. "June brought her little friend Dee in this evening about 7 P.M. and dressed her in a hot, red pair of flannel pajamas [this is July]. June only dressed herself after much coaxing from me. This is quite typical of June, to dress her brother, sister, or friend, comb their hair, and so forth, and then refuse to do anything for herself. The purpose of dressing Dee in P.J.'s was to have her stay overnight. On another occasion, much to my surprise (without my asking) June came to me one morning and said: 'Leslie and I are going down to *clean* up the basement.' June always manages to disappear when I mention cleaning the basement or picking up toys. After about 45 minutes of working, I found that she had picked up most of the toys off the floor. . . . Yesterday morning before 6 A.M., June undressed Leslie, wrung out a soiled diaper, put it in the diaper pail, gave Leslie a bath, and washed her hair. Then she dressed her in a robe and slippers. The only thing June couldn't do was to pin another diaper on Leslie. So, instead, she put a pair of training pants on her. Pretending to be asleep, I watched most of this from bed and felt there was no need to interfere, since June was handling Leslie as well as I would have myself."

At the Clinic also we allowed June to determine for herself, within limits, the activities that she was interested in pursuing; but once she was set upon a task, we always insisted that she carry it through. Frequently, however, in order to correlate our work with her with the experiences she had at home and at school, we would set up a playful but structured situation for June. Thus for instance, when Halloween came, and June showed up at the Clinic with the costume she was to wear in school, our game with her that day involved cutting out a real pumpkin to make a "Jack-O-Lantern." This included having June first trace on a paper the pumpkin's face, outline carefully the eyes, the nose, and the mouth; then she would have to cut out these features and paste them on the pumpkin as preliminary steps to her actually using a knife to cut out the features in the pumpkin. It took a full hour to do this, and June, at no point, was deterred from her task; she was very pleased with herself. At the end of the hour, to remind us that she didn't really need us in order to be happy, she said no when we asked whether she wanted to take the pumpkin with her. On her way out, however, she picked up the pumpkin and took it home with her.

Similarly, we were very pleased when June agreed to bring her jump rope to the clinic. This was at the request of her mother: "June's little girl friends and her brother John have mastered the art of jumping rope. This is something June has had a difficult time with even after I have tried to show her. I know this frustrates her. Since you are working with the other three children and their bikes, and since June has been riding a bike for some time, would it be all right if she brought her rope for a session? Maybe if you show her she'd catch on as she did with paper cutting." (We had constructed an entire school playground out of colorful construction paper, and June had spent a great deal of energy mastering the use of scissors, a feat of which she was very proud.) Fortunately, June brought two jump ropes, one for us and one for her. She had so much fun seeing us jump at her insistence that there was no stopping her from mastering this exercise. We cheered her on, and even when she had completely perfected this art, she would deliberately step on the rope at some time in order to hear the therapist scream, "Watch it!" Eventually, when the therapists were exhausted from jumping, and when it appeared that June was ready for a different game, we used the two ropes to mark off on the floor the sides of a hopscotch game and, using tinker-toy sticks, marked off the inner squares. In this game, just to tease us, June insisted on calling her "token" a "totonut" (as in coconut).

The playful and imaginative qualities in June required also that they find expression in structured channels and disciplined ways. We never allowed her fantasy to run wild, but we never destroyed it. June liked very much to design and construct mansions and apartment buildings out of blocks. In these tasks, we always required of her that she proceed in an orderly fashion and account fully for every aspect of her architectural scheme. When, however, one day she decided to build a boat with the blocks, we had to know what the boat was for and who would use it. June immediately responded by fixing herself a little bench at one end of the boat, and we began chanting, "Row, row, row your boat." She cheerfully and loudly interrupted us to explain the purpose of her boat. She was "going to the Specific [Pacific] ocean." We immediately cheered her on by singing "California, Here We Come" and clapping our hands. To our delightful surprise that's exactly where June intended to go. She apparently had had a long discussion with her friend Dee, whose parents had planned a vacation to Disneyland. That's where June was going, she informed us, as she went into excited descriptions of all the animals to be seen there, elephants, giraffes, crocodiles, and even porpoises (we had trouble understanding that one). To insure that her trip would be complete, we showed her pictures of all these animals.

The effort to provide June with structure, in order to enhance her capacity to cope with and master her widening world, was rewarded in the success she achieved when she was tested after six months. The examiner notes: "June was friendly and cooperative during all testing sessions. For the first time she was tested in two of the sessions by herself. She entertained herself between items by helping the examiner put test items away in the box. There were times during the sessions that she would grin quite slyly and give opposite responses, but she could easily be persuaded to give this up (her testing negativism) and produce the correct responses. Her attention span is considerably lengthened. Noteworthy also was her ability to come close to me by placing blocks in my lap. She demonstrated no fear or awe in my presence. This is a very different child from the one who had to be tested in the waiting room. . . . In this testing we introduced the Leiter International Performance Scale as it measures nonverbal factors and is an untimed test. On the Leiter, June earned a mental age of 5 years, 3 months and an IQ of 102 (corrected to Stanford-Binet). Areas of difficulty included mostly number concepts and also the idea of continuation or progression. Within her range of successes there is evidence of good concept formation that involves more than mere perceptual matching—for example, matching on the bases of use. . . . The Stanford-Binet shows a small IQ increase from 93 to 96, but the test items that show increase reveal consistent and strong improvement in verbal concept formation (Opposite Analogies and Differences). . . . In summary, June continues to develop at a steady rate. At present there is no essential discrepancy between verbal and nonverbal functions, and she continues to be above average in social functioning (Vineland Social Quotient 134, age equivalent 7 years, 5 months)."

Sixth through 12th month of treatment. In the following months, June maintained her steady rate of development. It was during this period that she had to go to the hospital for a few days for a hernia repair operation. This experience in many ways highlighted those personality features in June which were so typically characteristic of her emerging self. Her mother in her notes tells us of her own qualms with regard to how she expected June to react away from home; they tell us also how well June found in this experience an opportunity for new gains in maturity and mastery. "June is going into the hospital in about two weeks (I'm not sure of the exact date). A year or two ago I wouldn't have been too concerned, since June was so cold and detached; she wouldn't have minded being away from home and from me; but now that June has become somewhat overly attached to me, it will be much more difficult for her. She has already asked me if I'd stay all night with her in the hospital. Should I tell the nurses she's autistic so they won't be impatient with her if she doesn't talk or answer any questions? But even if I did tell them, they probably wouldn't really know what autistic meant. Or if they did know and had read Dr. B., they'd think of me as a murderous mother!" This was written April 6, 1967. In a later note dated April 25, we read: "June was a darling patient in the hospital and everyone seemed to like her. Each time I came, she mentioned that she missed John and when was she going to see him? Otherwise, her stay didn't seem to bother her. She became attached to two other children there. One was a two-year-old Negro boy, Chris, who was in another wing. The other was a two-year-old girl, Debbie, in the room across the hall from June. This was a *silent* relationship however. Neither of the two-year-olds could speak (or they were too ill or weak to talk), so June didn't need to speak. She was attracted to these two children in somewhat the same manner that she has been to little Tommy at the Clinic. She insisted on following Debbie around the hospital so religiously that I wondered if Debbie's mother would finally object. It was such a pleasure to be with June in the hospital that I found it disappointing when she resumed her old negativistic behavior as soon as she returned home. On the other hand, I spent more concentrated hours with June alone in the hospital than I could ever spend at home, and June was never negativistic there. Having June away from home these few days made me realize how much she fills up the house. I am as much aware of her presence as I am of all the other three put together. Even at her best, she keeps us on our toes with her busy activities."

June's "busy activities" at home included, besides breaking a few thermometers, setting up the entire hospital experience for the benefit of John, Leslie, and all their friends. As Nurse-in-Charge, she was obviously at her peak as far as ordering patients around and demanding that they conform to hospital regulations and procedures. It also gave her the opportunity to care for the sick and the injured with a great deal of concern and attention. Here again there was on her part the possibility of expressing both her understanding of the world around, and also her creative talents in enthusiastically getting into the childhood game of make-believe. The home observer, in her last visit, captures in her notes the hospital game in all its details and complexities. Excerpts from these notes follow.

"Following the first half-hour of play the children all went down to the basement where June set up a hospital game. She moved all the furniture around the bed and used the high stool for the nurse to sit on. She plays a very domineering role, pushing, pulling, and carrying Leslie who is the patient.

" 'You are to stay in bed,' she says to Leslie, 'because you're so sick. I'm a nurse.'

"John asks: 'What did you dream about?'

"June: 'I'm a nurse, I didn't dream about nothing.' She puts Leslie back into bed again. Leslie gets up and June says to Dee, 'You're the nurse,' and busies herself setting up the high stool as the nurses' station.

"June to Dee: 'Nurse, will you hold her?'

"Then June takes out the dishes and feeds Leslie in bed. And John screams: 'What do you have? Can I have a bite?'

"June to John: 'Get it upstairs in the kitchen.'

"As John leaves for the kitchen, June asks: 'Dr., will you watch her?'

"John answers: 'The nurse will watch her.'

"June rushes upstairs to get a piece of bread: 'Look, look what we have! Look what my mommy made! Toast! Only for the baby [Leslie]!'

"Dee: 'Can I have toast?'

"June: 'No, Dee, remember I gave you popcorn. The toast is for the baby.'

"At this point, the patient gets out of bed and June decides to lift her on the teacart and wheel her back and forth as in a wheelchair. Mother gets concerned that June picks up Leslie too often and might hurt herself. June pretends to ignore mother but says: 'We have to go outdoors now. Do you want the bottle, baby?' And then adds: 'Now she's all better,' but John gets into the act saying: 'I'm sick,' which immediately seems to remind June of her nurse's function and she screams: 'Leslie, get in here!' And Leslie dutifully climbs on the cart with John following her, and saying: 'Pretend I'm sick.' At this point the mother, addressing June, states: 'June, let John be sick someplace else.'

"June's feelings are hurt and her feathers ruffled; while she regains her composure, Leslie escapes. Mother, seemingly having a change of heart, uses the opportunity to interject: 'June, give John a chance to be sick, Leslie is tired of being sick. You know, you can get tired of being sick. You took such good care of Leslie, she got better. Why don't you pretend that Leslie got better and snuck out of the hospital. Call the police and tell them Leslie snuck out of the hospital. That's what a nurse would do!'

"June: 'Police, police!'

"Dee: 'She runned away and sneaked out and she's still sick!'

"June: 'Police! Police!' And she runs upstairs after Leslie. 'Police! Police! If you find her, don't drag her down, be gentle.' "

Such are the games of children, and June obviously was developing truly like a normal child. She still wanted her way, and she still used tantrums and scenes to have her way. But as far as life was concerned, she was now really with it. At the clinic we treated her like a "big girl." We had her accompany us every place we went, so that she could meet many people and see a variety of new situations. She especially liked, with us, her excursions to the vending machines where, proudly using her own money (the first few times we had to lend her a dime), she would pick out her "own" meal, chocolate bars or cookies, and her own drink, mostly cherry cola. In such circumstances, she still felt that she could maintain the upper hand, insisting that she should serve us were we to have coffee or milk from the machine. Nothing was too serious in these excursions, and June knew it so well that she never hesitated removing the cushion from the therapist's chair, causing him to lose some of his dignity. There were never any tantrums or scenes when June was on a "trip" with us, but somehow there were always games. For instance, on the way back to the Clinic, June would run ahead of us and then pretend, having lost us, to look all over for our whereabouts, giggling all the time she was supposed to be frantic at our absence. A big reunion scene always climaxed her relentless search. This was what she wanted.

The final psychological test evaluation made clear that, as had been said earlier, June's personality growth was proceeding at a steady rate. In social maturity, of course, she was a star (SQ 139: age equivalent 7 years, 10 months), and we weren't surprised at this in view of her complete involvement in family life. This was further reflected in the ratings on the Fels Scales, where typically her highest rates of improvement involve those scales which define behaviors demonstrating the child's affective engagement with people (Affectionateness 1.1; Friendliness 3.14; Gregariousness 3.15; Sense of Humor 7.1); and those behaviors which reflect the child's response to interpersonal contacts (Obedience 3.22; Suggestibility 8.2; Patience 4.1; Negativism 6.1). With regard to her environment and to the variety of experiences to which she was exposed, June's behavior also changed from aloofness and disinterest to curiosity about people and places (Curiosity 2.11); from haphazard and erratic activities to imaginative and organized behavior (Planfulness 5.1); and from indifference to attentive and concentrated awareness (Tenacity 8.3). Her intellectual development reflected gains in concept formation, but she still had difficulties in number concepts. With an IQ of 102 on the Stanford-Binet (mental age 5 years, 10 months at CA of 5 years, 9 months), June seemed ready to move from kindergarten to normal first grade placement. At the end of one year of treatment, we were looking forward to this, though we knew that such a first grade experience would be of profit to her only to the extent that the abilities and competencies she possessed could be channeled in well-structured and interesting forms of activities. Without such structure, so much of her good energies could be dissipated. More clearly than any of the other children in our program, June's progress and continued awakening during her first year with us made us feel that the level she had shown herself capable of achieving could be the level to be reached by all; because for her, like for the others, once her eyes were open, life appeared to her as a brand new day.

Table 6

JUNE

	4 Mo. Prior to Treatment	Initial Evaluation	Months in Treatment			
			3 Months	6 Months	9 Months	11 Months
Chronological age	4 years 5 months	4 years 10 months	5 years 1 month	5 years 4 months	5 years 7 months	5 years 9 months
Vineland		SQ 118 AE 5–10	SQ 125 AE 6–6	SQ 134 AE 7–5	SQ 139 AE 7–10	
Merrill-Palmer	IQ 77 MA 3–4	IQ 84 MA 4–1	IQ 82 MA 4–2			
Stanford-Binet	IQ 70 MA 3–2	IQ 87 MA 4–3	IQ 93 MA 4–9	IQ 96 MA 5–2		IQ 102 MA 5–10
Peabody picture vocabulary			IQ 96			
Leiter				IQ 102 MA 5–3	IQ 99 MA 5–3	

Follow-up

Many readers will want to know to what extent the developmental gains made by the children have been maintained. We have, for nearly one year now, followed both the children and their parents through monthly visits to their homes and to their schools. Except for Tommy, who is currently attending a special nursery school on the east coast, and about whom we have had only indirect information, our visits with the other children have left us very encouraged.

Though we have not been able, as of this writing, to measure objectively the present developmental level of the children, our clinical observations, as well as the reports of the parents and the teachers, indicate continued improvement in the acquisition of communicative skills and in social competencies. There still exist, however, many problems which, as far as we can evaluate at this time, appear to be traceable to the tendency in these children to experience rather quickly a drop in their affective arousal, unless an intensive flow of affective and sensory stimulations is available to them. By the same token, any drop in the children's alertness appears to have a depressing effect on the parents, who find it difficult, without frequent directives and reassuring support, to carry on the major therapeutic-educational effort with their respective autistic child.

Kathy, for instance, had a wonderful summer, following termination of the program with us. Her parents, upset by our departure subsequent to our inability to secure funds to continue the program, but greatly encouraged by the progress their child had made—"we know now that Kathy can be a real little girl; she is not hopeless"—were determined to allow no letdown in their work with her. Kathy was taken on a wide variety of outings which she enjoyed fully; she went by train with her mother to visit relatives in another state; she spent five weeks in nursery school where she continued to improve in social behaviors and in language development. As long as the "arousing" pressure was on, Kathy, still typically independent and mischievously negativistic, maintained the positive direction of growth of which she was capable.

In September, she returned to nursery school for a half-day period, and her teachers were delighted with the extent of her social progress ("she joined the group in singing!"). But at home and at school there were still many daily problems, which taxed the ingenuity of the teachers and demanded, of the parents, considerable patience and energy. Her mother frequently complained that Kathy would not entertain herself or play by herself! In Kathy's case, this could be viewed as an extraordinary change in a child who had spent the first part of her life alone and isolated! But for practical purposes, Kathy's demands to be constantly playing with her mother, her brother, or her father could create exasperating difficulties at times. Kathy, for instance, had nearly one half of her days to spend alone with her mother, who had many other chores to perform besides entertaining her child! Similarly, when Kathy's brother returned from school, he had, legitimately, many other interests that had little to do with his younger sister; he had "sessions" with her, teaching her to build block designs, color pictures, and read out words from cards; but when his friends came along, or when the day was fine for a bicycle ride, it was natural that he should leave Kathy behind. Her dad continued, in the evening, to include her as an "inspector" and a small "helper" in his various benchwork and artistic activities, but Kathy went to bed early and "inspecting" is not as exciting as spreading sawdust on the living room carpet! Thus, inevitably, Kathy had to be left to her own devices rather frequently, and just as inevitably, the activities with which she chose to "entertain" herself acquired annoying and attention-seeking self-stimulating qualities. She would sit in front of her mirror, repeat various behavioral injunctions (such as "Kathy, don't spit"—while she was spitting out saliva; "Kathy, hit head"—while she was banging her head against the wall; "Kathy, pull hair"—while she pulled her hair from her arm or from her head) and kill time waiting for someone to come and play with her.

Kathy's attention-seeking efforts appeared always to include defiant and oppositional characteristics. At school, she found it necessary to wet on the floor, for instance, in the hope of having the teachers replace her pants with "school issues" which Kathy thought were more interesting than her own. At first the teachers "fell" for this maneuver and were eventually led to complete despair by Kathy's fiendish exploitation of their concern, and by her seemingly inexhaustible capacity to wet! Finally, the school's director, with her typical good sense, advised her teachers to ignore Kathy's "water, even if it overflows through the windows!" Very shortly afterward, Kathy gave up, in search of new, annoying behaviors! At home, she discovered she could drive her mother "batty" by pulling her own hair from her head. All her mother's efforts to extinguish such behavior were ineffective, and Kathy's mom had unhappy and horrible visions of a baldheaded Kathy! For a while, most of the mother's ingenuity was devoted to finding ways of covering ever-widening bald spots on the child's head, and, in desperation, she consulted us many times on what to do about this problem. Our analysis—at a distance—of the circumstances of Kathy's unacceptable behavior led us to the obvious conclusion that Kathy was left alone too much, since no one in the family could actually report having "seen" or "caught" Kathy in the act of pulling her hair. Much of the hair-pulling was done after the child was in bed; some of it, when Kathy was alone in her room. We insisted that someone keep Kathy company until she fell asleep, quietly talking to her, singing, or simply holding her hand or rubbing her forehead; during the daytime, Kathy should always be recruited in helping her mother with her household chores, and any relaxed moments of reading a good book would have to be postponed for Kathy's benefit. Such requests did not imply that the entire pattern of family life should be dominated and tyrannized by Kathy; on the contrary, it meant that, for the most part, Kathy should be included more and more in every aspect of the family life.

Many problems crept up also in June's upbringing after the program terminated. Mostly, however, June's development was marked by increased social maturity, and the acquisition of a much broader and effective speaking vocabulary. Though the parents continued to be concerned with June's tendency to put on a tantrum whenever anyone interfered with her planned activities or with her wishes and whims, we were impressed, in our visits during the past year, with the amount of self-control the child displayed, and the degree of social awareness and consideration she was able to show.

Our greatest worry came from June's apparent lack of interest in regular classroom activities. She had been placed in the first grade of a local public school, and her teacher—a most dedicated and skillful woman—found her behavior baffling and unyielding to usual amounts of incentive and interest shown. We had a number of meetings with this teacher, her principal, and the home-school coordinator. June was behaving like a retarded child, and yet everyone agreed that, under certain specific circumstances, they had witnessed in June behaviors which, in their opinion, could not possibly be that of a retarded or defective youngster. We knew, of course, that June had better than average intelligence, but we also knew that for her, more clearly than for any of our other subjects, the purpose of learning anything had to be a personal experience. We were able to demonstrate this fact to the teacher, on the occasion of one of our visits, when we were shown June's written work or, more accurately, June's lack of written work. The teacher had tried so many different ways to get June interested in writing, and that day she had everybody's work on the blackboard, and June's space was empty! We told the teacher to make sure to tell June that we had wanted very much to see her writing. That afternoon, June not only brought us her written work (we were then having a meeting at home with her mother), but she insisted on spending the time with us writing notes! Obviously she was sure that we would truly appreciate it!!

To help the teacher and her principal have a clearer idea of June's competence, and to instill in them a more enlightened confidence in June's abilities, we suggested that she be referred for examination to the Board of Education's certified school psychologist. June had not performed well in the routine paper-pencil group tests for grade placement, but we were sure that, on an individual test like the Stanford-Binet, or the Wechsler Intelligence Scale for Children, she would hold her own very well. We have no official results of that testing, at this moment, but we know that no recommendation was made to have June transferred to an EMH (Educable Mentally Handicapped) classroom placement.

Another interesting development took place during this follow-up period of June's progress. Her mother took her to the family pediatrician for her regular checkup; he noticed June's tendency to become quickly, and successively, too interested in too many things; she was too easily distractible and the pediatrician decided to have her take a small dose of Dexedrine. This drug appeared to have a mild arousing effect on June's affective responses without increasing her motoric reactions. June was calmer but more alert; she was not only more interested but was also more attentive; she appeared more confident and had fewer of her temper tantrums. The parents were very pleased with this turn of events, and we felt that a new area of future research had been opened to us.

We had somewhat of a similar reaction when we received extensive communications from the "special school" which Tommy was attending on the east coast. Tommy, according to his teacher, was doing well "under the circumstances"! According to us, as we reviewed descriptions of his behavior there, he was doing terribly. What the teachers meant by "under the circumstances" amounted to saying: You really cannot expect too much from an autistic child, and therefore we should all rejoice at the little he does! In our opinion, the big mistake here was that Tommy, being placed in a "special" school, was also surrounded by "special" children and, more important, by personnel whose training was geared to treating pathology rather than educating children. Everyone in the school appeared afraid of demanding too much of this little boy, who had clearly shown us that he operated best when he was pushed and forced into utilizing his best talents. The disappointment we experienced in this respect led us also to wondering how much better it might have been had Tommy been placed in a normal nursery school. We have no way, at this point, of answering this question without further research; but what came home to us very forcefully in the face of Tommy's marking time in a situation where he could have been expected, under expert direction, to continue his normal development, was the effect that such a placement could have on the parents. By turning their child over to "experts," they easily tend to forget that they are the most important therapeutic and educational agents in their child's development. They still know they have an important part to play; but it is not difficult for them to fear that, if the "experts" can't do it, why should they be expected to do better! Tommy's parents never gave up their hopes, nor their conviction, that theirs was the first line of responsibility in his life; but whatever doubts they had in their own capacity to carry it through successfully appeared to be enhanced by the timidity of the experts in Tommy's school.

We saw no such timidity, or doubt, in Elizabeth's parents or in her teachers at nursery school. They had their problems after the program stopped, but Elizabeth's own enthusiasm for life gave them all the encouragement they needed to carry on the work of keeping Elizabeth aroused. A recurrent and absorbing problem, both at home and at school, remained that of toilet training. Elizabeth preferred to wet her pants, and though she seemed to understand very well what a masterful accomplishment it would be for her if she just allowed herself to go to the toilet, she maintained her right to do it elsewhere. Not that she liked having wet pants. On the contrary, she could change herself and would daintily deposit her discarded pants in the wash bag. We understand that she is making real progress in her toilet habits now, and that, at school, this is no longer a difficulty.

At school, the outstanding difficulty was reported to us as Elizabeth's inclination to absorb herself in tasks interesting to her and, though very much aware of the other children around her, be easily incensed by their intrusions into her activities. The school principal was deeply concerned over this lack of "emotional maturity" in Elizabeth, as he discussed with us plans for the child's next year in school. She was getting too old to stay in nursery school; but should she be placed in junior kindergarten— a glamorized version of nursery school—or should she be "promoted" to kindergarten? We knew of Elizabeth's good intellectual assets, and her speech and her vocabulary had increased considerably during the months since the end of the program. Optimistically, we would have preferred that kindergarten be the choice for Elizabeth, but her capacity to function there, in a mature emotional and social way, depended very much on how affectively aroused and alerted she would be kept at home and at school. We compromised with the principal and his dilemma, requesting that Elizabeth spend the summer months in junior kinder- garten and that in September she be promoted to the real thing if her behavior warranted it.

At this point (May, 1968), then, the follow-up information available to us can be summarized as follows:

1. All the children continue to be affectively involved with other people; none have regressed to an autistic and isolated position.
2. The children have suffered from a slowing down of the high affective impact which had become part of their lives, and with this slow-down the optimal level of arousal in them has not been consistently main- tained; their progress in general has not continued as rapidly as before.
3. Progress has been mainly in the areas of speech and of social compe- tencies; there has been less progress in self-sufficiency and in affective social adaptability.
4. The parents have continued to work hard but a certain level of de- spondency has at times prevented them from responding to their chil- dren with as many impactful, stimulating activities as might have been necessary.

Many new questions, as we noted in passing, are raised by these follow-up observations. Some of them are taken up in the following chapters.

Chapter XI

A Brave New Family

the parental response to
the therapeutic impact

When Kanner (1943) reported the data which he had accumulated for many years and from which he was able to describe carefully and comprehensively the specific syndrome of Early Infantile Autism, he painted also a picture of the parents of autistic children. This picture has remained relatively untouched by most investigators, who apparently never doubted its fidelity or never saw fit to challenge its accuracy. There were basic commonalities in the personality features of parents of autistic infants: Kanner described them as upper-middle-class individuals, well educated, tending to be aloof and distant in their relationships, and usually of Jewish extraction. Though Kanner never stated that these parents were pathologically incapacitated in their parental roles, his views were for the most part used by others as clear indications that the autistic condition of the infant could be securely brought home to the unhealthy quality of the parents' personality functioning. Bettelheim (1967), for reasons of his own, went far beyond Kanner's impressions and made himself the champion of the autistic child by declaring the parents unfit, giving no data in support of this extravagant conclusion other than questionable interpretations he had made from statements of the child or of the parents.

Though we disagree with Bettelheim's main position with regard to the parents of autistic infants, our disagreement, as we have indicated earlier, stemmed from the difference in the theoretical position we took to understand and explain the autistic infant's behavior and arrested development. If, in our view, the developmental arrest could be explained without postulating an early parent-child trauma or a destructive parental rejection in the early months of the child's life, then we did not have to regard the parents of these children as abnormal, unfit, or morbidly tangled up in their personal neuroses or psychoses. We could look upon them as normal parents, puzzled, baffled, and ineffectual in the face of a child who is not with them. By the same token, we could anticipate also that given the chance to see their child come alive and be responsive to them in their parental involvements with him, they would in turn discover within themselves those normal patterns of action and behavior which would stimulate the growth and liveliness of their child.

It was part of our project, then, to gather as much data as we could to test out the validity of our stand with regard to the parents of autistic children. Two questions were at issue: Were these normal parents, or did they have such psychological or personality difficulties that they were incapable of being appropriate and responsive parents to an autistic child? The second question: Would the attitude and behavior of these parents change from one of bafflement, impotence, and puzzlement to one of understanding, responsiveness, and involvement if the child began actively making demands on them for interaction and communication?

We are deeply grateful to Dr. Gerald Motz and to Dr. Vita Krall for the careful assessments they made of the parents during the entire period of our project, through interviews, psychological tests, home observations, and behavior rating scales. The discussion which follows is based on the data which they obtained, and whenever our understanding of these data is at divergence with their views, it will so be stated and discussed.

The evaluation of the parents

Connie's family. Of the five families with which we are concerned here, only one (Connie's family) was reported to us from the beginning as possibly unstable. This family had been referred to us by a social agency, where the parents were receiving marital counseling because of basic disagreements between them with regard to the care and attention to be given to their autistic young girl, Connie. Nevertheless, we accepted this child and her parents in our program, both because Connie, in her developmental history as well as in her behavior, fitted the criteria for selection of our subjects and because we hoped that the parental discord over the child was an exacerbated response to long years of frustrations and disappointments (Connie was 5 years old when she joined us) rather than an expression of serious personality difficulties in the parents. The fact that Connie was withdrawn from the program after nine months of treatment, at a time when she was making slow but steady progress in many areas of emotional and social behavior as well as in intellectual growth, and at a time when the parents themselves appeared to have overcome some of their differences and were hopefully involved in raising a new baby and moderately invested in our work, confronted us with a situation which, at face value, looked very much like a case of Bettelheimian parental rejection. It was as if the parents were intent on making sure that their child would not have a chance in life and that though, to alleviate their consciences, they had been willing to give lip service to the program, the destructive forces within them could not be stemmed, and they were just waiting to "put the child away" someplace. The temptation to draw such conclusions was great, and had it not been for the support we found in the data on our other four families, we would have felt that a deadly blow had been inflicted on our naïvely optimistic view that the parents of autistic infants were not, as they had been described, unloving, rejecting, and merely wishing that their child be dead.

Connie's parents were both very insecure individuals, whose dependence on each other, instead of leading to understanding and strength, appeared to feed on each other's personal difficulties. The father, 37 years old, a college graduate of good, average intellectual endowment, demanded of his wife emotional concern and attention and a warm and responsive interest in him as a person. He felt, in this regard, deprived and disappointed. The mother, 30 years old, a college graduate of average intellectual functioning, needed from her husband dependability and strength, a structure for her own inclinations to diffuse and vague feminine aspirations. This, she felt, her husband could not provide. There was in both the immature egocentricity of childhood, so that, faced with a child who gave them nothing, each made it a project to use the child to gratify in themselves those needs which were not met through each other: The mother looked to Connie for motherly pride; the father, for unconditional affection. They received neither, and, tragic as it may sound, it would have been easier, in some respects, for both of them if this child had not existed.

This last statement, speculative and after the facts, underlines the clinical fallacy of asserting one conclusion when many alternative ones are just as cogent. Though it is true that Connie's autistic condition made her incapable of fulfilling her parents' dreams and needs, it is just as true that the parents would not have turned to her with their dreams and their needs had they wished her dead from the beginning! Their disappointment in this child is unquestionable; it had a shattering effect on their lives. The father refused to believe that Connie would never be a real daughter to him; the mother, unrewarded and narcissistically hurt, had the driving resignation of someone who keeps hoping when all she feels is futility. At the age of 5, when Connie was brought to us, it was evident that her father had reached the end of his faith—he distrusted everyone—and that the mother was seeking some sort of refuge for her battered hopes in allowing what she considered another exercise in futility. At this time, Connie was a large, well-built child, weighing nearly 60 pounds; she could walk, but not climb stairs; she made "razz-ing" sounds but could not talk; she used her hands for very little except to clasp and unclasp them constantly; she was untrained. At 5 years of age, Connie was in every way, physically and emotionally, too much for her parents. With faith dwindling and their hope crumbling, would it be unreasonable to ask: What was left of their love for this child after five unbearable years. Or had they ever loved Connie?

For this is the question: If you wish your child dead, do you hate your child? Consciously or unconsciously, there is no love there for your child. But we cannot measure one person's love for another except by his behavior, by his actions. To say that Connie is an autistic child and that therefore the behavior and actions of the parents communicated to her, somehow, that she was unwanted and unloved, is begging the question. On the other hand, many motivations may lead to those pat-terns of behavior which at first blush, may seem to express love: There is guilt, fear, ambition, or even sadomasochistic impulses. At what point can we say that love is really there? Only when whatever one does for the loved one is the best that one can do. Observations of Connie's parents at home reflect clearly that, absorbed as each one may have been with his or her own egocentric preoccupations, both parents were totally devoted to their child: the mother in a patient, understanding, and quiet way; the father in an affectionate, boisterous, excitedly inconsistent manner. In a paradoxical sense, the center of their egocentricity was Connie, who demanded of them, obviously, much more than they could give but to whom, nevertheless, they gave the best they had. It is easy to say: "These parents gave Connie the wrong things, others could have done better." If a child, at home, dying of pneumonia and in urgent need of an oxygen tent which is not available, demands more than all the air there is, are the parents criminals for giving the child only the air that is there, even though it turns out to be inadequate?

Throughout the treatment period, Connie's parents, in our view, gave their child all they could. As the child responded to the program, became more alert to people around her and more consistently expressive of her feelings; as she began to learn to control her movements and attend independently to many small tasks; as her initiative and curiosity developed, and as she learned to clumsily express some of her needs, her parents' behavior took on also a more relaxed quality and a somewhat more hopeful character. Father and mother alternated in bringing the child to the clinic. At home the mother patiently allowed Connie to experiment with a variety of tasks: climbing stairs by herself, grasping a spoon to feed herself, or holding a cup to drink, picking up objects from the floor, or clapping her hands to the rhythm of a song. Whatever time he could spend there, the father used totally with the child, playing swinging games with her, having her run after him, singing songs to her, and keeping up a running conversation with her. During this period, a new baby was born, and it was evident that a greater degree of happiness had entered this home. Connie's mother, her hands full with two babies, demanded and received individual counseling: She wanted to be a better mother and a better wife. The father, faced with new responsibilities, worried that Connie might be too much for her mother, who had to give attention to the baby; he wished that the treatment could be accelerated and tried to make arrangements to have a maid help at home, mostly so Connie would never be neglected.

We would have wished also that Connie's progress be more rapid and that her parents be more mature individuals. The results of our work with their child served as an opening wedge in their lives; it brought out the qualities and deficiencies of their personality functioning. It brought home to us, in a most dramatic and telling way, the actual issue of parent-child relationships, which is a quality of communication of a psychosomatic nature (see Introduction) where messages are sent and received through reciprocal transactions attuned both to the sender and to the receiver of the communication. Connie had very few resources to send out or to receive messages. To those few that she managed to send through her entire body and through her autistic behavior, her parents were not properly attuned; they needed more from this child than the child could give, and, therefore, they themselves became less capable of truly being with this child. Connie made manifest in them both the depression which her condition created, and the depression which led them to despair of her. This depressive factor in Connie's parents made the task of "awakening the child" a nearly unsurmountable one; but, by the same token, it alerted us, as we reviewed and analyzed the data on our other families, to wonder whether a central characteristic of the parents of autistic infants should not be sought in the underlying, pervasive, depressed quality of their psychological responses to life.

Elizabeth's parents.   In contrast to Connie's family, where a good deal of disharmony existed and where both parents seemed to use the child to gratify their own unfulfilled needs and to assert the weakly differentiated aspects of their own personalities, Elizabeth's family can be pictured as a wholesome, united, stable, and rather secure group. Two brothers, ages 8 and 6, had preceded Elizabeth and at no time had shown any developmental problems out of the ordinary, so that the parents, delighted at having their first daughter, were somewhat reluctant to recognize in this child's "good baby" behavior anything about which to be too alarmed. "She (Elizabeth—as told to us by her mother) sat up late, but our pediatrician didn't seem concerned, so we were not either. She used to sit and play by herself and was never demanding. Our friends used to remark on what a good child she was. We didn't think this was unusual. The boys had been very good at this age, and we thought Elizabeth was even better because she was a girl. I had always heard that girls were easier to take care of than boys."

But Elizabeth was too "good" to be true; she had the goodness of being progressively more and more "invisible." She wasn't there. "Elizabeth made very little progress during the next few months, and we became worried about her. We took her to the doctor again, and this time he suggested we take her to the Evaluation Center. This was the lowest point for us. I was very upset and depressed. We realized that we could no longer hope that Elizabeth was normal and would catch up with other children. By the time Elizabeth started her tests, we had come to accept the fact that Elizabeth was probably mentally defective in some way."

Thus Elizabeth's parents, crushed at the realization that the daughter they wanted so much might be a defective child were, nevertheless, prepared to accept her this way because, in spite of everything, she was theirs, a member of the family. This acceptance eventually took on a humorous quality, when, after treatment had been initiated and after the parents had begun to understand the autistic meaning of Elizabeth's behavior, the two older brothers, awed and amazed that there should be a "special" sister in the family, boasted to their friends at school: "We have an autistic child, do you?"

In spite of this climate of unity which they had created in their home, Elizabeth's parents were very different individuals. They had married during the Korean war: The mother, of English parentage, had retained, besides her English accent, the quiet and reserved quality of a well-bred woman, proper and ladylike even in her most exuberant moments; the father, an American-born, only son of Czechoslovakian parents, was a tall, broad-shouldered, husky man of 36, who, in personal contacts, came across as a quiet, calm, diffident sort of individual, with a warm and friendly smile. Both had been raised in the Catholic religion, and their faith was part of their philosophy of life. At 34, the mother, a bright high school graduate, continued to have an avid interest in literature, and her main pastime was reading, whenever her household responsibilities allowed her the leisure. The father, a college graduate of superior intelligence, worked as a systems analyst in the computer division of a large department store; sports were his main hobby. In the suburban community where they owned their own home, they appeared well liked by their neighbors (at different times, neighbors volunteered to bring Elizabeth to the Clinic when the parents couldn't), and thanks to the grandparents who served as baby-sitters, they were able to maintain an active social life.

Elizabeth's mother, in the pretreatment evaluation of her personality functioning, appeared anxious, reticent, and depressed. Her anxiety inclined her to hold back, to doubt herself. Her depression constricted her ability to verbalize her thoughts freely and dulled her imagination. To operate at full capacity, it was evident that she needed the security of a familiar situation, well structured and defined. Faced with the unusual and the unexpected (such as Rorschach Ink Blots), she tended to seek external support rather than rely on her own inner resources to meet the situation. Thus her characteristic mode of dealing with difficult problems appeared to be to seek from others, in a dependent sort of way, the stimulating and encouraging responses from which she could derive the strength to mobilize the good assets she possessed but which she could not always use. This central feature of her personality functioning may give some understanding of her pattern of reaction when confronted with a child who was a complete mystery to her. Typically, she found herself not daring to do too much about it, but counting on others around her whom she trusted to give her some direction and some encouragement. Her anxiety did not arouse in her any creative or imaginative response, but only a deep sadness at not being able to do anything but be resigned.

On the other hand, her characterological mode of personality responses made her open and available to support from the outside: She would respond quickly as soon as she was told what to do and made to feel capable of doing it. At first her pediatrician gave the direction, then the personnel at the Evaluation Center, then the therapists in the program, and then, more importantly, her own Elizabeth, when the child began to reach for her and demand of her attention, affection, and life. "Since Elizabeth has been in treatment (this was written four months after treatment began) she has changed quite a bit. She is now a happy child; she smiles and laughs often. She is much more interested in people. Now that I look back, I realize she always liked things better than people. She allows more affection now; at one time she didn't like to be hugged or cuddled. We are happy about Elizabeth's progress during the last four months, and although we realize she may never be normal, we have some hope for her future."

This last statement of hope was made with some reservation. After four months of treatment, it was obvious that Elizabeth's mother was gaining more confidence and was reacting with pleasure to the child's progress. But she kept her fingers crossed, so to say, and her characteristic tendency to doubt herself required that constant reassurance and support be given her, both by Elizabeth and by the therapists, in the following months. Elizabeth, fortunately, was quite willing to help her mother be a real mother to her. Six months after the first home visit (December 30–31, 1966), Dr. Krall, our home observer wrote: "The most remarkable change that has occurred since the previous observation period is

Elizabeth's immediate recognition of me and smiling greeting as I entered the house on each day of this visit. She also seemed to be considerably more aware of the adult interacting with her. She spontaneously hugged her mother on one occasion, although she pushed her brothers away when they tried to hug and kiss her.

"The degree of interaction between mother and child has also shown a qualitative change. Instead of being a mere observer, mother now participates actively in Elizabeth's play. She will say 'that's right,' 'that was good,' or 'that's not right' about the child's play with puzzles, and so forth. She also actively encourages and accelerates language development. She asks, 'what's this?' frequently, and helps Elizabeth to give verbal responses. As a consequence, language development is improving. Elizabeth has about 35 words now in contrast to 10 or 12 words as of six months ago."

The following period (December, 1966–April, 1967) brought further improvement in Elizabeth and a greater feeling of security in her mother. "Both parents," writes Dr. Krall, "engaged Elizabeth in almost constant activity and interaction during this visit (April 21–22, 1967). The mother allowed Elizabeth to swing alone outside for awhile, but she finally joined her. Later she told me that they try to alternate her swinging with other activities and to combine the swinging with singing so as not to encourage withdrawal into previous autistic-like behavior. Elizabeth responds well to the games and songs introduced by the parents. She often repeats parts of these songs, such as 'Bah, bah, black sheep,' 'swing, swing,' and 'ee-i-ee-i-oh.' Greater warmth is evidenced on the part of both mother and child. Elizabeth ran to her mother, and was mildly upset when mother went in to get a Kleenex. Elizabeth seems to be more affectionate, holding mother, and running to father to kiss him on request."

Thus it is clear that Elizabeth manages to draw out her mother more and more; we see more alertness, assurance, and spontaneity, as well as imagination and intelligent concern in the mother. Yet such behavioral changes do not affect the basic characterological pattern of personality functioning in her. She continues to look to outside stimulating forces and support to maintain, at its peak, her capacity to give, in a sensitive and effective way, her maternal responses to Elizabeth's need for her. The satisfactions and pleasures she derived from the child's live and meaningful communication to her, as exciting and fulfilling as they may have been, could not meet all of her adult needs as a woman. Characterologically, in the same way she needed a real Elizabeth in order to be a real mother to her, she needed also the forceful presence of a real man, Elizabeth's father, to support and gratify her as a woman. Before discussing this issue, let us turn first to what sort of a man Elizabeth's father was.

On first contact, as was mentioned earlier, Elizabeth's father gave the impression of a quiet, reserved, somewhat shy individual. Yet there was also a quality of confidence and solid self-control which was reflected in his attentive and sensitive perception of situations confronting him. It was easy for him to accept Elizabeth, whatever her condition might be, because, first of all, she was his child and that made her part of the family and, second, because he would do whatever needed to be done, once he understood what action could be taken. Thus, for Elizabeth's father, his characteristic response to difficulties appeared to be less one of resignation than one of what might be called thoughtful passivity; he needed to understand and think through a problem before he could bring himself to act on it. There were two things he had to grasp with regard to his child's autistic condition: her low capacity to experience and express feeling and the possibility of increasing this capacity through intensive affective and sensory stimulation.

As soon as he understood this, Elizabeth's father went into action, and his interest and talents in sports activities served him well in his hard, intensive, physical, and stimulating play with the child. Every day, after work, he had a physical activity session with Elizabeth, and on weekends, swinging games, ball games, rough-and-tumble games included the boys, so that Elizabeth, as far as the father was concerned, was kept at a high level of pleasurable stimulation. She responded well to her dad's intrusions and he, in turn, found himself confronted with having to come to grips with other ways of expressing his feelings outside of hard, physical play.

For Elizabeth's father, the spontaneous expression of feelings did not come easily; he tended characteristically to be ill-at-ease with feelings, and it is very possible that a good deal of his thoughtful and quiet ponderings before action, as well as the hearty quality of his physical involvement once he went into action, were habitual protections he had developed to avoid having to confront himself too much with too many feelings. In other words, although he could readily hold the child in his arms and warmly allow her to hug and kiss him, he appeared more comfortable actively playing with her, that is, expressing through activities his interest and love for her. Thus, whenever strong feelings were part of a situation, he tended to distance himself somewhat, to isolate the feelings, to reduce the situation to an intellectual challenge, or to divert it into action channels.

There were good and bad points to such an attitude. Elizabeth obviously found in her father's interaction a great source of pleasure, and through his intensive activities, she came alive and became responsive. On the other hand, there are more ways to express love and feelings than just in fun and games; and Elizabeth's own inclination to "perseverate in the repetition of sameness" tended to place limits on the variety and types of physical activities through which her dad was present to her. We kept hoping, throughout the treatment period, that Elizabeth herself would help him lose some of his fears in the spontaneous expression of his feelings, and it is interesting that in the last months of treatment, the home observer notes that the father taught Elizabeth to run to him, hug him, and kiss him in public! This small step may have represented a large improvement in the father's attitude but did not represent any major change in his characterological pattern of behavior. His final personality assessment shows him still struggling against allowing too full an expression of feelings, and this natural reticence on his part, though far different from aloofness and coldly distant behavior, limited the range of affective involvements he could have in his transactions with his autistic child. This is especially true with regard to problems of discipline for Elizabeth.

The father—as most fathers are wont to do—was quite happy at leaving most of the disciplining to Elizabeth's mother, who, herself, tended to be lenient, especially when she received little or no support from the father in this connection. On her second visit to the home (December, 1966), Dr. Krall remarked: "In general, both parents have made little effort to place limits on Elizabeth. She rarely has to wait for anything, and she is given preference in any activity. The boys are asked, at all times, to wait for and accede to Elizabeth's wishes." And in her notes on her last visit (April, 1967), she wrote: "In contrast [to their handling of the boys], both parents seem at a loss as to how to set limits for Elizabeth. They will carry on a strenuous activity beyond their own physical endurance in order to please her." There is no question of the parents' good intentions here, but rather, a genuine reluctance on the part of the father, to move in strongly and with firm and clear structure in order to teach Elizabeth the controls that she needed to develop over her behavior. The father's discomfort with his own feelings prevented any assertive expression of himself in "setting limits," because, confronted with Elizabeth, for whom a rational explanation of any disciplinary action would have been well-nigh useless, it was easier to respond to her demands for physical activities, even if these demands became at times unreasonable.

It can be speculated that this difficulty in the personality functioning of Elizabeth's father also influenced the development of the child in a somewhat indirect way, through its possible effects on the mother. We have indicated how dependent this mother was, in her relationship and communication to others, on receiving from others the stimulating responsive support which could alleviate her anxieties and give her confidence. Elizabeth's father, reserved and reticent, shying away from any ebullient or assertive expression of feelings, may have also, indirectly, limited the mother's security in handling her child. She may have felt "desperately lonely" sometimes. The task of awakening the sleeping Elizabeth demanded of both her parents a steady, patient, relentless dedication, which taxed every ounce of their physical and psychological strengths. That they should have succeeded as well as they did is a tribute to their genuine love for this child. Their personalities, under clinical scrutiny, may show good and bad points, but Elizabeth is not concerned with clinicians; she knows she had good parents!

Kathy's mother and father.   In Kathy's parents, we also found good and bad points, because that is part of the "human condition" and of the "phenomenon of man" on this earth. Her parents, each in his or her own way, found in Kathy the ultimate test of all their personality resources and deficits. This child, who, for two years prior to treatment, had puzzled and baffled them in her isolation and in the inaccessible strength of her "circle of silence," continued, when she began coming out of her sleep, to confront them daily, as she did her therapists at the clinic, with unending behavioral problems which would have discouraged any normal parents. Kathy's mother was inclined to such moments of discouragement, but when everything seemed lost except despair, Kathy always came through with such new signs of growth and aliveness that hope appeared worthwhile again, and the task of awakening Kathy looked like a new and beautiful adventure. Signs of discouragement were not as noticeable in Kathy's father. He hid his feelings better. He had what might be considered the engineer's approach to Kathy's problems: He always proceeded with her from the easy to the difficult, from the simple to the complex, and when the situation appeared impossible, he escaped from the scene to his workbench in the basement.

By profession Kathy's father was a chemist. At age 34 he seemed rather secure in his position, and though he read mostly technical articles pertinent to his work, his main leisure time was spent either in painting or in making a variety of articles of furniture for the home. Like Elizabeth's father, he tended to be somewhat reserved and timid in interpersonal contacts, but, in contrast, he sought more aggressively to assert his own personal views and to challenge the opinions of others. The pretreatment personality evaluation revealed in him a quality of sensitivity which had some of the features found in artists. But he never gave free rein to his imagination, as if, having been brought up in a strictly conventional and regulated pattern of living, he sensed that it would be dangerous to go beyond the rules and regulations of a well-ordered society. There is evidence that he may have wished to give in to less conventional or socially acceptable impulses, but the frustrations he experienced in curtailing such "devil-may-care" moments he expressed in what clinicians call "passive-aggressive" behavior.

Thus, confronted with his autistic child, as long as no answer appeared available to the questions and problems which her behavior raised, he seemed content to bide his time; and since he was reluctant to use too much of his imagination in any attempt at offering any solution to the child's difficulties, he was quite willing in his frustration to turn Kathy over to her mother. This did not represent any lack of interest in, or concern on his part for, the child; rather he, too, needed very much some cues from Kathy as to what he should do for her. Kathy gave him no inkling of her needs, and, therefore, he felt impotent in his responses to her.

When treatment began with Kathy, and her father was told how the autistic isolation could be breached, he found in the unconventional approach taken by the therapists support for his less conventional drives and for his sensitive and creative imagination. On his second "observation period" in the therapy room at the clinic a few months after Kathy had started responding actively and affectively to the therapeutic efforts, we see him organizing his interaction with his child around the playful handling of a big red balloon which he had brought with him. This toy not only bounced around in a variety of directions leading the child to move and run freely after it, but it could be pinched and regain its shape to the amazement of Kathy; it also made strange and raucous

noises when both Kathy and her dad would start pulling at it in opposite directions. These were most delightful moments of interaction for
both the father and his little girl, and when, toward the end of this
session, he placed the red balloon under Kathy's shirt the child ecstati-
cally ran around the room showing her dad how grown-up her stomach
was, quite amazed that her dad had been able to do that for her in such
a short time!

Thus the affective understanding of her autistic condition, which
Kathy's behavior helped her father reach, stimulated in him creative and
imaginative ways of responding to her and of eliciting behavior from
her to which he could respond. He didn't go wild, but as long as Kathy
reached out for him, he found in her contacts inspiration to design and
build a wide variety of toys and playthings useful to her development;
he built a recreation room in the basement of his home so that Kathy
could have more space to romp around in with her brother; he rede-
signed, through painting and reupholstering, the entire interior of the
house so that Kathy, interested in colors, could easily recognize the various rooms of the home. Unfortunately, Kathy had, in her amazing development, periods which earlier we referred to as "plateaus." At such
times her stubborn negativism made her difficult to understand; at such
times she had little inspiring effect on her father.

It was in those situations that his characterological modes of behavior
would come to the fore. Frustrated and angry at his ineffectiveness with
his child, Kathy's father was inclined to leave the battlefield; passively,
he tended to withdraw from any close interaction with Kathy, and in a
sort of displacement of his aggressive impulses, allow the mother to bear
the full brunt of Kathy's baffling and punishing behavior. To Kathy's
credit we must add that these "plateaus," though apparently frequent
in the eyes of those who had to daily contend with them, never lasted
too long. The surge in growth which always followed them, also always
gave a new spurt to the father's enthusiastic capacity to respond to her
and be with her.

He was the one who found ways to teach her how to hold a spoon and
feed herself; how to use—after Kathy had wondrously discovered colors,
thanks to her brother's "sessions" with her—crayons to fill in a variety of
simple pictures which he had ingeniously arranged so as to force her to
utilize appropriate colors. It was mostly he who taught Kathy how to
imitate sounds and begin to form words. With great, affectionate patience he would crouch in front of the child (seated in a chair) and for

each sound or articulation effort that Kathy would imitate or initiate, he would happily give her a big hug and, to her delight, swing her in the air or playfully toss her about. Then he would proceed to help Kathy articulate her sounds better by following with his own voice whatever sound Kathy made, so that he progressively would bring her to form a word, and give her the joy of a new mastery. It is important to add here that thanks to her father's pedagogical efforts with her, Kathy not only discovered words but truly discovered speech, because in teaching her words, to the accompaniment of a great deal of affective and sensory stimulation, the father always made sure that the words he taught her had some meaning and made some sense to the child.

After two years, when we attempted to measure in what ways and to what extent Kathy's awakening to life had influenced basic attitudes and characteristic personality modes of behavior in her father, we were struck on the one hand by how effective Kathy had been in bringing out of her dad creative and productive energies, which he was able to use to her benefit and that of his entire family; on the other hand, we could have wished that these behavior changes in the father could have been reflected more clearly and strikingly in the results of those clinical evaluative measures which were used to assess his personality functioning. The sources of creative and imaginative energies which Kathy is so obviously capable of stirring and tapping, he is still inclined to keep locked and ineffectual when Kathy gives him no clues to go on. His anxiety over letting himself go for fear of going too far remains unquestionably a difficulty in his personality makeup and precludes his having available for Kathy, at times, the full impact of his presence to her. We could wish, ideally, that this difficulty did not exist, but when we look at how much this man did and continues to do for his child, we can only rejoice that this was, in strength and weakness, Kathy's father.

Inevitably, the strengths and the weaknesses noted in this father's personality functioning were bound to affect his relationships to other members of the family in a variety of ways. We indicated earlier that Kathy's mother was inclined to periods of depression and discouragement. We can only speculate, now, as to the influence which the passive-aggressive moods of her husband may have had in eliciting these dysphoric feelings in her. In many ways, she was a very different person from her husband. Though tending to be timid and quiet like him in social situations, she could, much more easily than he, let herself be caught up by the excitement and emotional qualities of a situation, so that there were fewer constraints in her behavior and even her aggressive impulses could be allowed to find more overt expressions. Kathy's mother, an only child, had been raised by parents both of whom were teachers. She had retained from this upbringing a sort of compulsive dedication to orderliness but, more important, a strong interest in intellectual matters and in literary achievements.

She was married after three years of college, and her son Marc was born while she was in Germany, where her husband was stationed as an Army engineer. Three years later Kathy was born, and for the next two years Kathy's mother sought in vain to establish with this child some sort of gratifying and useful communication. At age 28, when she first brought Kathy to the clinic, she was seeking desperately for some help in reaching her child and some support for her dwindling hopes. It is striking that in spite of the depressive qualities which we had come to accept as underlying so much of her behavior, Kathy's mother appeared to possess an infinite capacity to use any support given her to rekindle her hopes. It was not difficult for her to believe that the help offered her at the clinic was the long-awaited answer to the baffling problems which her child's behavior presented. She trusted and believed in the therapeutic program which was outlined for Kathy, and she assumed her part in this program with zest and dedication. Her superior intelligence, her good sense of humor, her ability to observe and describe a situation objectively and yet imaginatively, served her well in coming to grips, under our guidance, with the problems involved in the difficult task of bringing up Kathy.

There was a stubborn determination on her part in this effort, yet there were many fears in this woman. One could probably say that to react with fear when confronted with a strange and unpredictable situation was a characteristic reaction on her part; by the same token, it can also be said that she never allowed her fears to paralyze her capacity for action whenever action was needed. Her love for Kathy and her determination to reach her kept her going even when her fears obscured her good judgment, clouded her imagination, and cramped her good sense of humor. In moments of fear, as when Kathy seemed to revert to previously held autistic positions, and when the plateaus on which she chose to stand appeared to be unending, Kathy's mother needed desperately to find in others the stimulating force that would start her functioning effectively again. In this respect, it would be accurate to say that she was a very dependent individual, but once pointed in the right direction her own inner resources would easily be available to her in her transactions with Kathy.

During those periods when Kathy appeared to be fully responsive to the urge in her to discover the world about her, to master every new situation, and to thoroughly enjoy being alive and part of a family, the mother, caught in the excitement of such refreshing new life in the child, could find herself leading the entire family into putting on, with Kathy, a ballet performance complete with leotards, pirouettes, and graceful dance steps. She could also, when Kathy was so afraid to put anything in her mouth, invent an after-meal game where everyone had to sit around Kathy with lollipops in their mouths, demonstrating en masse, to the amazement and questioning look of Kathy, that this was neither a fatal nor even dangerous activity.

There were many such imaginative and effective "games" which Kathy's mother could invent when her confidence was high. But in difficult moments, when her fears took hold of her, she seemed incapable of inventing any solutions to any of Kathy's problems. She was, for instance, completely perplexed when the child tyrannically refused to have her hair washed or cut; the mother kept at it, but it was in the face of such monumental resistance in the child that the mother came out of it spent and exhausted. When told, however, that Kathy would probably enjoy this hair washing or cutting if the entire adventure was surrounded with "pomp and circumstance" by cloaking the child with a cape and preparing some impressive ceremonial protocols to accompany the event, Kathy's mother could easily catch on to the humorous and playful quality of the suggestion and add to it. Not only was she then able to wash Kathy's hair, but before taking her to her boudoir, she would wrap her hair in a colorful turban and then in front of the mirror install rollers in Kathy's hair to the child's utter delight.

Thus it would seem that the communication pattern between the child and her mother throughout this period of treatment fluctuated in line with the ebb and flow of the depressive tides in her which so frequently threatened to flood over her. As best she could, and to the rhythm of her own anxieties conflicting with the push in her for survival and life, Kathy kept up her end of the communication. This was not enough by itself to change in her mother those sources of insecurity which seemed to be part of her personality. But the challenge of Kathy's behavior constituted in her mother's life what clinicians might call an antidepressive regime. It kept her going, and what we witness at the end of two years in the behavior and attitude of Kathy's mother is the entrenched confidence that what has been started with Kathy in giving her a chance to be a normal little girl must be continued.

Moments of discouragement still exist and, looking to the future, Kathy's mother still worries whether her little girl will ever fit in a regular classroom at school, and whether each step of her development will be fraught with problems which always appear insurmountable. But less and less do these questions trigger off desperate feelings of weariness and hopelessness. What Kathy has done for her mother is reflected in the quality of the weekly notes which the mother wrote for us, and in which we see her struggles with her child and the fluctuating aspects of her communication with her. But in these notes, as in a song of hope, we see also expressed, even in their literary style, a mounting crescendo of infinite expectation that her intellectual assets, her imagination, and her sense of humor will see her through the task of fully awakening Kathy in spite of their mutual fears and of however long it takes. (Excerpts from these notes can be found in Chapter 10.)

Tommy's parents. In Tommy's mother, it was less a tendency to depressive moods that we saw than an inclination to be easily overwhelmed by the magnitude of the task of dealing with an autistic boy. The strength she would have needed in this regard was not always available from her husband, whose interest, love, and concern for the child were constantly offset by his bafflement in the face of his child's autistic behavior. Both parents were quite young (they were, in fact, the youngest couple in our parents' group), and Tommy was their first child. Both parents were of high intellectual endowment, and their educational background included a B.A. degree for the mother and a Master's degree in journalism for the father. In their youthful search to find a place in which to best use their talents, they had enlisted in the Peace Corps.

Shortly after their return from Southeast Asia, where they had been assigned, Tommy was born. A year later, the birth of a daughter brought new worries and hardship to the parents, especially to the mother, who suffered from some degree of anemia. The relative instability of home life created by the successive journalistic positions which the father pursued, only added to their concern in the face, very early, of what they both recognized as abnormal behavior and delayed development in Tommy. It was at the time when the father had been appointed to a secure and permanent position in a local university that Tommy, not yet 3, was brought to us at the Clinic. In their search for help, they had encountered a number of disappointments, and therefore it was with a certain skeptical and critical attitude that they welcomed the treatment program offered to their son. They were especially intrigued with the part that they were asked to play in this program, since it gave them the feeling that finally they also might be able to do something for Tommy.

This was strikingly true of the mother, who was able, as soon as she understood what was wanted of her, to put a youthful zest and enthusiasm into cooperating with us in this therapeutic adventure. This did not always come easily to her; she understood quite readily that Tommy needed a great deal of affective and sensory stimulation, but she felt somewhat awkward in allowing herself to interact freely at this physical level with her son. Though very affectionate and quite responsive herself to affection, she seemed to lack in her actions the spontaneity that she could very well express in her thinking. It was as if she understood what her little boy wanted and needed and could think it through very clearly and meaningfully, but when it came to having to express this in action, she tended to do it somewhat halfheartedly and awkwardly.

The presence of Tommy's sister in the home, who also demanded a great deal of physical attention and care, taxed to the limit this conflictual aspect of the mother's personality. That she should be overwhelmed so many times by the task of being insistently present to two youngsters, who needed her so much this way, is quite understandable. Yet, as Tommy began to come out of his shell and instead of angrily rejecting or avoiding her approaches to him, initiated, himself, many affectionate and exploratory moves toward her, she also began to find this direct form of communication and interaction with her children quite rewarding and gratifying. We have indicated earlier how wondrously delightful it was for her to find herself spontaneously gamboling and dancing with Tommy in the kitchen, while at the same time carrying on the chore of feeding her daughter. In her notes, written in a humorous, tongue-in-cheek style, she frequently describes these moments of acrobatic prowess when she would lend herself to having Tommy on one side of her lap, intent on discovering every part of her face, and his little sister on the other side, intent on making sure that she wouldn't miss a mouthful of the meal being fed her.

Obviously, for Tommy's mother the program was very demanding; to a certain degree this was due to her lack of good organization in the management of her household. Not all mothers are first-rate housekeepers; and, given the choice between carefully planning the effective distribution of the various chores required in their household and curling up quietly on the sofa to read a good book, Tommy's mother admittedly preferred to do the latter. It would be easy to see this behavior as an escape from her maternal responsibilities; more accurately, this behavior was less an escape than a moment of true relief from tasks which demanded so much physical strength from her and, by their unending complexities, appeared to overwhelm her so easily.

Unquestionably, part of her dismay in these situations can also be attributed to her immaturity as a person; her heart was in the right place, and time and time again she would say to herself: "Tomorrow, let's get organized." When tomorrow came, however, the same demands of the children appeared to defy any effective organizational intention on her part. Yet she never gave up, so that even in her somewhat scattered way, she began finding more and more effective methods of putting her tendencies to disorganization in the service of the growth and development of her children. In a colorful and humorous way, she describes how she exploited her little daughter's blossoming altruism by having her feed dry cereal flake by flake, like potato chips, to Tommy. And on another occasion when Tommy, obviously aware that his younger sister was preempting some of his time with his mother and was upstaging him in her demands for attention, took it upon himself to push her away in a most ungentlemanly fashion, the mother describes how pleased she was with Tommy, and how much every bit of her heart was cheering him on. Tommy was growing up, and his mother was rooting for him all the way.

Tommy remained with us 14 months. The personality assessment of his mother, which was made after his first year of treatment, indicated how much he and his little sister had contributed to their mother's personality maturation. This is reflected in the quiet and thoughtful way in which she could now meet new and unexpected situations; in the confidence she displayed that whatever physical interactions she had with her children would be rewarding to all and not harmful to the children; and in the capacity she showed in taking steps to insure that her part in Tommy's awakening would remain her central concern. Thus one could say that she both "loosened up" and "tightened up" in her maternal behavior. She could now be more easygoing in the physical display of her affectionate responses to Tommy and his sister. To some extent this little sister, who had now developmentally passed Tommy, supplied to the mother, in her initiative and spontaneous responses as well as in her refreshing capacity to entertain her with chatter and questions, those stimulating experiences which Tommy could not.

On the other hand, Tommy's need for structure and consistent predictability led his mother to more effective and economical distribution of her time and energies. The total family situation appeared less overwhelming to the mother, even though after one year of treatment Tommy was still far from being the wide-awake child she could wish for. Without having lost any of her youthful zest, Tommy's mother seemed to have acquired some of the wisdom of maturity. Her choice, in difficult moments, may still be to curl up on the sofa and read a good book, but the relief she found in such activity can be said to be easily offset now by the relief she finds in brief moments of close affectionate contacts with Tommy, and in long, lady-to-lady conversations with his sister. Tommy's mother grew up with the children!

But what about his father? The striking aspect of this man's personality was that, from the beginning, his behavior gave the impression that he wanted very much to come across to others as a mature, knowledgeable, intellectually curious, and sensitive individual. When he had been advised of Tommy's autistic condition, he had made it a point to read extensively on the subject of early infantile autism, to investigate what was being done for such conditions, and to evaluate critically whatever information he gathered from his inquiries. He wanted to approach the problem in an intelligent and mature fashion. But, in truth, he was stymied as far as what he himself could actually do for Tommy; and when the clinic program was presented to him and discussed, it was evident, though he maintained the position that the whole thing should make sense to him, that his response was one of relief that his love and concern for Tommy could now find more effective outlets than just an intellectual understanding of Tommy's condition. He was ready to do his part.

Because Tommy's father was somewhat the athletic type he could easily let himself get involved in close physical contacts with his children. After witnessing, at the Clinic, the amount of affective tactile, kinesthetic, and proprioceptive stimulations included in Tommy's interactions with his therapists, he had no hesitation, in contrast to his wife, in relating freely to Tommy in this preverbal psychosomatic way. So pleasurable and rewarding were such contacts between Tommy and his father that for a good while Tommy would not leave his father alone whenever the father was at home. It still remained very important to the father that he should continue his searching inquiries in scientific literature concerning early infantile autism and that outwardly he should remain in the eyes of others an intelligent seeker of truth. But clearly he was delighted to have a chance through his active participation in Tommy's therapeutic program, to shed, so-to-say, his academic garb and wearing slacks and a sweatshirt, allow Tommy to climb all over him.

The sources of warm affection and of spontaneous affective responsivity which were so available to the father he felt obliged in most situations to cloak under the garment of intellectual and academic respectability. Except with Tommy. And it is somewhat humorous that Tommy himself should have sensed this personality characteristic in his father. In the flush of his delight at finally being able to overcome his fears and begin to explore every part of his home environment, Tommy one day discovered his father's precious books. Just as he was in the midst of pulling them out of the bookcases the presence of his father in the room struck him, apparently, as giving great significance to this moment of uninhibited curiosity. Tommy stopped his activity short, turned to look at his father, and as quickly as he could, madly began pushing the books back where they belonged. A certain level of academic respectability still needed to be maintained, and Tommy was just the one to know that!

It would be wrong to conclude from the description given of this father's personality functioning that here was a man who was afraid of his feelings and had to defend himself against their free expression by hiding them behind a mask of intellectual curiosity and professional respectability. This young father was, in truth, a rather timid person and one who, though very dependent in his needs for affective fulfillment, had apparently learned to act as if he did not have any such dependencies. Of high intellectual endowment (as measured by standardized tests), he attempted to achieve this by utilizing the best assets he had. The front he tried to put on reflected his effort at independence, but in many ways he was uneasy and uncomfortable with such a front. Though from habit he still felt obliged to rationalize his behavior, he welcomed the first good chance he had to do away with such artificial independence and acquire that more mature and more appropriate form of independence which he found in the free and spontaneous expression of his feelings toward Tommy.

It is this change in his overall personality functioning which we found most clearly expressed in the behavior of Tommy's father after one year. During her last home visit (April, 1967), the home observer writes: "In contrast (to the mother's quiet handling of the children), Tommy's father was more active from the beginning of the home visit. In addition to rough-and-tumble play, he will also hold and hug Tommy, which Tommy does not reject but rather seems to enjoy." Tommy's limitless needs for unconditional and intensively direct expressions of affection and presence had apparently helped release the father from a self-imposed and arbitrary intellectual façade, offering him an opportunity not only to be truly and effectively himself but to be the father that Tommy needed.

June's family. When we first met June, it was her father who introduced her. He appeared somewhat self-conscious and apologetic at having to explain that his wife could not come that day to the clinic because she was still recovering from the recent birth of their fourth child. But unquestionably he was a proud father. We knew, from the social worker's notes, that as a family man his devotion to his wife, helping her in every way he could, had created a happy and stable atmosphere at home. We knew also that he had serious doubts about ever being able to think of June as a "normal" child. Thus part of his self-consciousness at the Evaluation Center, where we first met him, was also related to the fact that though he tried very hard to engage June in some interaction with him, she staunchly avoided and ignored him. It was this behavior which, he explained, had lead him to conclude that his child was probably autistic, since he had just read a book on this condition. Thus, self-conscious, apologetic, ineffectual in his handling of June, he nevertheless wanted to make sure that we would recognize in him an informed person and an intelligently concerned father.

Like Tommy's father, it was obviously important to June's father to let us know quickly of his intellectual standing. He was, in fact, a college graduate with a major in psychology and one year of graduate work in business administration. Though he was aware that we knew that the recent addition to his family represented the fourth child in less than five years and that therefore family responsibilities laid heavy on his shoulders, he felt compelled to act as if what mattered most to him at that moment was to enter with us in a long and erudite discussion of the scientific aspects of "June's case." There were so many puzzling points to that case, and it was so gratifying to him to have finally found, as he expressed it to us, scientists interested in tackling these enigmatic points. He would do whatever he could to help us; and when we told him that all he had to do was help June, he volunteered every ounce of his energy to this task. There was nothing bombastic or boisterous about his volunteering, yet it had some of the qualities of the high-powered salesman intent on convincing us that nothing would stand in the way of our helping June, including him. The picture to be drawn from these highlights is that of a generous, well-intentioned individual, terribly afraid that the genuine and warm concern he had for his child would not be understood unless he gave it some sort of a dramatic twist, either through a pseudointellectual presentation of it or through giving a mildly hypomanic "go-go" quality to it.

Yet June's father was neither an "intellectual" in the sense of being introvertively lost in abstruse thinking, nor was he an action-oriented extrovert. In some ways, he could be described as an artist or as somewhat of a dilettante. He had dreamed of being an actor, and his most important relaxation still remained attending theatrical performances. He played golf, also, but had no real confidence in his game. His business was selling, and his success in this line of work, as we understood it, appeared linked to the dramatic flair with which he approached an opportunity rather than to the convincing virtues of his selling determination. Colleagues in his field called him "gutsy" because his biggest successes were always in difficult situations and always flamboyant. But he was really more like a commando than like a professional soldier: He went in and out of a situation quickly, but when the action required was of a steady, patient, carefully painstaking quality, he tended to be restless and insecure and his determination sagged.

The inadequacies he experienced so deeply in his dealings with June —his first child—reflected and enhanced the feelings of low self-esteem which seem to underlie so many of his interpersonal relationships. He was willing to drive himself into action if action was needed to help June, but his tendency to doubt that anything he did could truly effect the changes he wanted, stood as an obstacle and a barrier to any spontaneity or consistent initiative and structure in his transactions with his daughter. On the other hand, because he truly wanted to have her as a central part of his concern and love, he felt compelled to maintain her in his mind as a "case" whose puzzling features he could always use as the starting point for long, involved, and fruitless intellectual discussions.

Whatever the sources of his underlying lack of self-confidence and of his insecurities, these experiences in him progressively gave way, under the steady and dramatically revealing evidence of growth and maturation in his child June, to a quiet and confident acceptance of himself as a man and as a father.

June had to work at this very steadily. She would not allow her father to make her just an object of intellectual explorations, nor would she allow him to remain uninvolved with her. To the many overtures she made to him, either in a positive way by seeking physical expressions of affection from him or in negativistic ways by provoking some sort of reaction on his part to her behavior, he learned to respond as time went on, with less doubts about himself and more rewarding faith and trust in her. He learned, for instance, that he could exploit June's curiosity and tendency to wander about in the neighborhood by giving her small errands to run, and by giving her opportunities, when he would drive her to the shopping center, to discover how to operate vending machines or make small purchases as normal children do. He also learned that he could deal successfully with negativistic moments by adopting what the therapists had described to him at the Clinic as "reverse negativism," which amounted to saying no to the very behavior to which a yes answer on the part of June was desired. These successes with June in his handling of her behavior progressively gave him more confidence as a father and less tendency to view her as a "puzzling case" than as a delightful and understandable child. Especially was this true when June was accepted as a regular student in the public school system. He had convinced himself so well that this could not happen to June that, confronted with it, his final reaction seemed to say: "Well, maybe we're not doing so bad after all."

The final assessment of his personality shows June's father to have gained a truer and more mature capacity to accept in himself the strengths and the weaknesses which were part of his behavior when he first brought June to us at the clinic. It seems that the more June demanded that he be a real "Daddy" to her, the more the doubts he had about her and about himself tended to disappear. There is a striking correlation here between the improvements in the father's general attitude about himself and his family and the awakening of June to the lively realization that she truly had a father and a family. As the most advanced child in our program, June had somehow rallied the entire family into letting the father know that he need only be what he truly was, with his assets and liabilities, to be fully acceptable to her and to them.

Somehow it is to June, also, that we owe the very striking changes which occurred in her mother's pattern of communication with her. The first time she brought June to the Clinic, we were somewhat disheartened at witnessing how inept this mother appeared in her handling of June. It was as if she were completely perplexed and immobilized in the face of June's aggressively clinging and erratically arbitrary activities. Our reaction was: "How can this woman deal with three other younger children?" In a conversation with us a few months later, June's mother explained to us why she had been so paralyzed by June's behavior that day. "This was the first time June had ever clung to me, and I didn't want to discourage her."

A warm and maternal person, June's mother was by no means as ineffectual as she had first appeared to us. Like her husband, whom she had met on the stage in a college play, she was somewhat of an artist, but her creative abilities were expressed less in dramatic performances than in the graphic arts. Because her artistic talents took second place to her primary and central concerns as a wife and a mother, she tried nevertheless to combine them, and for each child that was born in the family, there was also a painting completed in her studio. A sensitive woman, who reacted with diffidence and insecurity whenever she was left on her own to meet a strange or unusual situation, she could, whenever she was on her home grounds and surrounded by the reassuring presence of those she loved, assert herself with a strength always tempered with a fine sense of humor.

June was her first child. She sensed very early that this was an unusual baby, who left her without those clues necessary to bring forth from her sensitive and effective maternal responses. In the face of such a situation, similar in some respects to the one we witnessed on the first visit to the Clinic, the anxiety in June's mother tended to become expressed in perplexed inaction; restrained by the fear of doing wrong, the mother preferred to do only those gestures which she felt would be safe and cause no damage. Thus it is not surprising that, in our eyes, she appeared incapable with June of imposing the necessary structure through which to permit effective action to take place. And though this characteristic behavior of hers may tend to foster disorganization and even at times chaos in her disciplinary efforts towards her children, it also has the refreshing beneficial effect of eliciting from the children a form of independence which is not all oppositional and negativistic, but rather creative and spontaneously productive. This is especially seen in the fact that each child in the family takes care of the others. One of the most touching scenes which we observed in the Clinic involved June taking charge of the two babies in the family while the mother, somewhat harried and distraught by the extent of the task that was hers, was frantically trying to regain possession of June's rambunctious brother.

It would be tempting to suggest that June's mother lacked in aggressive self-assertion but such a suggestion would be misleading. In those situations where because of their social and conventional nature she felt more at ease and relaxed, she could assert her views very forcefully and handle herself very effectively in interpersonal exchanges. This paradoxical aspect of her personality we also saw in the striking contrast at home between the orderly management of the household in general and the obvious absence of any effective discipline in her dealings with the children.

In attempting to understand these contradictions in the personality of June's mother, we had to give weight to what might be seen as an assumption of a "feminine" role. She was in many respects more secure and self-sufficient than June's father, but it was important to her that he remain in the eyes of all the strong, assertive, self-reliant head of the household. Thus one could say that her fears and her timidities were to some extent assumed, and in the same way that June managed to help her father feel more comfortably adequate with her, she seemed also to have helped her mother discard any borrowed fears and use the strengths of her personality to be a more efficient mother.

One year after our original appraisal of her personality functioning, we have clear indications that these strengths have become available to June's mother. She has little doubt now that she can deal in a much more structured way with the demands of her children and their "independent" behavior, because somehow June's own demands on her and her brand of autistic independence have lead the mother to a much more assertive expression of her maternal concerns. She has discovered that June need not wander aimlessly throughout the neighborhood; by clearly defining for June the exact route she should take, and giving her clear signposts by which to orient herself, the mother could effectively transform June's useless wanderlust into a pleasurable journey with a definite destination and a route of return.

Similarly, instead of being helpless in the face of the tyrannical manner with which June so frequently was inclined to "boss around" her siblings and her friends, the mother could now put June in charge of entertaining her siblings and her friends, thus again utilizing June's inconsiderate independence in a much more structured and productive way. Especially did her security and self-confidence as a mother become evident to us when, on the occasion of June's sitting on her mother's lap and attempting to impose on her arbitrary and selfish demands, we saw this mother, who one year previously had appeared to us so inept and perplexed in handling June, quietly and effectively transform an unpleasant and disagreeable situation into a playful and relaxed, kidding conversation with June. "Mother always, always listens to June and always does what June wants, isn't that so, June?" Paradoxically, this in fact was so. June needed the strongly assertive and yet warmly maternal structure that her mother could now impose on her, and that the mother found herself capable of such behavior at this point was truly another good effect of June's awakening from her autistic sleep.

Discussion

At this point, having taken such a close look at the parents of our group of autistic children, we can wonder indeed what common characteristics in behavior or in psychological makeup these parents might possess. However, one is more impressed by the differences between them rather than by the similarities. In common they have good intelligence, good education, good family background, a certain degree of shyness and reserve, an inclination to be conventional and conservative, a capacity to respond to the human condition of stress and trial with sometimes more than the usual amount of sensitivity and anxiety, and possibly a penchant toward depressive feelings. But mostly what they have in common appears to be their genuine love and concern for their children.

With regard to their intellectual endowment, none of them was a genius, nor did any of them give evidence of being an aborted genius. As for their educational achievements, though the majority had either completed college or had had several years of college work, none of them could be said to be lost in the high spheres of literary or scientific absorption. We indicated that they seemed inclined to shyness and reserve in their interpersonal attitudes; but as is evident, this is a far cry from cool detachment and emotional aloofness. They were in the upper-middle level of economic life, but though this enabled them to afford attention and treatment for their child, none of them could be called highly prosperous. In their upbringing, all of them had acquired the conventional respect for what is proper and socially acceptable; they were conservative in their views, not because any one of them couldn't experience at times an urge to break the rules and regulations but because they had learned to live in the security of a well-defined and predictable society. All of them could react with anxiety and helplessness, and sometimes despair, in the face of the most baffling situation which they had encountered as parents; and they seemed, all of them, to be truly human in the variety of ways, some positive, some negative, in which they dealt with these anxieties. These were sensitive people who could laugh and cry, work and play, hope and despair; they had in common that ordinary quality that ordinary human beings possess—the quality of doing the best they could with whatever assets or liabilities they possessed.

The differences between these parents far outshine, however, the commonalities. This fact alone may be the strongest support for the view that parents of autistic infants can be thought of as plain, ordinary, normal parents. From a clinical point of view their personality pictures represent a wide spectrum of personality organizations or types. Some of them might be called obsessive-compulsive individuals; others, hysterical-compulsives (mixed neurotics); others might be seen as schizoid; others as having character disorders; still others we might characterize as passive-aggressive or sadomasochistic or oral dependent. All these arbitrary nosological attributes may have psychopathological connotations, but who is to say which one of any so-called normal people walking down the street at any hour of the day or night would escape such potential psychopathological labeling, were he or she to be placed under clinical scrutiny. We have tried with our group of parents, for the first time in any systematic study of Early Infantile Autism, to verify as accurately as we could whether parents of autistic infants were, in truth, a special breed of human beings. We did not think so to start with; this in some ways may have biased our analysis of their test protocols and our interpretations of their behavior. Their test data and the observational notes we possess remain available for those who may want to do their own analyses and their own interpretations.

"Normal" as our group of parents may have been—and possibly for the reason that they were normal—the simple truth is that their autistic infant's behavior had defied their attempts at breaking through the fortress of affective isolation in which these infants were imprisoned. We stated as part of our working hypothesis in this research that the parents could not reach these children because they were given by the infants no clues and no messages to guide their responses and structure their reactions. The direct corollary of this hypothesis was that if the children somehow could be made through their behavior to give clues and to send messages communicating their needs to the parents, the parents then would be in a position to answer these needs and offer their children those responses most appropriate for the children's development and personality growth. Certainly the evidence which we have presented tends strongly to support these views.

Yet when we look closely at the wide variety of responses given by the parents and make a critical evaluation of the effect of their reactions on the children's growth and development, many questions are raised. Obviously, not all parental responses had direct or demonstrable developmental benefits on the children. But taking into account the wide variety of individual personality makeup which we found in this group of parents, is it possible that for one or the other of these parents the existing personality inadequacies may have constituted an additional barrier to the child's messages, even when the child was obviously attempting to communicate. In other words, could the developmental progress of any one of these children, dramatic as it generally was under the circumstances, have been even more striking had the parents been "perfect" personality-wise, or had the children had a different set of parents?

Though this question is truly speculative, our point in raising it allows for the underscoring of what we consider to be a central issue of parent-child relationships. We have discussed that issue in the Introduction to this book and referred to it as the biological and psychological correspondence between parent and child. As we indicated earlier in this chapter, a feature of our parents' personality functioning which seemed to crop up in varying degrees in all of the parents was the tendency to depressive reactions. It would have been easy to deal with this feature by simply stating that this depression in the parents was reactive to the autistic condition of the child. However, our basic position with regard to what we consider to be the central component of Early Infantile Autistic behavior (that is, a low capacity in the child to be stimulated by and respond to affective inputs) alerted us to the possibility that this defective or "depressed" capacity in the child represented the exaggeration of the parental characteristic (that is, the tendency to depressive reactions). If this be so—and only further research could help substantiate it—then in a most meaningful sense we can say that these autistic children had the best parents they could have.

What we are saying here is this: Of all psychosomatic (as defined in the Introduction) forms of pathology, the reactive depression presents us with a situation where the only possible form of effective communication with the depressed individual is through "preverbal and nonverbal channels" (Ref. Grinker, 1964; Hollon, 1962). And isn't it through these channels of preverbal and nonverbal communication that the autistic infant can best be reached? The depressive inclinations in the parents of our group of autistic children would seem to have attuned them well to the language of their child, since they themselves possessed in their own personality makeup an affinity for the basic psychosomatic modes of communication essential to growth and personality development in any infant. The kinds of physical sensory and affective stimulating activities which we requested that they have with their child were exactly the very kinds of communicating instrumentalities they needed themselves for their own personality integration and functioning. It is in that sense, then, that we speak of the biological and psychological correspondence between the parents and the child; in truth they very much needed each other.

NOTE: This chapter had been completed when we came across a recent book which, in its honest and dramatic expression of the struggle of a mother to reach her autistic child, sheds considerable light on the views expressed in the preceding pages and gives them substantial support. *The Siege* describes the strategies, the tactics, and the battles of a mother determined to breach the walls of isolation in which her child, as in a fortress, was imprisoned and lifeless; she was determined to make that child know her, love her, be her child. Any one of our parents can take heart in reading the pages of Clara Claiborne Park. What she did without professional help and guidance, they were able to accomplish more rapidly and effectively with our support and belief that they were the true and natural therapists for their child. What they saw happening to their autistic infants repeats and reinforces the message of faith which Mrs. Park's *Siege* proclaims:

"Human beings fortify themselves in many ways. Numbness, weakness, worry, inattention, silence, suspicion are only a few of the materials out of which the personality constructs its walls. With experience gained in my siege of Elly I mount smaller sieges . . . however formidable the fortifications, they can be breached . . . of all the things that Elly has given, the most precious is this faith, a faith experience has almost transformed into certain knowledge: that inside the strongest citadel we can construct, the human being awaits his besieger."

Chapter XII

And She Walked

discussion of the results

It has been said of psychotherapy in any form that the degree of its success is directly proportionate to the enthusiastic conviction with which the therapist engages in it. When we embarked upon the adventure of awakening Kathy and her friends, we were guided by a number of convictions which may have made us enthusiastic and may have given meaningful direction to our work, but which we mainly wanted to translate into testable hypotheses to be verified and supported, or rejected. Our work with our group of children enabled us to look very closely at the behavioral manifestations of early infantile autism and relate our observations to the theoretical understanding of this condition that we had reached. The observations we made confirmed our view—a view in many ways shared by many other research workers in this field—that the autistic child's behavior, except in its affective manifestations, has all the characteristics of normal behavior in children, carried out, however, in a repetitious and unending way. It is in his lack of affective arousal that the autistic infant is so different from the normal.

At birth, however helpless he may appear otherwise, the normal infant possesses an unquenchable openness to affective arousal, so that his entire repertoire of behavior at that moment appears to have no other value than to insure pleasure and avoid pain. Under usual circumstances the communication by the baby of this affective openness is so clear that the entire pattern of maternal responses to the infant is completely modulated to support and maintain (giving pleasure, reducing pain) this affective position of the infant. For the autistic child and his mother such a communication appears impossible from the beginning. The autistic baby seems normal to everyone except his mother, because from him she receives no messages or clues or, as Bowlby might put it, no "releaser" that would permit in her the mobilization and direction of those energies involved in caring pleasurably and meaningfully for the baby. It is in this affective deficit, preventing any true communication between the infant and the mother, that we chose to see the specific core of the early infantile autistic condition.

Our program of work with the autistic child and his parents was directed at overcoming this affective deficit in the infant, and at restoring the possibility of a normal pattern of communication between the child and his parents (especially his mother). If such a deficit could be overcome, and if such a normal pattern of communication could be restored between the child and his mother, then we could expect a process of personality development and growth in the autistic child which would follow essentially the laws of normal personality development in children.

The autistic children in our program all showed growth and development in all areas of ego functioning, and at a rate which could only be interpreted as "making up for lost time." Their parents, especially their mothers, found themselves capable of meaningful and effective responses to their child's needs for them, so that a basis for true interpersonal communication was established between child and mother. In this communication they were very much present to each other; the child felt like a real child, and the mother felt like a real mother. To what extent these results of our program authentically give support or value to our stated hypotheses will depend very much on the extent to which it will be felt that our program, in its methods and procedures, represented a true test of these hypotheses.

In this discussion, however, we wish to concern ourselves more with some of the important questions raised by the results obtained in our work than with issues of methodology. A central aspect of our therapeutic or educational approach involved establishing, as a climate to our interactions with the autistic child, what we referred to as activities of high affective impact. We had to bring the autistic infant out of his aloofness, indifference, and affective isolation. This we saw as the main goal of our work, yet this turned out to be surprisingly easy. As we repeatedly stated in describing our experiences with all the children in the program, their responses to our affective bombardment seemed to imply, by the eagerness with which they were given, that these children had just been waiting for a chance to show how aroused they could become affectively. Was their affective isolation just a sham? Or were we wrong in viewing the affective deficit as the core problem of the early infantile autistic condition?

It is important to recognize with regard to the problem at issue that what appeared to us as the most difficult part of our work with these children was not penetrating their aloofness and indifference or arousing them out of their affective isolation but rather it was maintaining this affective arousal in them at a level which would make possible their meaningful involvement and communication with their human surroundings. As has been noted by so many other well-intentioned and enthusiastic therapists of autistic children, these children unexpectedly and to one's frustration and disappointment do "check out." "Now they're with you, now they're not." Thus when we describe the amount, the variety, and the intensity of our activities with these children, we are stating the simple truth that without this continuous and relentless impact of our presence upon them, it would have been impossible to maintain a meaningful communication with them.

In our experience, the tempo of such affect-arousing activities needs to remain high until the child himself, caught by the enlivening experience of such an affective arousal, finds himself impelled or driven to seek from others the contacts and stimulations that maintain his pleasure. When the autistic child reaches this level of affective arousal, we see him constantly seeking out human contacts; he prefers this to anything else, so that his entire waking life, far from being, as it was in the past, one of affective isolation, appears to be an endless effort at being with, exploring, and touching the important persons in his life. We could say that at this level of affective arousal the child in some respects is not autistic anymore. But to leave him at this level would, in many ways, be courting developmental disaster as far as his personality growth and learning are concerned.

There is no great developmental advantage for a child to spend his life clinging to his mother, as pleasurably satisfying as this may be to both. For each one of the children that we dealt with, we saw the dangers of such a "symbiotic" position, and it may very well be that the discouragement that many parents of autistic children (as well as many therapists) have experienced in relationship to such a child stems from their having allowed themselves to so much enjoy their newly found close contact with their child that they have permitted this situation to endure indefinitely. It is not enough to bring the autistic child to a level of affective arousal where human contacts are most pleasurable and gratifying to him, and it is not enough to maintain him there. For each autistic child there exists an optimum level of affective arousal which not only releases in him the drive to seek human contacts but also begins to give to each of the experiences he has in contact with himself— with his own body and its functions and with the discoveries he makes of his environment through his senses and motor activities—a higher degree or a different quality of affective arousal, derived from this experience of mastery and accomplishment. We could speak here of self-arousal (affective and meaningful) through initiative and curiosity in the discovery of an ever-widening world of gratifying and pleasurable experiences.

Take, for instance, the behavior of Tommy once he had discovered how wonderfully rewarding human contacts and stimulations were; he sought incessantly to engage others in pleasurable and playful physical activities with him but found little or no energy for, or interest in, activities which would have enlarged the range of his mastery over himself and his environment. Compare such behavior with Kathy's discovery that she could actually fit the pieces of a puzzle into a meaningful pattern, so that the swinging which she had previously sought with such eagerness became secondary to the delight she experienced at having mastered this complex task. The importance of creating and maintaining such an optimal level of affective arousal goes beyond what appeared to be the simple and easy task of transgressing the autistic child's isolation and having him become interested in human contacts.

What our results in this respect demonstrate most emphatically can be stated as follows: For each individual autistic child, the effort by the therapist at overcoming the affective barrier to the maximum extent needed for continued development requires a degree of intensity of affective stimulation such that not only does the affective arousal created in him lead to involvement and communication with important human beings in his surroundings but that through these contacts and communication a further degree of arousal is triggered off, of sufficient intensity to help the child find in his mastery over his own body and over his physical environment an experience of satisfaction and pleasure. We are, in short, speaking here of a *gradient* of affective arousal which for each child must reach an optimal level; therefore, to speak of overcoming the affective barrier is more than making him affectively responsive to human beings because, stranded at that level, the child would not fully be a human being. To be a human being is more. The child has to be made, through his affective arousal, to develop and enjoy the totality of his functioning organism as it deals with, adapts to, and copes with the variety of objects, situations, and circumstances that are part of living as a human being. Our experience as we met, in each of our subjects, this challenge of overcoming the affective barrier, unquestionably supports our conviction that the core problem of the early infantile autistic condition resides in an affective deficit.

Thus it may be useful to review the progressive development and awakening of the autistic child during the treatment process against the measuring stick of what we have referred to as "a gradient of affective arousal." At its lowest level, this gradient is represented by the self-stimulating, endless, repetitive, stereotypic behaviors engaged in by the autistic child; the gradient, at its highest level, reflects what can be described as self-sustaining arousal, which is characterized by the child's awareness that he can bring changes in his environment, through self-initiated and self-gratifying attempts at mastery over, and at learning from, the environment. In this context, the treatment process which we have described could be understood as a horizontal representation of the step-by-step progression in the autistic child from the initial condition of minimal affective arousal to that optimal point where the child is not only affectively responsive to his environment but appears capable as well of sustaining such affective arousal by consciously initiating activities which, in their interaction with the environment, give him the satisfying and pleasurable feeling of mastery.

Such a progression—as we have seen it take place and as it is clearly supported by our results—was possible through the high-impact, affective stimulation which we in therapy and the parents at home provided for the child. The relentless and impactful quality of this stimulation seems to have created the condition of optimal arousal that has prevented the child from remaining stranded in a sort of symbiotic attachment to the parent and has allowed him to reach that level of awareness and consciousness (which we might call reflexive consciousness) which is essential to learning, to generalizing from one experience to the other, to acquiring a wider grasp of his surrounding world, and to developing capacities to master his own functions and the objects in his environment.

If, on the other hand, we take what might be considered a vertical view of the range of behaviors displayed by the child at any one point in the treatment process—i.e., on the gradient of affective arousal—we are confronted with the clear possibility that whatever behavior the child is displaying at that moment is very much dependent on, and reflective of, the quality of the environmental stimulation being provided at that moment. What we are saying here is that the affective deficit in the autistic child is such that unless the human environment supplies him with that degree of optimal affectively arousing stimulation which he needs to begin to find, in his own self-initiated activities, a self-sustaining pattern of arousal, we can expect that earlier forms of behavior reflective of earlier developmental levels will tend to reappear and the developmental progression will be marking time.

Evidence from the limited follow-up which we have been able to conduct would seem to support these conclusions. We see, for instance in Kathy, that immediately following our departure, the parents—mobilized and enthusiastic in their drive to keep Kathy going—were able to help her sustain an optimal level of arousal whereby she continued to gain in her self-control and in her interest in, and mastery over, the environment. As time went by, however, and as the parents began to fall back into a less stimulating pattern of behavior, Kathy in desperation reintroduced in her behavior many activities which expressed her desperate need for more stimulation from the human environment and more affective excitement in her interaction with others.

This is illustrated by the fact, for instance, that during this period, whenever the parents took Kathy for a weekend outing, picnic, or new experience, she always returned home a much more "normal," happy, alert, and enjoyable child; her irritating negativistic behaviors disappeared for a number of days thereafter. Unlike the usual home environment of a normal child, which by its relative monotony supplies the child with a sense of security in which he finds freedom to experiment with mastery and self-initiated activities, it is evident, on the basis of our observations and findings, that the developmental progression toward mastery in the autistic child is contingent upon maintaining in the home environment what we might call an atmosphere of excitement, novelty, unpredictability—within, nevertheless, a consistent structure.

Let us then review the characteristic patterns of behavior in the autistic child in relationship to the stages or levels of affective arousal which he experienced as the treatment progressed, keeping in mind that the possibility of his reaching any one stage remained constantly contingent upon the ingenuity of the therapists, the parents, and the teachers in creating for the child (at times forcing them upon him) the necessary quantity and quality of affectively arousing stimulation. At the onset of treatment, which on the gradient of affective arousal in the autistic child we might refer to as point zero, the behaviors are essentially those characteristic of the autistic syndrome (aloofness, repetition, stereotypy, sameness). Under the continuous and forceful impact of our sensory and affective stimulation, the child begins rather quickly to respond with behaviors that reflect his awareness of the human stimulating environment and his enjoyment of such stimulations. Thus what we might call level I of arousal is represented in the autistic child by behaviors of satisfaction and enjoyment in the presence of the affectively intruding human environment; but these behaviors tend to disappear as soon as the human environment ceases its high impact of affective and sensory stimulation.

However, to the extent that such stimulations in therapy, at home, and in school, are relentlessly continued, a level II of affective arousal is ushered in, represented in the child by behaviors which not only express pleasure at the intrusions but also are characterized by the child's actively seeking out the human environment in order to elicit and experience these human intrusions. At this stage the child's behaviors might be depicted as "reflex-like" to the extent that the very presence of the human stimulating environment is sufficient to "trigger off" his active and aggressive search for a repetition of the pleasurable experiences he has had with this environment. In the affective progress of the child, this level II of arousal can be viewed as crucial, both in positive and negative ways. Positively, the child at this stage is not affectively autistic any more; he is aware of and enjoys the presence of others, and he aggressively asserts his own presence to others in seeking them out. On the negative side, the eminent danger exists that at this stage the affective responses of the child are so rewarding and gratifying to his human environment that the parents will tend to bask in the warmth of their discovery of a real child and in their effort at maintaining this enjoyment will be content with keeping the child at that level. Their fears of doing anything with the child which may in their mind destroy this wonderful, warm relationship can prevent them from introducing in their relationship with their child demands for new forms of experiences and more extensive varieties of behavior.

It is only on the basis of the existing good affective relationship reached at level II that further developmental gains can be achieved by the child. This requires not only that the high affective and sensory impact of the environment be maintained but that within this climate of affective arousal, new experiences, new circumstances, and new events be introduced in the interactions with the child. As these experiences, events, and circumstances are offered, a new level of arousal, level III, becomes possible. A break is made in the child's tendency to the repetition of sameness. In the security he finds in his affective contacts with his human environment, he dares to try out new behaviors in reaction to a varied and novel form of stimulating environment. Many fears born out of his affective isolation are overcome. On his own he practices and tries out his capacities for control over his own body and his potential mastery over the objects in his environment.

This level III of affective arousal is characterized by behaviors through which the child clearly experiments with a variety of circumstances and events as they are offered to him and rehearses on his own generalizing from one situation to another, the effectiveness of his controls over himself and of his mastery over his environment. At this level the child, like Tommy for instance, will practice at home his skills at climbing over the furniture which he had fearfully learned to enjoy in therapy through climbing up a chair to jump into the therapist's arms; or like Kathy the child will practice in front of a mirror how to modulate the various sounds that she found herself in therapy capable of producing and enjoying through imitation. At this stage, then, we see the child capable of overcoming, in the security and support of his affective interactions with others, his fears of new and different experiences and events; he does not seek these on his own initiative, but when the therapists or the parents offer them to him in such a way that he discovers that he enjoys them, he can then on his own try to reinstate their affective impact on him by experimenting with them and mastering them in other situations. This level III of arousal represents a base for development through learning, as more functions in the child come into play, provided new stimulations of a varied and novel quality and of increasing complexity are offered by the environment in a climate of high affective impact.

As the child is reinforced in these self-initiated attempts at mastering his own bodily functions and at coping with events and circumstances in the environment, a fourth stage or level of affective arousal emerges where we see the child alerted and aroused by his own behavior and the effects of this behavior on the environment. At this level we get the impression that the child finds enjoyment in the very act of initiating a behavior through which he somehow changes something in the environment. But even this form of what might be called self-sustaining arousal through his own activities, the child has to learn within the felt affective presence of the intruding human environment. Kathy for instance could discover the joy and satisfaction of having, herself, solved many complex puzzles only after she had experienced affectively the security of knowing that the people with her were just as interested in her puzzle as she was; and Elizabeth could begin to ask herself where was the best place for this or that object only after she had experienced from her interested parents that certain objects do belong in certain places and that she could make sure that through her activity such objects were placed where they belonged.

With this stage (IV) we witness the beginnings of what we have called a reflexive consciousness. This level of arousal obviously goes much beyond the degree of affective alertness required for the child to be interested in and satisfied with the presence of another human being interacting with him. Now the child has to be made to feel that the responses he gives and the activities he engages in are recognized by others and supported and given value by others as being the child's own behaviors and own activities; that is, the child must begin to feel that his behavior is him and that his activity expresses him and is valued by others as such. The affective impact of the environment, to create such a level of affective arousal in the child, must in a more forceful way than ever be directed at reinforcing the self-initiated and autonomous qualities of the child's attempts at mastering a task, at coping with a situation, at learning. None of our children could be said to have reached completely such a degree of affective arousal that it could be considered self-sustaining in their attempts at controls over their own bodies and in their mastery over their environment. Yet to the extent that within the context of pleasurable and gratifying feelings a constant flow of varied, novel, and surprising stimulations were supplied to the child to challenge him and to provoke him into activity, to the same extent did we see the emergence of this reflexive awareness in which the child expressed his autonomy and his pleasure at mastering more and more of his surrounding world. That is, at this stage the child must almost always be pushed into a new potential situation of mastery, but once in it, he (the child) will then be capable of sustaining himself in the mastery of the situation.

Consider, for instance, Kathy's wonderment and delight at discovering the letters of the alphabet. For each letter there was a word, for each word there was an object, for each object there was a color, and for each letter that Kathy recognized there was also the enthusiastic and spontaneous response of the teacher. Kathy quickly learned the entire alphabet (in fact she was the first in the class to learn it all) and, aware of her achievement, she couldn't wait to have a chance to recite it. The teachers quickly recognized this and exploited Kathy's awareness of her own achievement by setting up a wide variety of situations involving different classrooms, different teachers, different material to challenge Kathy's capacity to generalize her learning. Kathy was kept very excited by all these maneuvers and it was this level of arousal which enabled her to progress quickly from letters to numbers and to begin to learn to print the letters she had learned. As we have indicated earlier it is clear that with the autistic child the degree of alertness he reaches appears contingent upon the degree of variety and novelty in the stimulating circumstances and events in the environment where he behaves, provided a stable structure of high "affective push" is maintained by the intruding human environment.

Clearly, monotony, which is one of the central characteristics of the syndrome of Early Infantile Autism, is deadly to the developmental process of the autistic child. The repetition of sameness with regard to any task, which is a standard procedure in most ordinary teaching methods and which is a central feature of most behavior modification practices, has such limited stimulating value, because of its lack of novelty and surprise, that it has little learning impact on the autistic child. We do not mean to say here that tasks to be learned do not need to be repeated but rather that the conditions and context in which the tasks to be repeated are presented must always include elements of variety, novelty, and surprise. Paradoxically as it may sound, this is possibly just as true for exceptionally bright and advanced youngsters in a classroom, who often also lose their appetite for learning whenever the situation becomes monotonously boring for them.*

As we indicated earlier, none of the children in the project has thus far achieved a stable level of self-sustaining arousal. When we terminated the project, their behavior in many instances, as we have pointed out, gave indications that they were coming close to that degree of reflexive consciousness which would allow for self-sustaining affective arousal. This degree of arousal which we label level V is the ideal toward which the developmental process in the child is striving and which in the autistic child could be attained only if the affective deficit in them could be constantly compensated for. In terms of our descriptions of a vertical view of the behavior of the child at any one moment in the treatment or developmental process, we can see how dependent he is on the affective and sensory stimulating qualities of his environment. At any one time his behavior appears like a barometer of the affective climate surrounding him. When there is too much calm and monotony, behaviors in the child reappear that reflect earlier levels of development as if the child had to fall back on the basic forms of self-stimulating experiences which were characteristic of his original autistic position. Such behaviors are more an expression of the limited repertoire of activities available to him through which to express or assert some degree of autonomy than true forms of regressive behavior. This statement is supported by the fact that such "regressive-like" behavior will be immediately given up by the autistic child as soon as he is intruded upon and affectively aroused.†

---

* Another comment suggests itself in this regard. This concerns the school placement of the autistic child. Our decision to provide wherever possible a normal school environment for the children in the project appears to have been clearly vindicated by the fact that only in such a normal environment could both the children and the teachers function under optimal circumstances; that is, the autistic child was constantly confronted with new situations, and the teacher never had to contend only with autistic or disturbed children. Thus, whatever additional energy drain on the teacher might be presented by an autistic child was readily compensated for through the constant affective feedback the teacher received from the normal children in the classroom. For this reason "special schools" dealing only with severely disturbed children would have to be viewed as having a built-in limitation in the amount and quality of affective energies available to the teachers in keeping alive in the children a level of arousal sufficient to promote growth and personality development in the children. The limited information we have on Tommy's progress following his placement in a "special school" strongly tends to support this view.

† This conclusion also supports the view expressed earlier (Introduction, Part II) that the Early Infantile Autistic condition represents truly a developmental arrest (failure to develop ego functions) rather than a psychosis of childhood (disintegration of acquired ego functions). The regressive behavior demonstrated by the psychotic

It is in this light that a second problem raised by the results we have obtained assumes a crucial importance. This problem involves the parents. Within the context of our total program with autistic children we viewed and accepted the parents as the natural and appropriate instruments of education and of therapy for their respective child. The continuity of our own work at the clinic could be maintained at home only if the parents, and the mothers especially, were willing to put forth more than the usual amount of maternal energy required in being present and responsive to any one of their children. With regard specifically to the question of affective arousal in the autistic child, our experience makes it obvious that the degree of carry-over and generalization from the clinic to the home of the child's initiative, curiosity, learning, and developing skills and competencies was directly related to the degree and intensity of the parents' active and persistent involvement in keeping their child aroused affectively beyond the point of his seeking only human physical contacts. In the same way that at the clinic we had to use every opportunity of pleasure and satisfaction in the child to introduce him to new and interesting situations and objects in the environment, it was of crucial importance that at home the parents also exploit to an optimal level every situation of pleasurable interaction with their child to arouse the affective involvement of the child in the mastery of his own bodily functions and of his physical environment.

The question of structure and discipline is very much to the point in this connection. As we mentioned earlier, it is quite understandable that a mother who has waited many years to receive from her child a pleasurable and affectionate expression of his acknowledgment of her presence may find it very difficult, for fear of alienating the child again, to push her luck, so to say, and demand of, or impose on, the child behavioral responses which if they were dealing with a "normal" child they would automatically demand and expect. It may be fun for instance to have a child finally enjoy sitting at the table with the family to eat a meal, but the entire event could easily become a disaster and a nightmare if the child, left to his own devices, spends the majority of his time there throwing food on the floor and messing up the table. In such circumstances the parents had to have the courage of risking the displeasure of the child and, with their hearts clearly attuned to what ultimately would

---

child does not disappear simply by making the child alert to, and gratified by, his interactions with the environment. Rather it requires that the integrative function of the ego be restored through an affective cathexis of existing body ego functions (see DesLauriers, 1962).

be best for the child, impose on him through whatever measures their own imagination and initiative might dictate, the structure and discipline necessary to bring up the child properly. We venture to say in this respect—and the follow-up work to this time amply supports this view—that the continuing progress of the autistic child in his total human development will ultimately remain contingent upon the capacity of the parents to constantly retain in their attitude and approach to their autistic child the same quality of structure and discipline that they find so natural to maintain in relationship to their other children; only more so.

We might add here one more comment suggested by our results. The pattern of development which we witnessed in the autistic child appeared as an exaggerated expression of the usual pattern of development followed by normal infants and children. There was unevenness, with spurts of apparent sudden growth; there were also many so-called plateaus. In the face of such plateaus parents were easily inclined to wonder whether their child would be forever stranded there, and experienced feelings of discouragement. In our experience the developmental plateaus which the child reached represented one of two things: Either this child needed some time to assimilate the new experiences which were part of his emerging life and to accommodate to the ever increasing demands of a world which he was just beginning to discover; or else, the plateaus were unduly prolonged because the therapists or the parents were not sufficiently alert and at times courageous enough to push the child ahead beyond the level at which he seemed somehow to choose to remain. Autistic children are not fragile, especially once they have discovered how good it is to be alive and part of the human family. To refuse to impose on them human structure and discipline when their normal personality growth process demands it is not only unfair to the child but it also involves the risk of allowing the child's undifferentiated behavior to go on tyrannizing the environment in which he lives.

Our follow-up information to this point makes it amply clear that unless the parents are prepared to maintain with their autistic child the level of arousal which had enabled the child to begin functioning with some degree of reflexive consciousness and with real pleasures in his efforts at mastery and control over himself and the environment, the process of growth in the child tends to be unduly delayed. We have indicated in our discussion of the parents (Chapter XI) the depressive component that seems to be a common personality characteristic of all of them. They, too, obviously need to be pushed in order to provide for their child an environment of optimal arousal and supply him with a stimulating environment of surprise and novelty. For these parents, more easily perhaps than is general, the tendency to yield to monotony in the household under the guise of security and predictability is very strong and deep-seated. They like routines and adhere to them whenever they are not reminded that something more is needed to alert and interest their autistic child. It is striking to note that, as we have described earlier, these parents can become very energetic and dedicated as long as they are given support, inspiration, and direction; yet their level of energy drops rather quickly when such supports are not forthcoming. It is very much in this light that we can state that for the autistic child the ultimate possibility of maintaining a self-sustaining level of arousal appears contingent upon not so much the availability of a continued treatment program for the child, once he has emerged from his affective isolation through treatment, as the availability of reinforcement for the parents.

In Kathy's case for instance we see, in terms of our latest follow-up information (approximately one year after termination of treatment), two contrasting forms of behavior: at home, where life eventually returned to its "minor key" routines, Kathy's behavior took on many fluctuating characteristics reflecting all those behaviors described earlier as part of the early levels of arousal; these behaviors were discouraging to the parents, who without the previous support continuously available to them were inclined to mark time and be resigned to the child's erratic ways. On the other hand, at school, where the teachers had found in Kathy the greatest challenge to their ingenuity and creativity and where there was always an unending supply of variety and novelty in situations and events, Kathy showed amazing progress in her capacity to learn new behaviors and in her general interest in involving herself more and more in such a stimulating environment. We have noted earlier that even at home whenever something exciting happened, like a visit to the zoo or an excursion to the aquarium, Kathy always returned from these experiences highly alert and capable of functioning at a higher level of achievement and involvement for several days thereafter.

In a somewhat different way June, who found little stimulation at school (in a classroom of 35–40) and therefore little appetite for learning, was able to do at home the work she wouldn't do in school; this required, however, that her parents communicate to her that they had absolutely no doubt that she could do this work and that they were genuinely delighted at seeing her do it. June, who had refused to write in school, had no trouble copying words on birthday and valentine cards to send to us. A somewhat better balance with regard to an optimal level of arousal appeared to exist for Elizabeth between the home and the school. In either place the people tended to be readily pleased by the behavior of such a sweet and lovable child and therefore tended to sometimes forget that she needed to be pushed and challenged; however, both the parents and the teachers were able to recognize these tendencies in themselves and actively cooperated in offering new and more exciting situations to the child. Thus Elizabeth's growth was maintained with less fluctuation and more infrequent appearances of "regressive" behaviors.

In brief, then, our follow-up information at this time, convinces us that the continued possibility of growth in the autistic child rests above all on the degree to which the family, the closest human environment he has, is capable of maintaining a climate of high affective arousal. It is our impression—and this is not offered as a scientific conclusion, but rather as a substantially documented opinion—that the autistic child is quite capable of pursuing a normal rate of personality development (accepting, of course, his late start) if the human environment closely available to him—his home, his parents, his family—can offer, through novel, surprising, and highly affective stimulations, an arousing impact on the child. Thus, what we are saying, in terms of our work, its results, and its long-range effectiveness, is that the continued personality growth process in the autistic child appears to be essentially contingent upon the child's parents' ability to give up the natural tendency (in all families) to set up routine, predictable, and "secure" patterns of family life. The autistic child, if he is to grow up, requires (because of his inner-imposed sensory deprivation) an environment of high affective stimulating quality, where there is no "white noise" and there are no undifferentiated affective elements. If the parents of the autistic child can receive the support they need, in maintaining in their relationships to their autistic child, a highly personal and intensively affective environmental climate, the child, in our opinion, will continue to grow. Once the child has discovered and experienced how good it is to be part of the human race, it is up to the parents to keep high in their child the level of affective arousal that enables him to acquire those functions that are very much part of developing as a human individual.

Our results raise questions also with regard to specific functions and their integration in the total personality development of the child. One such question concerns the acquisition and development of meaningful expressive speech. Because our main effort with autistic children was directed at establishing with them a basic level of communication of a psychosomatic and preverbal nature, which we saw as essential and natural to their ultimate capacity to develop normally, we placed little emphasis on their acquiring and developing verbal language and speech. We proceeded with the general expectation that if we were able to trigger off a normal pattern of development in the autistic child, such a child eventually, like any normal child, would experiment with sounds, develop sounds into words, and at some point use words for meaningful communication. These may have seemed naïve expectations. We were no specialists in language formation or speech development. Specialists in these areas continue to be baffled by the mysterious and wondrous achievement of any normal developing child in acquiring and mastering the complex task of communicating meaningfully through speech (see Chomsky, 1968). Furthermore, we were quite cognizant of the fact that a great amount of work had been done with autistic children, especially through behavior modification methods, to have them acquire words and utilize sentences, since from a social communication point of view such an achievement is so desirable both at home and at school.

In spite of this we chose to be patient with our group of autistic children and pursued our "humanizing" efforts with them in the same general way as a parent would do at home with a normal child. That is, we constantly talked and sang to the children, we reacted with genuine pleasure and interest to any sound they made or to any response they gave which appeared to be an imitation or an effort at articulated speech. Like the usual parent we "ooowed" and "aaahed" whenever we heard what appeared to be an expressive sound and followed through in making clear to the child how pleased we were with his efforts and accomplishments. The net result of all this was that three of the five subjects in our program developed appropriate speech (the other two are only just beginning to say words), by which we mean that their use of verbal communication is neither odd in terms of tonality nor meaningless and inappropriate in terms of content or circumstance. The grammar and syntax of their language has no "autistic" quality; it is the ordinary language of a child attempting to communicate verbally in a meaningful fashion with his human environment. None of the children spoke too much, but what they said made sense and was relevant to the situation in which they wanted to express their needs or their feelings.

Whether we could have achieved results in a shorter time with a procedure specifically aimed at speech development cannot be answered here. We had no doubts, however, that the parents were most eager to see their children acquire appropriate communicative speech and, therefore, that they would, much more than we did, make constant and determined efforts at encouraging their child in this accomplishment. Furthermore, the children's involvement in kindergarten and nursery school offered them, as we expected, many opportunities to discover new words and new patterns of language in communicating with their teachers and their little friends there.

With the acquisition of expressive language as well as with the mastery of so many other skills by these children, our experience underlines two other major points which we would like to make here. The first is that the autistic child not only demonstrates new forms of behavior when he seems developmentally ready to give such responses but also when such responses appear to him to be worthwhile giving. This is not easy to explain. Perhaps the best way of suggesting what is involved here might be to say that with a child emerging from an autistic condition and manifesting in his behavior a progressively widening mastery of his own body and of his environment, one can never demand, with respect to his new achievements, what might be called a "command performance." We may be certain that the child is very well able to draw a square, or sing a song, or participate actively and pleasurably with others in a table game, because he has just done it a minute before. Yet he may refuse to do it again when asked, simply because, from his point of view, at that next moment there is no point to it. There is a spontaneity and an independence in such a child which brook no submission to senseless conventional requirements. Like any normal child he may at times enjoy very much "showing off" but never on demand because apparently he has no inclination nor interest in "keeping up with the Joneses." From this point of view it may be said that when the child gives up his autistic position, he never surrenders his individuality. Whatever he does retains the spontaneity and freshness of truly being enjoyed by him as if he always experienced it as something meaningful and just newly discovered.

The other point we wish to make touches upon this idea of novelty and spontaneity as conditions to the child's acquiring new forms of behavior. As we review our work and its results, we are struck by the fact that the element which pervades so much of our transactions with the autistic children is an element of *surprise*. There is no room here to discuss at length the place which a factor like surprise holds in the normal learning process nor its relation to the entire arousal phenomenon, but there are good reasons to consider that the probability of any event or circumstance having an impactful value in changing the behavioral response of an organism is directly related to the timing of that event or circumstance, that is, to the fact that such event or circumstance occurs unexpectedly and surprisingly within an ongoing routine of interaction. Such event or circumstance acts then in the same general way as a meaningful sound would act against a background of white noise; it stands out, makes an impression, has strong alerting and arousing value to the organism. The awakening of an autistic child could be described as an endless series of responses to a never ending sequence of alerting and arousing surprises. This is possibly why when the child's eyes are finally opened to a new and delightful experience of life, the response he gives to this brand-new vision contains all the spontaneity, delight, and freshness of childish awe and wonderment.

Part V

'In the beginning
is relation.'

Buber, *I and Thou*

Chapter XIII

The Child's World of Communication

the implications of the results for other childhood deviations

The central theme throughout this book has emphasized the simple truth that for a human being there exists nothing more important in life than another human being. The process of growth and development through which a child goes to achieve, through separation and differentiation from others, a human identity which defines him clearly as a person in his own right cannot take place without constant communication and relationship between the developing human organism and its human environment. This is what Buber meant when he wrote: "In the beginning, there is relation. . . ." We have recognized and fully accepted this basic condition of human personality development in our efforts at helping a group of autistic children become truly human and establish themselves as separated and differentiated individuals. What we have learned from this work and its results appears, in our judgment, to have wide implications for the understanding of various other forms of de-

Intro.

velopmental deviations in children, as well as for a clearer conception of
the factors involved in educating children, that is, in bringing them
up as truly human individuals.

At a theoretical level we conceptualized the behaviors of early infantile autism as consequent to a form of sensory and affective deprivation.
To explain this "inner imposed" form of sensory and affective deprivation, we constructed, on the basis of recent advances in the study of the
neurological mechanisms of sleep and consciousness and their implications for the understanding of the bases of learning, a neurophysiological model which underscored the importance of a relationship and of a
functional balance between two Arousal Systems in the human brainstem. The existing sensory and affective deprivation in the autistic child
was the result, we said, of an "imbalance" between the drive-response
system (Arousal System I, the reticular formation), and the incentive-
motivation system (Arousal System II, the limbic system). The autistic
child, in our view, had such a high threshold of affective Arousal (was
so hyporesponsive with respect to System II), that the effects of this system in moderating and modulating behavioral responses triggered off by
the drive mechanisms of System I, were never allowed to occur, and,
therefore, the possibility of reinforcing effectively any behavioral response, that is, the possibility of fostering any learning, was absent. Our
work with autistic children was designed to overcome the functional imbalance between Arousal System I and II, by activating the latter through
impactful affective stimulations, thereby permitting the normal reversal
of system ascendency to take place. Under such conditions of normal
balance or dynamic equilibrium of these two systems, System II, the
affective system, could appropriately suppress System I long enough for
normal learning (through reinforcement) to take place.

The success we achieved through our approach in bringing about substantial modifications and changes in the behavioral responses of our
autistic subjects does not warrant any claim to the validity of our neurophysiological model. Such a model, after all, was of speculative value
and was intended only as a rational framework in structuring and guiding our efforts. But the positive results we obtained appear to make it
imperative to take into account, whenever we are faced with problems
of developmental delays or arrests in children (we are speaking here of
personality development) or of severe learning disabilities, the neurophysiological substrates of learning and growth, by directing our attention to the existence of a possible imbalance between the drive-response

system (I, reticular formation) and the incentive-motivation-affective system (II, limbic system).

Any child, to develop as a human being, has to go through a slow— and yet it is so rapid!—process of acquiring and learning an ever more complex and diversified repertoire of adaptive and coping responses, to relate to and enjoy an ever increasing and widening world of human events, situations, and circumstances. This process cannot take place when obstacles and barriers exist to the child's capacity to experience affectively the presence of others to him, or to express in a humanly meaningful way (affective) his presence to them. "In the beginning, is relation. . . !" Without such relation, without such communication, no human growth or development takes place. Our work with autistic children has made clear that the quality of the relationship and communication that needs to be established from the beginning must be at the basic level of sensory-affective, bodily experiences if a normal developmental process is to take place. To transgress the high threshold of affective arousal, to break down the barrier to affective communication, one has to reach the child in a preverbal, psychosomatic way. This approach was successful with autistic children.

There exist, however, many other children, who do not fit, from a behavioral point of view, the diagnosis of early infantile autism, yet their behavior reflects severe developmental deficits and deviations. We are thinking here of children who are deprived at birth of important sensory modalities, such as the congenitally deaf or blind children, and of others who for a variety of organic reasons appear incapable of learning and, to a greater or lesser degree, seem forever stranded on the interminable plateau of a developmental arrest. In all these children we find dramatic examples of a basic type of communication defect such as we saw in the autistic infant. Sometimes such children present in their behavior "autistic" mannerisms, and they are viewed as having "secondary autistic adaptation"; but usually they do not appear as affectively isolated as the autistic infant, nor is their repertoire of behavioral responses, perceptually, motorically, or emotionally, as limited as that of the autistic infant. They give evidence of having been able to reach, developmentally, a certain level of personality functioning, primitive and in many ways undifferentiated, and then their growth stopped as if the task of acquiring the vast number of adaptive responses needed to maintain an effective and integrated functioning in the face of the complex demands of their environment had turned out to be an overwhelming and impossible challenge. What they can learn is so limited that specialists have classified them for educational purposes as "educable" or "noneducable." This meant that they either could be made to acquire some useful behaviors—such as dressing themselves and attending to their physical hygiene, feeding themselves and having good table manners, taking adequate care of their belongings and respecting the property of others, playing simple games with other children, communicating their needs verbally, writing their names, orienting themselves with respect to their environment, running small errands, counting simple numbers, reading simple words, and so forth—or else the majority of these behaviors were impossible for them to learn. To be "educable" in this sense, then, meant to possess certain elementary and useful skills; with such skills they could "get along," more or less, in this world, and their behavior could be viewed as more or less acceptable to society.

The guiding principles of our approach to autistic infants also implied that we viewed these children as "educable." But the meaning we had of educability in this effort went beyond the narrow sense of developing a limited number of skills in dealing with the environment or in being acceptable to society. Our primary concern in "educating" autistic infants was to offer them the possibility of first experiencing themselves as human beings, alive and responsive to other humans, and capable, through their communication and relationship to them, of growth and development as human individuals. Whatever skills were needed to master the environment or to be socially acceptable we saw as secondary to a basic capacity in them of affective and enriching communication with those important people in their environment, the presence of whom they could experience and to whom they could affectively make their presence felt. This communication, achieved through the reciprocal presence of the child and of his mother, helped define the structural conditions of human personality growth, by creating, through a mutuality of pleasurable and gratifying sensory and affective experiences in the mother and in the child, their individual limits, their body image, and their separation and differentiation from each other. On such a pattern of basic, physical, sensory, preverbal and presymbolic communication, human personality development could take place, with its ever increasing movement toward individuality, mastery, independence, and freedom. To what avail to know how to count or how to read, if one is forever to be, for the most part, outside of the stream of human life.

In the autistic infants, we postulated the existence of a strong barrier to the type of communication we have just described, and we set ourselves upon transgressing this barrier in order to free these children from their "unhuman" condition. We should like to suggest that a similar type of approach may very well be even more effective with those children, whom we mentioned above, who are also arrested in their human development, but for whom, in general, nothing more is offered than a form of education, which, far from being an "upbringing" in the truest human sense of this word, appears to be just a "training" in conformity and social acceptability. These children also could be freed to grow; their limitations may not be directly consequent to a primary imbalance between their affective arousal and their capacity to be alerted by external stimuli. But their limitations have direct bearing on their capacity to establish with other important persons in their life that level of communication through which affective arousal is possible and through it, learning and growth.

Some of these children can relate affectively, and, compared with autistic infants, they can even be said to be warmly responsive. But the gradient of their affective arousal never seems to go beyond the level of human contacts. They enjoy these, but such contacts do not appear to be of such arousing quality that they trigger off in the children a zest for mastery of self and of the environment. Their learning capacities remain limited because fundamentally there is no purpose in learning. It may be said that affective contacts and human communication have little to do with learning impairments related to basic sensory and perceptual deficits. But one may want to look at the person and life of Helen Keller before putting too much emphasis on such a statement. When learning becomes experienced as the finest and most gratifying expression of one's human individuality, there is purpose in learning. For such a purpose to become a driving force in a child's life requires more than that he just be made to feel the pleasurable rewards of warm, affective, human contacts. In the affective arousal created by such contacts, the child must be led to whatever level of affective excitement is optimal for him. This will be the level when he feels exhilarated and wondrously delighted at finding himself master of his own body, of his own functions, of his own feelings, and at spontaneously and with curiosity reaching out toward the mastery of his environment.

The preceding considerations which may appear to have direct bearing on what is commonly referred to as the area of "special education" also have wide implications for the development and translation into action programs of more meaningful conceptions of general education.

Nicholas Hobbs (1967), in his Re-Ed project, offers a striking demonstration of the humanizing value of an educational effort which does not forget the human quality of the child to be educated. In a similar way the work of Maria Montessori (1949), in its intuitive grasp of the child's human aspirations for autonomy and freedom, also affirms the crucial importance of the human quality which education should retain. Unfortunately, what seems to have been retained of her contribution to the child's upbringing are the ingenious methods, materials, and techniques of learning which she developed rather than the humanistic spirit that had guided their development. For it is indeed a sad commentary on current general programs of education that they emphasize more materials and ingenious techniques than the awakening in the child of a true zest and purpose in learning.* Changes in the pattern and quality of behavioral responses, to make them adaptive in a meaningful and effective way to the stimulating environment under a variety of circumstances and situations, can occur in a child only to the extent that an associative link becomes established between the various aspects of the stimulating events and the appropriate response he progressively becomes capable of giving to them. Our work in developing such a repertoire of appropriately responsive behaviors in the autistic child serves, in our opinion, to emphasize once again a truth which seems to have been lost in most educational efforts: That the associative and integrative link that enables a child's response to an event to become fixated, stabilized, and generalized as a learned pattern of behavior is the affective component that surrounds and accompanies the stimulating event. Through this affective component, with its elements of pleasure, discovery, and surprise, the child's organism is aroused and his awareness of what is happening to him is reinforced and expressed in interested concentration and attention. His memory which is crucial to learning is also alerted; for as we discussed earlier, in detail, what is remembered (or forgotten) is largely a function of the affective components surrounding the event or circumstance to be remembered.

It is important, however, to make very clear that the affective component of which we are speaking must retain its basic human value if it is to arouse the child to a level of learning that gives a true purpose and a true meaningfulness to what he learns. The learning process in the child

---

*A refreshing exception in this regard was demonstrated to us at the (Pied Piper) Nursery School which Kathy attended and whose principal, Mrs. Jones, made sure that while encouraging the use of much of the Montessori materials and equipment the human spirit intended by Maria Montessori pervaded all the children's activities.

is part of his development as a human individual, and we have seen that this development cannot take place unless the child experiences himself in affective relationship and communication with his human environment. If there be a "reward" that reinforces and triggers off adaptive and appropriate behavioral response in the child, that reward must be sought in the consciousness, affectively aroused, that the child has of his own aliveness and delight at being in the presence of another human being whose presence to him gives true meaningfulness and purpose to all of his behaviors. Such a reward, in the sense that we have described it in previous chapters, might be called a primary reward; but it has little to do with what in certain current learning situations is commonly called a primary reward. When a piece of candy is systematically presented to a child as a reinforcement to an imposed behavioral response, the affective arousal created by such a so-called primary reinforcer never attains that needed optimal level of arousal in the child which would permit the reverberation and the generalization of such a response to develop in the child's organism. In such situations we seem to have a closed-circuit effect where all that is accomplished is a sort of second-rate symbiosis between the child and the candy offered. Truly, a learning situation of this type has no humanizing effect on the child, and any purpose in learning as the expression of an individual's drive to enrich and expand his own individuality becomes completely lost.

Thus, what we have outlined of the requirements of "educating" an autistic infant would seem to contain basic principles of general education. These principles assert that learning takes place when there exists a purpose in learning. This purpose lies in the human individual's need to be fully human through an experience of himself in communication with other human beings. Such an experience requires in the child a degree of affective arousal that cannot be left to a level of vegetative and autonomic functions. For each child to learn and enjoy the delight of an ever expanding behavioral mastery of himself and of his environment, an optimal degree of affective arousal is required which only the impactful and alert presence of a meaningful individual in his life can supply to his personality growth and development.

Chapter XIV

The Child Is Not Dead...
She Is Sleeping

the child's infinite expectation

"One has no need to be a great scholar to perceive that the greatest danger which may frighten humanity is not some external catastrophe or famine or plague, but rather that spiritual sickness (the most terrible because the most directly antihuman of all scourges), the loss of appetite for living" (p. 171). In writing these lines, Teilhard de Chardin (1966) meant to underscore his view that life, in our universe, had found in man "in the awakening of his sense of humanity" through reflexive consciousness, the ultimate point of convergence of all its strivings and expressions. Thus, when a child is born we could say that life again is attempting to move forward and that in this child, as Nietzsche puts it, life is saying, "I am the one who forever incessantly attempts to surpass itself." There exists from the beginning in every child that is born from human parents an infinite expectation that all his needs as a newborn human will be met and that he will be allowed to become part of humanity. Life represents initiative, autonomy, and adaptive creativity, and from the beginning the newborn accepts the terms of life. In the

361

helpless display of his undifferentiated and unspecialized functions at birth, the child nevertheless asserts as loudly as he can the simple and yet so dramatic fact that he is here. With everything that he is he affirms his presence and his appetite for living. At that moment, through the openness of his capacity to be affectively aroused and with the totality of his bodily and sensory responses, the child speaks a language that can only be understood by another human being, capable of being affectively and physically present to him with her entire body, through an incessant pattern of stimulating activities that keeps saying in response to the child: "I am here with you, my baby, and I'm so happy that you're here with me." In this reassuring and welcoming pattern of early communication between the child and his mother, the child's appetite for living is given its most arousing boost, and the infinite expectation he has that the world he has come into belongs to him is given its strongest justification.

It is in the reciprocity of this direct physical, preverbal, and affective communication between the child and his mother that the foundations are laid for the development in the child of a truly human form of life expression. And precisely because in this form of communication nothing else is communicated but the real and impactful presence of one human being to another, this communication remains for the child the model of all truly meaningful relationships he might have with other human beings. In some ways this could be called a silent language, where words are not needed, nor images, nor symbols; it is a communication expressed in the direct physical presence of one to another, in the activities and movements that make this presence very close or very far, in the quality with which the responses appear, immediate or delayed, and in the climate, sunny or cloudy, in which the presence of one is communicated to the other. This then is a language of body, of physical space, of time, but mostly of affective and sensory arousal and stimulation.

To understand and to respond to this silent language is to insure that the child's appetite for living will never die and that his infinite expectation will never be destroyed. For it is in the security of his having been understood, accepted, and welcomed to the family of human beings that all the energies of the child begin to find expression in the development of an ever increasing number of differentiated functions through which he discovers himself and his mother, progressively moving into an awareness of himself as separated from his mother and finding within himself the spontaneity and initiative to progressively shape the mother into the person that he needs most as a life-giving object for him. With each response he receives from her, his appetite for life increases; and he reaches out for more and more experiences and contacts which, in their affectively arousing quality, maintain and support the direction of his initiative and the zest of his spontaneity. With each new experience the world of the child widens and with the mastery he progressively achieves over each one of his developing functions, he discovers himself capable of possessing and mastering more and more objects in his environment. He acquires more forms of behavior, he learns to adapt to an increasing variety of circumstances and events, he relates one experience to another and builds up for himself an understanding of the world he lives in, because underlying this tremendously complex structure which is evolving as his personality develops there exists the solid and unshakable foundation of the affective conviction he possesses, a conviction born out of the answers he received early in life to the silent language through which he expressed his delight at being alive and his hope that he would be truly given a chance to live.

There is, however, a child born into this world whose appetite for living is muted and whose infinite expectation appears forever doomed. Such is the early infantile autistic child. In him life seems to have come to a standstill; there is no effort at surpassing itself; there seems only the spiritual sickness of waiting to die. This child gives the appearance of being in this world and yet not of or with this world. Unlike the normal child, who with his entire body loudly asserts and communicates his presence and demands forcefully and provocatively to be attended to, the autistic infant appears to enshrine himself in the awesome silence of an empty temple from which the gods of life have fled. He asserts nothing except his isolation; he demands nothing except to be left alone; seemingly without feelings or emotions, he ignores his mother to the point that she feels rejected and unwanted by him, so that the distance which originally his behavior had established between him and her becomes eventually compounded by her own desperate inclination to desert this child by whom she is never made to feel like a mother. Between this mother and this child the basic lines of normal human communication never had a chance to exist, so that at no time could the child say to her, "I am here" nor could he hear from her the reassuring answer, "It's so nice to have you here." In this seemingly unbreachable silence, the autistic child vegetates, no boost being given to his muted appetite for living and no reassurance to the infinite expectation of life in him.

Thus he never develops as a person, and he never learns to live and experience himself as truly part of humanity. In the autistic child, human life appears to have failed.

Confronted with this failure of life in the autistic child, we tried to make sense out of it. In the understanding we reached, we caught a glimpse of hope, and in the sustaining and prodding value of this hope we were lead to develop, on a research basis, a program of therapeutic intervention aimed at restoring in the autistic child the conditions of a truly human life. We have, in the preceding pages of this book, reported as completely as we could the planning, implementation, and outcome of this program. Five autistic children and their families participated in this work and experienced with us, as it developed, the wonderful vision of life being born anew in a child, and with it, the appetite for living and the infinite expectation which any child needs, to be part of humanity. From these five autistic children we have learned a great deal about the Early Infantile Autistic condition. But mostly we have learned about the human condition of every child born into this world. For if there is one central discovery which our work with five autistic children has made available to us, it is that human life fails in a child only to the extent that we confuse its silent and muted expression for death and fail to recognize that sometimes life can be asleep. Perhaps it is this truth that Christ wanted to suggest to us when, called upon in faith to restore life to a dead child, He said to the grieving and wailing onlookers, "Why do you make all that noise and weep? The child is not dead but sleeping."

To be awake is to be aroused and conscious of the stirrings and strivings of life within oneself. This experience of awakening to life cannot fully take place unless certain conditions are met, which are identical with the conditions necessary in a child for the birth of a self. Earlier in this chapter we have defined these conditions and made explicit the central position of affective and meaningful communication between the infant and his mother in arousing in the child an exciting appetite for living and in channeling the infinite expectation he has of possessing and mastering a world that belongs to him. Awakened and aroused, the autistic child has shown us that he too could express through his ever increasing mastery and control of his ego functions the consciousness he had of being somebody in his own right and of being able to assert, through the communication of his individuality, his presence to the world around him. The awakening of his consciousness and awareness of his place in this world in relationship to the important human beings in his life and of the acceptance he received from them could not have been achieved without overcoming the barrier which his own functional organic weakness created for him. His high threshold of affective arousal could have easily been mistaken for a "spiritual sickness" in him or for a wish for death. In truth, this weakness in him was a form of sleep from which he was waiting to be aroused, because in him, as in every other child, human life wanted also "to surpass itself."

In the communication and dialogue which was possible for the autistic child to have with his human environment, once he had been awakened and made conscious of it, the strivings of life seeking to express the child's infinite expectation could not be allowed to be dissipated in inhuman directions. In the reciprocity of the communication between the child and his human environment, the channeling and disciplining value of the parents' communication in answer to the child create what we have called the "human condition" in the child's development. What the child expects is to be given a chance to be fully human and to be accepted unconditionally as such. To the extent that life in him expresses this expectation and seeks through the development of instrumentalities and functions to enlarge in the child an ever increasing repertoire of behaviors, to the same extent must the response of the human environment to the child's initiative and drive be modulated and geared to sustain the child's initiative and to channel his behaviors into effective and rewarding forms of activity and mastery over himself and the environment. The maintenance of the human condition, what we have called structure and discipline, in the upbringing of a child, insures a basic consistency and integration to all of his experiences and to all of his activities.

We have emphasized in this connection the fundamental difference we saw between, on the one hand, creating human conditions of growth and development and, on the other hand, conditioning, bit by bit, for various sorts of reasons, a child's behavior. The human condition involves a communication between mother and child through the immediate and felt presence of one to the other and when the acceptance of the child by the mother is unconditional. The child's capacity to grow, to discover, and master the world is not immediately dependent on the approval of his mother, but rather it is directly consequent to the experience he has of her presence to him in his pleasures and in his pains. Approval comes easily when what is approved of is what was wanted in the first place. But if the mother who approves or disapproves of her child's behavior does not, through her actions, communicate at the same time her presence to him, the risk is great then that the only behavior that the child will pursue will be essentially an "avoidant" type of behavior: that is, he will avoid being disapproved of. In other words his behavior then may achieve conformity, be socially acceptable; he will be like others want him to be. But in the process the child will not learn to be with others, that is, truly part of humanity.

Our work has demonstrated that any behavior which the autistic infant learns through social approval or disapproval will retain its basic avoidant quality unless the person who approves or disapproves has managed first to communicate his or her presence to the child by arousing him affectively to their presence in which he feels secure and accepted. The end result of socially acceptable behavior is represented in conformity; people are alike. The autistic child can be "like" any other child if being like another child means only to sit quietly in a chair, avoid spilling food on the floor, keep his pants clean, or say "candy" when he wants an M&M. But unless he feels and experiences himself as alive and human, that is, in exciting and stimulating contact and communication with someone whose entire meaningfulness to him is that this someone is there, immediately present to him, then the autistic child cannot be like any other child whose zest and lust for life is expressed in his aliveness, his play, his curiosity, his surprise, his discoveries, and wonderments. What we have learned from the autistic infant is that he, too, can be like others once he has experienced the pleasure that comes from being with others. Such an experience takes place only if a human condition, rather than a conditioning, is given to the child's growth and development.

It is probably one of the most serious and most devastating tragedies of our time that we have somehow been led to lose our sense of humanity in educating our children. Education has become conceptualized as a grandiose conditioning experiment, available to all, in which the behaviors of our children are shaped and programmed to meet the challenges and demands of the pseudo realities of social conformity, social acceptability, and social expectations. This, in itself, would not be of such destructive value to the individual had not society, which originally was intended to insure for each individual a greater consciousness and expression of his humanity, betrayed this fundamental awareness in him and choked off any possibility of real autonomy and freedom. For the true realities of life to become manifested and expressed, the human quality of the individual must be attended to and respected. It is not for society to define the purpose and meaning of an individual's life; rather it is for the individual to shape and define a society in which the relationships of one individual to the other as well as the communication between individuals make possible an ever increasing appetite for living, because it allows the individual to define his own purpose and meaning by giving him a keen sense of being a part of the family of human beings. Without such a purpose, education fails, like life itself, and the possibility for each child to be fully awakened to life is choked off.

These reflections are suggested to us as we look back over our work with five autistic infants. In them life appeared to have failed as long as their behavior was looked upon as not fitting the acceptable norms of social expectations and so-called educability. But given a chance to feel like human beings, given an opportunity to experience within themselves an awareness and consciousness of their human identity, they responded with such a degree of love for living that it is clear that what had appeared in them to be a strange form of death was really only a mysterious form of sleep. By awakening them to their own sense of humanity, we were able to open up for them the gates of learning; they showed us that they could grow and develop and learn, because there was a real purpose and value in doing so. They were expressing their human individuality. Paradoxical as it may seem, the conditions of their awakening were as humble, simple, and direct as the enjoyment of a mother's smile, the reassuring touch of a friend's hand, the quietening sound of a nursery rhyme, or the wonderful feeling of a father's embrace. It seems to take so little to "educate" a human being, that is, to bring out the dormant ferment of life which stirs in every child. Apparently, Christ understood this well. It might be presumptuous to assume that when He spoke the words, "The child is not dead, but sleeping," He may have been thinking of an autistic child. But without presumption we could say that He was thinking of all the children of this world who have a right to be awakened to a clear consciousness of their humanity. "Little girl, I say to you, arise. And immediately the girl got up and walked; . . . And immediately they were overcome with amazement. And He . . . told them to give her something to eat."

The last time we saw Elizabeth, she jumped on Carole's knees, and with a bright smile illuminating her eyes, and her hands extended to her best friend's hands, she began, in her thin soprano voice, to sing: "Holy, Holy, Holy!" We chuckled; Elizabeth had never liked to go to church. But had her friends Kathy, June, Tommy, and Connie been present, we were sure that they would have joined her in this hymn. After all, this was a definite improvement over "Row, Row, Row Your Boat!"

Appendix

Appendix

Statistical Data on Vineland
and Fels Behavioral Scales

As stated in Chapter VI describing the design of the project, each child was used as his own control and was evaluated on an individual basis. Therefore, where possible, statistical analyses were made for each child on each of the scales involved. This was possible because each child was rated several times (at specific intervals) during the course of treatment.

Using the Friedman Test on the Fels Behavior Scale ratings (see Table I in text for list of these scales) for the four children who remained in the project for at least one year (Connie was withdrawn before the final one-year rating period) indicated a pattern of significant change in all children by all four raters beyond the 0.001 level of significance.

Analysis of the data from the Vineland Social Maturity scale (administered at three month intervals) showed a significant improvement in all cases beyond the 0.001 level using the Friedman Two-way Analysis of Variance Test. Agreement as to the pattern of subscales within the Vineland over the successive three-month administrations was significant in all cases beyond the 0.01 level using the Kendall Coefficient of Concordance.

371

Table 1

KATHY

Vineland Data—Frequency Count

	C	SHG	S	O	SHE	L	SHD
Initial	1.0	7.0	1.0	0.0	3.0	2.0	0.0
6 months	2.0	11.0	3.0	5.0	3.0	5.0	1.0
9 months	3.0	11.0	3.0	5.0	3.0	5.0	1.0
12 months	3.0	11.0	3.0	5.0	3.0	5.0	1.0
15 months	3.0	12.0	3.0	5.0	3.0	5.0	1.0
18 months	3.0	12.0	4.0	5.0	6.0	5.0	2.0
21 months	3.5	12.0	5.5	7.0	7.5	5.0	3.5
24 months	4.0	12.0	5.5	7.5	7.5	5.0	5.5

X^2_r (Friedman) $p < .001$
W (Kendall) $p < .01$

C:	Communication	SHE:	Self-Help Eating
SHG:	Self-Help General	L:	Language
S:	Socialization	SHD:	Self-Help Dressing
O:	Occupation	SD:	Self-Direction

Table 2a

KATHY

Fels Scales; Rater *Home Observer**

Fels Scales		1 year	1 yr. 6 mo.	2 years
1.1	Affectionateness	1.0	2.5	2.5
1.2	Aggressiveness	1.0	2.0	3.0
1.5	Cheerful-depressed	1.0	2.0	3.0
1.7	Conformity	1.0	2.0	3.0
2.11	Curiosity	1.0	2.0	3.0
3.11	Emotional excitability	1.0	2.0	3.0
3.14	Friendliness	1.0	2.0	3.0
3.15	Gregariousness	1.0	2.0	3.0
3.22	Obedience	1.0	2.0	3.0
4.1	Patience	2.5	1.0	2.5
5.1	Planfulness	1.0	2.0	3.0
6.1	Negativism	1.0	2.0	3.0
7.1	Sense of humor	1.5	1.5	3.0
8.2	Suggestibility	1.0	2.0	3.0
8.3	Tenacity	1.0	2.0	3.0

$X^2_r = 25.5; \ d.f. = 2; \ p < .001$

*Friedman Analysis (Using Kendall Conversion)

Table 2b
KATHY
Fels Scales; Rater *Mother**

Fels Scales		1 year	1 yr. 6 mo.	2 years
1.1	Affectionateness	1.0	2.0	3.0
1.2	Aggressiveness	3.0	1.0	2.0
1.5	Cheerful-depressed	2.0	1.0	3.0
1.7	Conformity	1.0	2.0	3.0
2.11	Curiosity	1.0	2.0	3.0
3.11	Emotional excitability	1.0	2.0	3.0
3.14	Friendliness	2.0	1.0	3.0
3.15	Gregariousness	1.0	2.5	2.5
3.22	Obedience	1.0	2.0	3.0
4.1	Patience	1.0	2.0	3.0
5.1	Planfulness	2.0	2.0	2.0
6.1	Negativism	1.0	3.0	2.0
7.1	Sense of humor	1.0	2.0	3.0
8.2	Suggestibility	1.0	2.0	3.0
8.3	Tenacity	1.0	2.0	3.0

$$X^2_r = 16.8; \ d.f. = 2; \ p < .001$$

*Friedman Analysis (Using Kendall Conversion)

Table 2c
KATHY
Fels Scales; Rater *Clinic Observer**

Fels Scales		1 year	1 yr. 6 mo.	2 years
1.1	Affectionateness	1.0	2.0	3.0
1.2	Aggressiveness	1.5	1.5	3.0
1.5	Cheerful-depressed	1.0	2.0	3.0
1.7	Conformity	1.0	2.0	3.0
2.11	Curiosity	1.0	2.0	3.0
3.11	Emotional excitability	1.0	2.0	3.0
3.14	Friendliness	1.0	2.0	3.0
3.15	Gregariousness	1.0	2.0	3.0
3.22	Obedience	1.0	2.0	3.0
4.1	Patience	1.0	2.0	3.0
5.1	Planfulness	1.0	2.0	3.0
6.1	Negativism	1.0	3.0	2.0
7.1	Sense of humor	1.0	2.0	3.0
8.2	Suggestibility	1.0	2.0	3.0
8.3	Tenacity	1.0	2.0	3.0

$$X^2_r = 27.3; \ d.f. = 2; \ p < .001$$

*Friedman Analysis (Using Kendall Conversion)

Table 2d

KATHY

Fels Scales; Rater *Therapist**

Fels Scales		*1 year*	*1 yr. 6 mo.*	*2 years*
1.1	Affectionateness	1.0	2.0	3.0
1.2	Aggressiveness	1.5	1.5	3.0
1.5	Cheerful-depressed	1.0	2.5	2.5
1.7	Conformity	1.0	2.0	3.0
2.11	Curiosity	1.0	2.0	3.0
3.11	Emotional excitability	1.0	2.0	3.0
3.14	Friendliness	1.0	2.0	3.0
3.15	Gregariousness	1.0	2.0	3.0
3.22	Obedience	1.0	2.0	3.0
4.1	Patience	1.0	2.0	3.0
5.1	Planfulness	1.0	2.0	3.0
6.1	Negativism	1.0	2.0	3.0
7.1	Sense of humor	1.0	2.0	3.0
8.2	Suggestibility	1.0	2.0	3.0
8.3	Tenacity	1.0	2.0	3.0

$$X = 28.8; \ d.f. = 2; \ p < .001$$

*Friedman Analysis (Using Kendall Conversion)

Table 3

CONNIE

Vineland Data—Frequency Count

	C	*SHG*	*S*	*O*	*SHE*	*L*
Initial	2.0	9.5	0.5	0.0	4.0	3.0
3 months	2.5	9.5	3.0	1.0	5.0	3.0
6 months	3.0	10.5	3.0	2.5	6.5	5.0
9 months	3.0	10.5	3.0	2.5	6.5	5.0

$$X^2_r \ \text{(Friedman)} \quad p < .001$$
$$W \ \text{(Kendall)} \quad p < .01$$

C:	Communication	SHE:	Self-Help Eating
SHG:	Self-Help General	L:	Language
S:	Socialization	SHD:	Self-Help Dressing
O:	Occupation	SD:	Self-Direction

Table 4

ELIZABETH

Vineland Data—Frequency Count

	C	SHG	S	O	SHE	L	SHD
Initial	4.0	10.0	3.0	3.0	2.0	3.0	0.0
3 months	4.0	10.5	3.0	5.0	5.5	3.0	1.0
6 months	4.0	10.5	3.5	5.5	7.5	3.5	2.5
9 months	5.0	11.0	4.0	7.5	8.0	4.0	4.0
12 months	5.0	12.5	4.0	7.5	9.0	4.0	4.5

$$X^2_r \text{ (Friedman)} \quad p < .001$$
$$W \text{ (Kendall)} \quad p < .01$$

C:	Communication	SHE:	Self-Help Eating
SHG:	Self-Help General	L:	Language
S:	Socialization	SHD:	Self-Help Dressing
O:	Occupation	SD:	Self-Direction

Table 5a

ELIZABETH

Fels Scales; Rater *Home Observer**

Fels Scales		Initial	6 months	1 year
1.1	Affectionateness	1.0	2.0	3.0
1.2	Aggressiveness	1.0	2.0	3.0
1.5	Cheerful-depressed	1.0	2.0	3.0
1.7	Conformity	1.0	2.0	3.0
2.11	Curiosity	1.0	2.0	3.0
3.11	Emotional excitability	2.0	1.0	3.0
3.14	Friendliness	1.0	2.0	3.0
3.15	Gregariousness	1.0	2.0	3.0
3.22	Obedience	1.0	2.0	3.0
4.1	Patience	1.0	2.5	2.5
5.1	Planfulness	1.0	2.5	2.5
6.1	Negativism	1.0	2.0	3.0
7.1	Sense of humor	1.0	2.0	3.0
8.2	Suggestibility	1.0	2.5	2.5
8.3	Tenacity	1.0	2.5	2.5

$$X^2_r = 26; \quad d.f. = 2; \quad p < .001$$

*Friedman Analysis (Using Kendall Conversion)

Table 5b

ELIZABETH

Fels Scales; Rater *Mother**

Fels Scales	*Initial*	*6 months*	*1 year*
1.1 Affectionateness	1.0	2.0	3.0
1.2 Aggressiveness	1.0	2.0	3.0
1.5 Cheerful-depressed	1.0	2.5	2.5
1.7 Conformity	1.0	2.0	3.0
2.11 Curiosity	1.0	2.0	3.0
3.11 Emotional excitability	1.0	2.0	3.0
3.14 Friendliness	1.0	2.0	3.0
3.15 Gregariousness	1.0	2.0	3.0
3.22 Obedience	1.0	2.0	3.0
4.1 Patience	1.0	2.0	3.0
5.1 Planfulness	1.0	2.0	3.0
6.1 Negativism	1.0	2.5	2.5
7.1 Sense of humor	1.5	1.5	3.0
8.2 Suggestibility	1.5	1.5	3.0
8.3 Tenacity	1.0	2.5	2.5

$$X^2_r = 26.4; \ d.f. = 2; \ p < .001$$

*Friedman Analysis (Using Kendall Conversion)

Table 5c

ELIZABETH

Fels Scales; Rater *Clinic Observer**

Fels Scales	*Initial*	*6 months*	*1 year*
1.1 Affectionateness	1.0	2.0	3.0
1.2 Aggressiveness	1.0	2.0	3.0
1.5 Cheerful-depressed	1.0	2.0	3.0
1.7 Conformity	1.0	2.0	3.0
2.11 Curiosity	1.0	2.0	3.0
3.11 Emotional excitability	1.0	2.0	3.0
3.14 Friendliness	1.0	2.0	3.0
3.15 Gregariousness	1.0	2.0	3.0
3.22 Obedience	1.0	2.0	3.0
4.1 Patience	1.0	2.0	3.0
5.1 Planfulness	1.0	2.0	3.0
6.1 Negativism	1.0	2.0	3.0
7.1 Sense of humor	1.0	2.0	3.0
8.2 Suggestibility	1.0	2.0	3.0
8.3 Tenacity	1.0	2.0	3.0

$$X^2_r = 30; \ d.f. = 2; \ p < .001$$

*Friedman Analysis (Using Kendall Conversion)

Table 5d

ELIZABETH

Fels Scales; Rater *Therapist**

Fels Scales	Initial	6 months	1 year
1.1 Affectionateness	1.0	2.0	3.0
1.2 Aggressiveness	1.0	2.0	3.0
1.5 Cheerful-depressed	1.0	2.0	3.0
1.7 Conformity	1.0	2.0	3.0
2.11 Curiosity	1.0	2.0	3.0
3.11 Emotional excitability	1.0	2.0	3.0
3.14 Friendliness	1.0	2.0	3.0
3.15 Gregariousness	1.0	2.0	3.0
3.22 Obedience	1.0	2.0	3.0
4.1 Patience	1.0	2.0	3.0
5.1 Planfulness	1.0	2.0	3.0
6.1 Negativism	1.0	2.0	3.0
7.1 Sense of humor	1.0	2.0	3.0
8.2 Suggestibility	1.0	2.0	3.0
8.3 Tenacity	1.0	2.5	2.5

$$X^2_r = 27.6; \; d.f. = 2; \; p < .001$$

*Friedman Analysis (Using Kendall Conversion)

Table 6

TOMMY

Vineland Data—Frequency Count

	C	SHG	S	O	SHE	L	SHD
Initial	1.0	8.0	2.0	3.0	2.5	3.0	1.0
3 months	2.5	10.5	2.5	3.0	4.5	3.5	1.0
6 months	2.5	11.0	2.5	3.0	5.5	3.5	2.0
9 months	2.5	11.0	2.5	3.0	6.5	4.5	2.0
12 months	3.5	11.0	3.0	4.0	9.0	4.5	2.0

$$X^2_r \; \text{(Friedman)} \quad p < .001$$
$$W \; \text{(Kendall)} \quad p < .01$$

C:	Communication	SHE:	Self-Help Eating
SHG:	Self-Help General	L:	Language
S:	Socialization	SHD:	Self-Help Dressing
O:	Occupation	SD:	Self-Direction

Table 7a

TOMMY

Fels Scales; Rater *Home Observer**

Fels Scales	Initial	6 months	1 year
1.1 Affectionateness	1.0	2.0	3.0
1.2 Aggressiveness	1.0	2.0	3.0
1.5 Cheerful-depressed	1.0	2.0	3.0
1.7 Conformity	1.0	2.5	2.5
2.11 Curiosity	1.0	2.0	3.0
3.11 Emotional excitability	1.5	1.5	3.0
3.14 Friendliness	1.0	2.0	3.0
3.15 Gregariousness	2.0	2.0	2.0
3.22 Obedience	2.0	1.0	3.0
4.1 Patience	2.0	2.0	2.0
5.1 Planfulness	2.0	2.0	2.0
6.1 Negativism	1.0	2.5	2.5
7.1 Sense of humor	1.0	2.0	3.0
8.2 Suggestibility	1.0	2.0	3.0
8.3 Tenacity	1.0	2.5	2.5

$$X^2_r = 19.8; \ d.f. = 2; \ p < .001$$

*Friedman Analysis (Using Kendall Conversion)

Table 7b

TOMMY

Fels Scales; Rater *Mother**

Fels Scales	Initial	6 months	1 year
1.1 Affectionateness	1.0	2.0	3.0
1.2 Aggressiveness	1.0	2.0	3.0
1.5 Cheerful-depressed	1.0	3.0	2.0
1.7 Conformity	1.0	2.0	3.0
2.11 Curiosity	1.0	2.0	3.0
3.11 Emotional excitability	1.0	2.0	3.0
3.14 Friendliness	1.0	2.0	3.0
3.15 Gregariousness	1.0	2.0	3.0
3.22 Obedience	1.0	2.0	3.0
4.1 Patience	1.0	2.0	3.0
5.1 Planfulness	1.0	2.0	3.0
6.1 Negativism	1.0	2.0	3.0
7.1 Sense of humor	1.0	2.0	3.0
8.2 Suggestibility	1.0	2.0	3.0
8.3 Tenacity	1.0	2.0	3.0

$$X^2_r = 28.8; \ d.f. = 2; \ p < .001$$

*Friedman Analysis (Using Kendall Conversion)

Table 7c

Tommy

Fels Scales; Rater *Clinic Observer**

Fels Scales		Initial	6 months	1 year
1.1	Affectionateness	1.0	2.0	3.0
1.2	Aggressiveness	1.0	2.0	3.0
1.5	Cheerful-depressed	1.0	2.0	3.0
1.7	Conformity	1.0	2.0	3.0
2.11	Curiosity	1.0	2.0	3.0
3.11	Emotional excitability	1.0	2.0	3.0
3.14	Friendliness	1.0	2.0	3.0
3.15	Gregariousness	1.0	2.0	3.0
3.22	Obedience	1.0	2.0	3.0
4.1	Patience	1.0	2.0	3.0
5.1	Planfulness	1.0	2.0	3.0
6.1	Negativism	1.0	2.0	3.0
7.1	Sense of humor	1.0	2.0	3.0
8.2	Suggestibility	1.0	2.0	3.0
8.3	Tenacity	1.0	2.0	3.0

$$X^2_r = 30; \ d.f. = 2; \ p < .001$$

*Friedman Analysis (Using Kendall Conversion)

Table 7d

Tommy

Fels Scales; Rater *Therapist**

Fels Scales		Initial	6 months	1 year
1.1	Affectionateness	1.0	2.0	3.0
1.2	Aggressiveness	1.0	2.0	3.0
1.5	Cheerful-depressed	1.0	2.0	3.0
1.7	Conformity	1.0	2.0	3.0
2.11	Curiosity	1.0	2.0	3.0
3.11	Emotional excitability	1.0	2.0	3.0
3.14	Friendliness	1.0	2.0	3.0
3.15	Gregariousness	1.0	2.0	3.0
3.22	Obedience	1.0	2.0	3.0
4.1	Patience	1.0	2.0	3.0
5.1	Planfulness	1.0	2.0	3.0
6.1	Negativism	1.0	2.0	3.0
7.1	Sense of humor	1.0	2.0	3.0
8.2	Suggestibility	1.0	2.0	3.0
8.3	Tenacity	1.0	2.0	3.0

$$X^2_r = 30; \ d.f. = 2; \ p < .001$$

*Friedman Analysis (Using Kendall Conversion)

Table 8

JUNE

Vineland Data—Frequency Count

	C	SHG	S	O	SHE	L	SHD	SD
Initial	6.0	13.0	5.0	8.0	11.5	6.0	10.0	0.5
3 months	6.0	13.0	6.0	8.5	11.5	7.0	11.0	0.5
6 months	6.0	13.0	7.5	10.0	11.5	7.0	11.5	0.5
9 months	6.0	13.0	8.0	10.0	12.0	7.0	12.0	1.0

$$X^2_r \text{ (Friedman)} \quad p < .001$$
$$W \text{ (Kendall)} \quad p < .01$$

C: Communication	SHE: Self-Help Eating
SHG: Self-Help General	L: Language
S: Socialization	SHD: Self-Help Dressing
O: Occupation	SD: Self-Direction

Table 9a

JUNE

Fels Scales; Rater *Home Observer**

Fels Scales		Initial	6 months	1 year
1.1	Affectionateness	1.0	2.0	3.0
1.2	Aggressiveness	1.0	2.0	3.0
1.5	Cheerful-depressed	1.5	1.5	3.0
1.7	Conformity	1.0	2.0	3.0
2.11	Curiosity	1.0	2.0	3.0
3.11	Emotional excitability	2.0	2.0	2.0
3.14	Friendliness	1.0	2.0	3.0
3.15	Gregariousness	1.0	2.0	3.0
3.22	Obedience	1.0	2.5	2.5
4.1	Patience	1.0	2.0	3.0
5.1	Planfulness	1.0	2.0	3.0
6.1	Negativism	1.0	2.0	3.0
7.1	Sense of humor	1.0	2.0	3.0
8.2	Suggestibility	1.0	2.0	3.0
8.3	Tenacity	1.0	2.0	3.0

$$X^2_r = 27; \quad d.f. = 2; \quad p < .001$$

*Friedman Analysis (Using Kendall Conversion)

Table 9b
JUNE
Fels Scales; Rater *Mother**

Fels Scales		Initial	6 months	1 year
1.1	Affectionateness	1.0	2.0	3.0
1.2	Aggressiveness	1.0	2.0	3.0
1.5	Cheerful-depressed	1.0	2.5	2.5
1.7	Conformity	1.0	2.5	2.5
2.11	Curiosity	1.5	1.5	3.0
3.11	Emotional excitability	1.0	3.0	2.0
3.14	Friendliness	1.0	2.0	3.0
3.15	Gregariousness	1.0	2.0	3.0
3.22	Obedience	1.0	2.0	3.0
4.1	Patience	1.0	3.0	2.0
5.1	Planfulness	1.0	2.0	3.0
6.1	Negativism	2.0	2.0	2.0
7.1	Sense of humor	1.0	2.0	3.0
8.2	Suggestibility	1.0	2.0	3.0
8.3	Tenacity	3.0	2.0	1.0

$$X^2_r = 16.5; \ d.f. = 2; \ p < .001$$

*Friedman Analysis (Using Kendall Conversion)

Table 9c
JUNE
Fels Scales; Rater *Clinic Observer**

Fels Scales		Initial	6 months	1 year
1.1	Affectionateness	1.0	2.0	3.0
1.2	Aggressiveness	1.0	2.5	2.5
1.5	Cheerful-depressed	1.0	2.0	3.0
1.7	Conformity	1.0	2.0	3.0
2.11	Curiosity	1.0	2.0	3.0
3.11	Emotional excitability	1.0	3.0	2.0
3.14	Friendliness	1.0	2.0	3.0
3.15	Gregariousness	1.0	2.0	3.0
3.22	Obedience	1.0	2.0	3.0
4.1	Patience	1.0	2.0	3.0
5.1	Planfulness	1.0	2.0	3.0
6.1	Negativism	1.0	3.0	2.0
7.1	Sense of humor	1.0	2.0	3.0
8.2	Suggestibility	1.0	2.0	3.0
83.	Tenacity	1.0	2.0	3.0

$$X^2_r = 26; \ d.f. = 2; \ p < .001$$

*Friedman Analysis (Using Kendall Conversion)

Table 9d

JUNE

Fels Scales; Rater *Therapist**

Fels Scales	Initial	6 months	1 year
1.1 Affectionateness	1.0	2.0	3.0
1.2 Aggressiveness	1.0	2.0	3.0
1.5 Cheerful-depressed	1.0	2.0	3.0
1.7 Conformity	1.0	2.0	3.0
2.11 Curiosity	1.0	2.0	3.0
3.11 Emotional excitability	1.0	3.0	2.0
3.14 Friendliness	1.0	2.0	3.0
3.15 Gregariousness	1.0	2.0	3.0
3.22 Obedience	1.0	2.0	3.0
4.1 Patience	1.0	2.0	3.0
5.1 Planfulness	1.0	2.0	3.0
6.1 Negativism	1.0	3.0	2.0
7.1 Sense of humor	1.0	2.0	3.0
8.2 Suggestibility	1.0	2.0	3.0
8.3 Tenacity	1.0	2.0	3.0

$$X^2_r = 27; \ d.f. = 2; \ p < .001$$

*Friedman Analysis (Using Kendall Conversion)

Bibliography

Bibliography

Anthony, J. (1958). An experimental approach to the psychopathology of childhood: Autism. *British Journal of Medical Psychology*, **31**.

Aubry, J. (1955). The effects of lack of maternal care: Methods of studying children aged one to three years, placed in institutions. In G. Caplan (Ed.), *Emotional problems of early childhood*. New York: Basic Books. Pp. 293–306.

Balint, A. (1938). Love for the mother and mother love. In M. Balint, *Primary love and psychoanalytic technique*. London: Hogarth Press, 1952.

Balint, A. (1954). *The early years of life*. New York: Basic Books.

Bartlett, F. G. (1932). *Remembering: A study in experimental and social psychology*. Cambridge: Cambridge University Press.

Bergman, P., and Escalona, S. K. (1949). Unusual sensitivities in very young children. *Bulletin of the Menninger Clinic*, **12**.

Bettelheim, B. (1959). Feral children and autistic children. *American Journal of Sociology*, **64**.

Bettelheim, B. (1967). *The empty fortress*. New York: Free Press.

Bosh, G. (1962). *Der Fruehkindlicke autismus*. Berlin: Springer.

Bowlby, J. (1951). Maternal care and mental health. *World Health Organization Monographs*. No. 2.

Bowlby, J. (1957). An ethnological approach to research in child development. *British Journal Medical Psychology*, **30**.

Bowlby, J. (1958). The nature of the child's tie to his mother. *International Journal of Psychoanalysis*, **39**.

Brody, S. (1956). *Patterns of mothering: Maternal influence during infancy*. New York: International Universities Press.

Bruner, J. (1961). The cognitive consequences of early sensory deprivation. In P. Solomon *et al.*, *Sensory Deprivation*. Cambridge: Harvard University Press, 195–207.

Buber, M. (1923). *I and Thou*. Edinburgh: R. & R. Clark, 1945.

Burlingham, D. (1961). Some notes on the development of the blind. *The psychoanalytic study of the child.* Vol. 16. New York: International Universities Press.

Carlson, C. F. (1967). An evaluation of consistent high impact sensory and affective stimulation therapy on early infantile autistic behavior. Unpublished doctoral dissertation, Northwestern University.

Chomsky, N. (1968). Language and the mind. *Psychology Today,* 1.

DesLauriers, A. M. (1960). The psychological experience of reality: Therapeutic implications. In L. Appleby (Ed.), *Chronic schizophrenia.* Glencoe: Free Press.

DesLauriers, A. M. (1962). *The experience of reality in childhood schizophrenia.* New York: International Universities Press.

DesLauriers, A. M. (1967). The schizophrenic child. *Archives of General Psychiatry,* 16.

Despert, L. (1951). Some considerations relating to the genesis of autistic behavior in children. *American Journal of Orthopsychiatry,* 21.

Eisenberg, L. (1956). The autistic child in adolescence. *American Journal of Psychiatry,* 112.

Eisenberg, L., and Kanner, L. (1956). Early infantile autism, 1943–55. *American Journal of Orthopsychiatry,* 26.

Escalona, S. (1945). Feeding disturbances in very young children. *American Journal of Orthopsychiatry,* 15.

Escalona, S. (1949). A commentary upon some recent changes in child-rearing practices. *Child Development,* 20.

Escalona, S. (1953). Emotional development in the first year of life. In M. Senn (Ed.), *Problems of infancy and childhood.* New York: Josiah Macy, Jr., Foundation.

Escalona, S. K. (1963). Patterns of infantile experiences and the developmental process. *The psychoanalytic study of the child.* Vol. 18. New York: International Universities Press.

Escalona, S. K. (1965). Some determinants of individual differences. *Transactions of the New York Academy of Sciences,* Series 2, Vol. 27.

Eveloff, H. (1960). The autistic child. *Archives of General Psychiatry,* 3.

Ferster, C. B. (1964). Psychotherapy by machine communication. In D. Rioch and E. Wernstein (Eds.), *Disorders of communication, Proceedings of the association for research in nervous and mental disease,* 42. Baltimore: Williams & Wilkins.

Ferster, C. B., and De Myer, M. K. (1961). The development of performance in autistic children in an automatically controlled environment. *Journal of Chronic Diseases,* 13.

Fiske, D., and Maddi, S. (1961). *Functions of varied experience.* Homewood: Dorsey Press.

Flavell, J. H. (1963). *The developmental psychology of Jean Piaget.* Princeton: Van Nostrand.

Freeman, F. S. (1962). *Theory and practice of psychological testing.* New York: Holt, Rinehart, Winston.

Gardner, R., Holzman, P. S., Klein, G. S. *et al.* (1959). *Cognitive Control; A study of individual consistencies in cognitive behavior.* New York: International Universities Press.

Gellhorn, E., and Loofburrow, G. N. (1963). *Emotions and emotional disorders.* New York: Harper.

Gesell, A., and Amatruda, C. S. *Developmental diagnosis.* New York: Paul B. Hoeber.

Gewirtz, J. (1961). A learning analysis of the effects of normal stimulation, privation and deprivation on the acquisition of social motivation and attachment. In B. Foss (Ed.), *Determinants of Infant Behavior.* New York: John Wiley.

Goshen, C. E. (1963). Mental retardation and neurotic maternal attitudes. *Archives of General Psychiatry,* **9.**

Grastyan, E. (1959). The hippocampus and higher nervous activity. In M.A.B. Brazier (Ed.), *The central nervous system and behavior.* New York: Josiah Macy, Jr., Foundation .

Grinker, R. R., Sr. (1961). *Psychosomatic research.* New York: Grove Press.

Grinker, R. R., Sr. (1964). Reception of communications by patients in depressive states, Ch. 25. In D. M. Rioch and E. A. Weinstein (Eds.), *Disorders of communication, Proceedings of the Association for Research in Nervous and Mental Diseases,* **42.** Baltimore: Williams & Wilkins.

Hall, E. T. (1959). *The Silent Language.* Greenwich: Fawcett Publications, 1961.

Hebb, D. O. (1949). *Organization of behavior.* New York: John Wiley.

Hebb, D. O. (1955). Drives and the CNS. *Psychological Review,* **62.**

Hebb, D. O. (1958). The motivating effects of exteroceptive stimulation. *American Psychologist,* **13.**

Hess, E. H. (1959). Imprinting. *Science,* **130.**

Hobbs, N. (1967). Helping disturbed children: Psychological and ecological strategies. *American Psychologist,* **21.**

Hollon, T. (1962). A rationale for supportive psychotherapy of depressed patients. *American Journal of Psychotherapy,* **16.**

Hunt, J. McV. (1961). *Intelligence and Experience.* New York: Ronald Press.

Hutt, S. J., Lee, C. H. D., & Ounsted, C. (1965). A behavioral and electroencephalographic study of autistic children. *Journal of Psychiatric Research,* **3.**

Kanner, L. (1943). Autistic disturbances of affective contact. *The Nervous Child,* **2.**

Kanner, L. (1944). Early infantile autism. *Journal of Pediatrics,* **25.**

388   *your child is asleep*

Kanner, L. (1946). Irrelevant and metaphorical language in early infantile autism. *American Journal of Psychiatry*, **103.**

Kanner, L. (1951). A discussion of early infantile autism. *Digest of Neurological Psychiatry*, **24.**

Kanner, L. (1954). Childhood schizophrenia, round table, 1953. *American Journal of Orthopsychiatry*, **24.**

Kanner, L. (1955). General concept of schizophrenia at different ages. *Proceedings of the Association for Research in Nervous and Mental Diseases*, **34.**

Kanner, L. (1965). Infantile autism and the schizophrenias. *Behavioral Science*, **10.**

Kanner, L., and Eisenberg, L. (1955). Notes on the follow-up studies of autistic children. In P. H. Hoch and J. Zubin (Eds.), *Psychopathology of childhood*. New York: Grune and Stratton. Pp. 227–239.

Kanner, L., and Lesser, L. I. (1958). Early infantile autism. *Pediatric Clinics of North America*, **5.**

Katona, G. (1940). *Organizing and memorizing: Studies in the psychology of learning and teaching*. New York: Columbia University Press.

Keeler, W. R. (1958). Autistic patterns and defective communication in blind children with retrolental fibroplasia. In P. H. Hoch and J. Zubin (Eds.), *Psychopathology of communication*. New York: Grune & Stratton. Pp. 64–83.

Leland, H. and Smith, D. E. (1965). *Play therapy with mentally abnormal children*. New York: Grune & Stratton.

Levine, S. (1962). The effects of infantile experience on adult behavior. In *Experimental foundations of clinical psychology*. New York: Basic Books.

Levine, S., and Lewis, G. W. (1959). Critical period for effects of infantile experience on maturation of stress response. *Science*, **129.**

Lindsley, D. (1961). Common factors in sensory deprivation, sensory distortion, and sensory overload. In P. Solomon *et al., Sensory deprivation*. Cambridge: Harvard University Press. Pp. 174–194.

Loewald, H. W. (1951). Ego and reality. *International Journal of Psychoanalysis*, **32.**

Lorenz, K. (1935). Der Kumpan in der Umvelt des Vogels. Der Artgenose als auslosendes Moment sozialer Verhaltungsweisen. *Journal of Ornithology*, **83.**

Lorenz, K. (1958). *King Solomon's ring*. New York: Crowell.

Lovaas, O. I. *et al.* (1965). Building social behavior in autistic children by use of electric shock. *Journal of Experimental Research in Personality*, **1.**

Lovaas, O. I. *et al.* (1966). Imitative speech by schizophrenic children. *Science*, **151.**

Lovaas, O. I. (1966). Some studies on the treatment of childhood schizophrenia. Paper presented at Symposium on Behavior Therapy at the University of Chicago.

Lovaas, O. I. (1968). Some studies on the treatment of childhood schizophrenia.

In J. M. Schlein (Ed.), *Research in psychotherapy*, Vol. 3. Washington, D.C.: American Psychological Association.

McCarthy, D. (1966). Affective aspects of language learning, Ch. 12. In A. H. Kidd, and J. L. Rivoire (Eds.), *Perceptual development in children*. New York: International Universities Press.

Mahler, M. S. (1952). On childhood psychosis and schizophrenia: Autistic and symbiotic infantile psychoses. *The psychoanalytic study of the child*. Vol. 7. New York: International Universities Press.

Mahler, M. S. and Gosliner, B. J. (1955). On symbiotic child psychosis: genetic, dynamic, and restitutive aspects. *The psychoanalytic study of the child*. **10.** New York: International Universities Press.

Moruzzi, C., and Magoun, H. W. (1949). Brain stem reticular formation and activation of the EEG. *Electroencephalography and Clinical Neurophysiology*, **1.**

Murphy, L. B. *et al.* (1962). *The widening world of childhood*. New York: Basic Books.

Nauta, W. J. H. (1959). Hippocampal projections and related neural pathways to the mid-brain in the cat. *Brain*, **81.**

Park, C. C. (1967). *The Siege*. New York: Harcourt, Brace & World.

Montessori, Maria (1949). *The absorbent mind*. Madras: The Theosophical Publishing House.

Piaget, J. (1952). *The Origins of Intelligence in Children*. New York: International Universities Press.

Piaget, J. (1954). *The construction of reality in the child*. New York: Basic Books.

Pribram, K. H. (1967). Emotion: Steps toward a neurophysiological theory. In D. C. Glass (Ed.), *Neurophysiology and emotion*. New York: Rockefeller University Press and Russell Sage Foundation.

Pribram, K. H., and Kruger, L. (1954). Functions of the "olfactory brain." *Annals of the New York Academy of Science*, **58.**

Provence, S., and Lipton, R. C. (1962). *Infants in institutions*. New York: International Universities Press.

Rapaport, David. (1950). *Emotions and memory*. New York: International Universities Press.

Reisen, A. H. (1961). Excessive arousal effects of stimulation after early sensory deprivation. In P. Solomon *et al.*, *Sensory deprivation*. Cambridge: Harvard University Press. Pp. 34–40.

Richards, T. W., and Simons, M. P. (1941). The Fels Behavior Scales. *Genetic Psychology Monographs*, **24.**

Rimland, B. (1964). *Infantile autism*. New York: Appleton-Century-Crofts.

Routtenberg, A. (1966a). Neural mechanisms of sleep: Changing view of reticular formation function. *Psychological Review*, **73.**

Routtenberg, A. (1966b). The two arousal hypothesis. Paper read at American Psychological Association Meetings, New York, September, 1966.

Routtenberg, A. (1968). The two arousal hypothesis: Reticular formation and limbic system. *Psychological Review*, **75.**

Ruff, G., Levy, E., & Thaler, V. (1961). Factors influencing the reaction to reduced sensory input. In P. Solomon *et al*, *Sensory deprivation*. Cambridge: Harvard University Press. Pp. 72–90.

Sandler, Anne-Marie (1963). Aspects of passivity and ego development in the blind infant. *The psychoanalytic study of the child*. Vol. 18. New York: International Universities Press.

Sarason, S. B. (1957). Psychological and cultural problems in mental subnormality: A review of research. *Genetic Psychology Monographs*, **57.**

Schain, R. J., and Yannet, H. (1960). Infantile autism: An analysis of 50 cases and a consideration of certain neurophysiologic concepts. *Journal of Pediatrics*, **57.**

Schultz, D. P. (1965). *Sensory restriction*. New York: Academic Press.

Scott, J. P. (1962). Genetics and the development of social behavior in mammals. *American Journal of Orthopsychiatry*, **32.**

Scott, J. P. (1963). The process of socialization in canine and human infants. *Monograph of The Society for Research in Child Development*. **28.**

Sharpless, S. K., and Jasper, H. (1956). Habituation of the arousal reaction. *Brain*, **79.**

Solley, C. M. (1966). Affective processes in perceptual development, Ch. 11. In A. H. Kidd, and J. L. Rivoire (Eds.), *Perceptual development in children*. New York: International Universities Press.

Solomon, P., Kubzansky, P., Leiderman, P., Mendelson, J., Trumbull, R., & Wexler, D. (1961). *Sensory deprivation*. Cambridge: Harvard University Press.

Sontag, L. W. (1941). The significance of fetal environmental differences. *American Journal of Obstetrics and Gynecology*, **42.**

Spitz, R. A. (1945). Hospitalism: An inquiry into the genesis of psychiatric conditions in early childhood.*The psychoanalytic study of the child*. Vol. 1. New York: International Universities Press.

Spitz, R. A. (1946a). Hospitalism: A follow-up report. In *The psychoanalytic study of the child*. Vol. 2. New York: International Universities Press.

Spitz, R. A. (1946b). Anaclitic depression. In *The psychoanalytic study of the child*. Vol. 2. New York: International Universities Press.

Spitz, R. A. (1957). *No and yes: On the genesis of human communication*. New York: International Universities Press.

Spitz, R. (1965). *The first year of life*. New York: International Universities Press.

Spitz, R. A., and Wolf, K. M. (1946). Anaclitic depression. *The psychoanalytic study of the child*. Vol. 2. New York: International Universities Press.

Teilhard de Chardin, P. (1957). *The vision of the past*, Ch. 11. New York: Harper & Row, 1966.

Teilhard de Chardin, P. (1965). *The phenomenon of man*. New York: Harper & Row.

The Holy Bible. American Bible Society, 1952.

Thorpe, W. H. (1950). The concepts of learning and their relation to those of instinct. *Symposia of the Society for Experimental Biology*, 4.

White, P. T., and De Meyer, M. (1964). EEG abnormalities in early childhood schizophrenia: A double-blind study of psychiatrically disturbed and normal children during Promazine sedation. *American Journal of Psychiatry*, **120.**

Witkin, H. A. *et al.* (1954). *Personality through perception*. New York: Harper.

Wicks, Sue (1966). Unpublished paper, Northwestern University.

Zeigarnik, B. (1927). Uber das Behalten von erledigten und unerledigten Handlungen. *Psychologische Forschung*, **9**, 1–85. Cited by J. Inglis in H. J. Eysenck (Ed.), *Handbook of Abnormal Psychology*. New York: Basic Books, 1961. P. 278.

Indexes

Author Index

Subject Index

This book has been set in 10 point Baskerville, leaded 2 points. Part numbers and chapter titles are in 24 point Baskerville. Chapter numbers are in 18 point Baskerville. The size of the type page is 26½ × 44 picas.